Principles of pavement engineering

Nick Thom
University of Nottingham

thomas telford

Published by Thomas Telford Publishing, Thomas Telford Ltd, 1 Heron Quay, London E14 4JD.
www.thomastelford.com

Distributors for Thomas Telford books are
USA: ASCE Press, 1801 Alexander Bell Drive, Reston, VA 20191-4400
Japan: Maruzen Co. Ltd, Book Department, 3–10 Nihonbashi 2-chome, Chuo-ku, Tokyo 103
Australia: DA Books and Journals, 648 Whitehorse Road, Mitcham 3132, Victoria

First published 2008

A catalogue record for this book is available from the British Library

ISBN: 978-0-7277-3480-8

Typeset by Academic + Technical, Bristol
Index created by Indexing Specialists (UK) Ltd, Hove, East Sussex
Printed and bound in Great Britain by MPG Books, Bodmin, Cornwall

Contents

viii

Foreword

Pavement Engineering has only been recognised as a discipline under this name in relatively recent years. This recognition came about as a result of developments in research and practice since the 1960's that are now having a major impact on how pavements of various types are designed, built and maintained. This rather slow evolution in a traditionally conservative branch of civil engineering has involved improved understanding of materials, design concepts and theory together with the availability of appropriate testing techniques for site and laboratory use. It has also involved a change in philosophy from a wholly empirical approach to design, supported by method and recipe specifications, towards the use of a theoretical framework for design and the adoption of performance-based specifications. The move towards Public-Private Partnerships in the highway engineering field in many countries has moved much responsibility from the public to the private sector and offered increased opportunities for innovation accompanied by appropriate assessment of the risks involved within the context of Whole Life Costing scenarios. To take advantage of this new way of doing business, engineers are increasingly in need of a sound, fundamental understanding of all the essential elements of pavement engineering. Unfortunately, few University degree courses include adequate coverage of the necessary material; pavement engineering often being treated only briefly relative to mainline subjects such as structures, hydraulics and geotechnics.

This excellent book sets out, for the first time, the material needed to equip practicing engineers and students alike with the fundamental understanding needed to undertake the design and maintenance of all pavement types in a professional manner. The Author, Nick Thom, combines a rare blend of experience as a consulting engineer in a specialist pavement engineering company with leading edge research and teaching at the UK's premier University centre in this field. In writing this book, he has provided a great service to the profession as no other publication has the level and scope of coverage that is set out here. The reader is given a real engineer's approach, involving theoretical concepts that are presented in a way that is easily understood, together with quantitative material to illustrate the key issues. The coverage given to such topics as planning, risk assessment, costing and management sit comfortably alongside detailed descriptions of material properties, design techniques, maintenance strategies and rehabilitation procedures. The topical issues of energy saving, sustainability and environmental improvement are tackled with the same eye to quantification of outcomes as the more traditional subjects. Excellent references are provided for background reading and to pavement engineering standards and design guides.

The essence of this very readable book is the fundamental treatment given to materials, design and forensic evaluation of pavements, illustrated by sample calculation sheets to show how answers can be achieved. The author provides his personal assessment of which methods and ideas are well-proven and which are less certain at this stage. His philosophy is one of encouraging the engineer to always have a logical basis for developing quantitative answers to problems but equally to use engineering judgement at all times by sensibly combining the quantitative with experience.

The book emphasises the importance of understanding the mechanical properties of pavement materials and soils, including their failure mechanisms under repeated loading, together with descriptions of how they can be measured in the field and the laboratory. This knowledge is then used within an analytical approach to design based largely on linear elastic analysis, while appreciating its shortcomings and adopting such techniques as crack propagation theory where appropriate. Methods for the computation of permanent deformations that accumulate under repeated loading are also presented. All types of construction are embraced as are their various applications for the different categories of roads from motorways to country lanes and for airports, container terminals and parking areas. The fundamentals of soil mechanics, asphalt technology and concrete are combined to provide the comprehensive range of knowledge required by the modern professional pavement engineer. I commend this book to all who are either practicing pavement engineering or are studying with a view to entering this interesting and rapidly developing civil engineering discipline, which provides many and varied challenges in developing and maintaining the world's transportation infrastructure into the future.

Stephen Brown
2008

Acknowledgements

This work could never have been written were it not for the contributions of my colleagues and ex-colleagues at the University of Nottingham. In some cases this involved direct feedback on early drafts; in all cases it involved a willingness to help and to enlighten me on issues with which I was relatively unfamiliar. I would particularly like to mention Andrew Dawson, Salah Zoorob, Andy Collop, Gordon Airey and Tony Parry. My thanks also go to Steven Brown for kindly writing the forward to the book. I should also say that I owe much to the accumulated knowledge gained by the authors of dozens of doctoral research theses on various pavement-related matters, too numerous to list here but many of which are referred to directly in the text.

I must also acknowledge the significant contribution made by colleagues at Scott Wilson Ltd. Much of Part 4 of this book stems from my own experiences working with Scott Wilson, but this has been greatly supplemented by the recent assistance of Bachar Hakim and Martyn Jones.

Finally, but most importantly, I owe a debt of thanks which I shall never be able to repay for the patient support of my wife Jackie.

Nick Thom

Part 1
Principles

1.1

Introduction

When all is said and done, the pavement industry deals in high-volume, low-cost materials. In the UK alone, there are approximately 14 000 km of trunk road and motorway with a surface area of some 250 km², between 5 and 10% of which has to be resurfaced each year. In the US, this figure can be multiplied by about six. And these are not figures that can be dramatically reduced while motor vehicle transport remains such a key factor in the economy. The choice of materials is therefore limited to those that can be easily and cheaply produced in large quantities – which inevitably means the raw materials of the earth, namely *rock*, *sand* and *clay*. Any additive used to give extra quality – such as bitumen or cement – has to be used relatively sparingly; otherwise society just couldn't afford it – to say nothing of the environmental cost of such additives. The job of the pavement engineer, therefore, is to maximise the potential of these cheap, readily processible materials. The unit cost of the bulk materials may be relatively low, but the quantities are very high indeed, which means a modest saving per square metre can multiply up to a very substantial saving overall. To put it another way: if the life of a road pavement can be extended by 10%, this represents a very large contribution to the local economy.

1.1.1 The long history of the paved highway
It is impossible to know where or when the wheel was invented. It's hard to imagine that Stone Age humans failed to notice that circular objects such as sections of tree trunk rolled. The great megalithic tombs of the third millennium BC bear witness to ancient humans' ability to move massive stones, and most commentators assume that

3

tree trunks were used as rollers; not quite a wheel but a similar principle! However, it is known for certain that the domestication of the horse in southern Russia or the Ukraine in about 4000 BC was followed not long afterwards by the development of the cart. It is also known that the great cities of Egypt and Iraq had, by the late third millennium BC, reached a stage where pavements were needed. Stone slabs on a rubble base made an excellent and long-lasting pavement surface suitable for both pedestrian usage and also traffic from donkeys, camels, horses, carts and, by the late second millennium BC, chariots. Numerous examples survive from Roman times of such slabbed pavements, often showing the wear of tens of thousands of iron-rimmed wheels. Traffic levels could be such that the pavement had a finite life.

Even in such ancient times, engineers had the option to use more than simply stones if they chose – but only if they could justify the cost! Concrete technology made significant strides during the centuries of Roman rule and was an important element in the structural engineer's thinking. Similarly, bitumen had been used for thousands of years in Iraq as asphalt mortar in building construction. Yet neither concrete nor asphalt was used by pavement engineers in ancient times for the excellent reason that neither material came into the cheap, high-volume category. As far as the pavement engineer was concerned, economics dictated that the industry had to remain firmly in the Stone Age. Even in the days of Thomas Telford and John Loudon Macadam – the fathers of modern road-building in the UK – the art of pavement construction consisted purely of optimising stone placement and the size fractions used.

Times have moved on; the massive exploitation of oil has meant that bitumen, an inevitable byproduct from refining heavy crude oil, is now much more widely available. Cement technology has progressed to the stage where it is sufficiently cheaply available to be considered in pavement construction. However, there is no way that pavement engineers can contemplate using some of the 21st century's more expensive materials – or at least only in very small amounts. Steel can only be afforded as reinforcement in concrete and, even in such modest quantities, it represents a significant proportion of the overall cost. Plastics find a usage in certain types of reinforcement product; polymers can be used to enhance bitumen properties; but always the driving force is cost, which means that, whether we like it or not, Stone Age materials still predominate.

1.1.2 Materials for pavement construction

In introducing the various building blocks from which pavements are constructed, it will not be possible to avoid entirely the use of technical terms such as 'load', 'strength' and 'stiffness'. Definitions of these terms can be found in Section 1.4.

1.1.2.1 Soil

Every pavement, other than those on bridges, self-evidently includes soil. The most basic design requirement of any pavement is that the underlying soil is adequately protected from applied loads. Thus, no pavement engineer can avoid the need to understand soil. Here are some key facts:

- Soils vary from heavy clays, through silts and sands to high-strength rocky materials.
- Soils are not usually consistent along the length of a road or across any pavement site.
- Soils are sensitive to water content to differing degrees.
- Water content will vary during the life of a pavement, sometimes over quite short timescales, in response to weather patterns.
- Some soils are highly permeable; some clays are virtually impermeable.

Inevitably, all this leads to one thing – *uncertainty*. However clever one tries to be in understanding and characterising soils, it is quite impossible to be 100% sure of the properties at a given time or in a given location.

This uncertainty makes life considerably harder. Nevertheless, it is necessary to categorise each soil type encountered in as realistic a way as possible, and there are two fundamental areas in which soil behaviour affects pavement performance. These are:

1. *stiffness* under transient (i.e. moving wheel) load
2. resistance to accumulation of deformation under repeated load, likely to be related to *shear strength*.

The various means of testing, measuring and estimating these properties will be covered in Part 2 of this book, as will the possibilities of soil improvement using additives such as cement and lime.

1.1.2.2 Granular material

Granular material refers to unbound material with relatively large particle sizes, and includes natural gravel, crushed rock and granulated industrial byproducts such as slag from steel production. Soils are technically granular materials, albeit often with a very small particle size (2 μm or less for clay), but the key difference is that a soil is not, in general, 'engineered' in any way. A granular pavement layer, on the other hand, will be selected and quite possibly deliberately blended to give a particular combination of particle sizes. It can also be mixed with a predetermined amount of water. One would therefore naturally expect that much of the uncertainty inherent in soil properties is removed in the case of a granular material. However, it may still be difficult to predict performance accurately since different material sources, most commonly different rock types, might be expected to generate slightly different properties due to their different responses to crushing or their differing frictional properties. Nevertheless, a granular material will be a much more controlled and predictable component than the soil. Even water content variation will be a little more predictable in both magnitude and effect than in the case of soil.

However, the properties of granular material of interest to the pavement engineer are actually more or less the same as those of soil, namely:

- *stiffness* under transient load
- resistance to accumulation of deformation under repeated load, related to *shear strength*.

1.1.2.3 Hydraulically-bound material

Nowadays the availability of Portland cement, and substitutes such as fly ash or ground granulated blast-furnace slag, means that it can be economic to use such a binding agent to strengthen a granular material. These binders are known as 'hydraulic' binders since they require the presence of water for the cementing action to take place.[1]

Hydraulically-bound materials, including so-called '*Pavement Quality Concrete*' (known hereafter as PQC) at the upper end of the strength spectrum, introduce a quite different type of behaviour and totally different design requirements. They possess a key property, lacking in soils and granular materials, namely the ability to withstand *tension*. Individual particles are rigidly bonded together by the binding agent and a definite tensile force is required to break that bond. In the case of a strong concrete, all the large particles are well bonded into a continuous matrix of fine aggregate and cement paste and the whole material is solid and rigid. It has a stiffness which is still partly governed by the

contacts between the large particles, but which is also heavily dependent on the qualities of the surrounding cementitious matrix. In the
case of a weaker hydraulically-bound material, the binding effect may
be less complete and there may be many particle contacts which
remain unbound, giving a certain freedom of movement within the
material and a reduced stiffness and strength. Nevertheless, even a
weak hydraulically-bound material will remain as a solid with negligible
permanent deformation until the bonds are fractured, i.e. until the
tensile strength is overcome. The key properties for the pavement
engineer are therefore:

● *stiffness*
● *tensile strength.*

One further property, which could arguably be added, is *fatigue
resistance*, i.e. the resistance of the material to failure under repeated
load at a stress level less than its failure strength. However, the relationship with tensile strength is so close that it is hardly a separate property.
It would also have been possible to add *curing rate* (the rate of strength
gain), since this certainly affects construction process and economics
significantly, and *thermal expansion coefficient*, since this property
strongly influences the tendency of a hydraulically-bound material to
crack under day–night temperature variation, requiring the introduction of movement joints in concrete pavements (see Section 1.3.2).
Part 2 will discuss all these properties and associated tests.

1.1.2.4 Bitumen-bound material
This is a material almost unique to pavement engineering, a material
whose beneficial properties were discovered almost by accident,[2] but
a material which is now very much at the centre of pavement technology. While proportions differ around the world, typically some
90% of paved highways have a bitumen-bound surface layer; whatever
the make-up beneath the surface, bitumen and bitumen-bound
materials (known from here on as *asphalts*) currently play a major
role. And asphalt is quite different from concrete or any hydraulically-bound material. Bitumen is a binding agent, like Portland
cement and the other hydraulic binders, but it has very different properties. Whereas hydraulic binders create a rigid material which cannot
deform appreciably unless it first cracks, bitumen remains a viscous
liquid at normal in-service temperatures. It therefore has the ability
to 'flow'.

An ability to flow may seem a rather undesirable quality in a material which is aiming to bind rock particles together, and it does indeed lead to the possibility that an asphalt can deform – hence the phenomenon known as 'rutting' or 'tracking'. However, it also overcomes some of the difficulties with rigid hydraulically-bound materials. For a start, the expansion and contraction with day–night temperature variation is accommodated simply by a small viscous strain within an asphalt, meaning that no movement joints are required and that thermally-induced cracking will only occur under the most extreme temperature conditions (continental winters, deserts). Asphalts are also able to accommodate any moderate movement within the foundation, for example minor differential settlement in an embankment, movement which might lead to the fracture of a rigid concrete slab. Furthermore, the tendency of asphalt to flow can be controlled by proper mixture design such that rutting is avoided.

However, despite the flexible nature of asphalt, it can still crack. It is impossible to define a tensile strength, since this will vary with temperature and rate of loading; the relevant parameter is the 'fatigue characteristic', defining resistance to cracking under repeated load. The key properties required for design are therefore as follows:

- *stiffness*
- resistance to *deformation* under repeated load
- *fatigue* characteristic.

1.1.2.5 Other materials

The four material types introduced so far represent the basic building blocks available to the pavement engineer. However, it is worth referring here to a couple of materials which do not fit so easily into any of the four categories. The first is *block paving*. Blocks are often made of concrete and so could have been introduced under 'hydraulically-bound materials'. On the other hand they can be cut from natural stone or may comprise fired clay bricks. Moreover, the discontinuous nature of block paving means that the properties of the parent material are less important than the effects of the discontinuities. The blocks themselves may have the properties of concrete, for example a stiffness modulus of some 40 GPa, but the effective layer modulus once the discontinuities are taken into account may be as little as 500 MPa. They are therefore a special design case and will be treated as such in Part 3.

The second special case is a hybrid material, known in the UK as *grouted macadam*,[3] although variant names exist around the world. This too does not fit neatly into any of the previous categories since it combines an asphalt skeleton with a cementitious grout, filling the voids in the asphalt mixture. It therefore utilises both bituminous and hydraulic binders. Having a two-stage production process, the material tends to be expensive and is used in particular heavy-duty applications such as bus lanes and industrial pavements. As will be demonstrated later, it actually resembles an asphalt much more than a concrete, but it is nevertheless distinct.

Block paving and grouted macadam are bulk-usage materials at the expensive end of the range. There are also specialist products which are only used in small quantities to strengthen or in some way improve a pavement layer. Here one could include *steel reinforcement* of concrete. There are also reinforcing products designed for asphalt; some are steel, others polymeric or made of glass fibre. A similar range of products is available for the reinforcement of granular materials. Generically, these products are known as *geogrids* and their use is widespread in some areas, for example as a means of stabilising roads over very soft ground. A closely related range of products are the *geotextiles*, produced in various ways and forming continuous layers separating two different pavement materials, commonly the soil and a granular layer. They too can have a reinforcing function but their most common usage is simply as a separator, ensuring that fine soil particles do not migrate up into the pavement and that stones from a granular layer do not lose themselves in the soil. The entire spectrum of geogrids and geotextiles is known under the collective name of *geosynthetics*, and although geosynthetics are specialist products, it is the responsibility of the pavement engineer to understand how (and whether) they work in particular applications rather than relying solely on the sometimes not unbiased opinion of a supplier.

1.1.3 Typical pavement structures

This section is included here principally so that the relevant terminology can be introduced. And the first terms which should be drawn to the reader's attention are *flexible*, *rigid* and *composite*, all words used to describe certain generic classes of pavement. Basically, a rigid pavement is one with a PQC slab as the main structural layer; a flexible pavement consists entirely of unbound materials and asphalt; while a composite pavement has an asphalt surface overlying a hydraulically-bound (e.g.

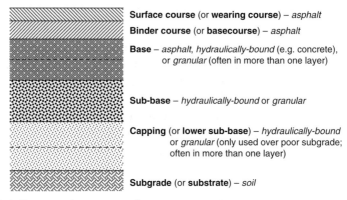

Fig. 1.1 Pavement layer terminology

concrete) base. The terms are rather loose and will be used only rarely in this book.

1.1.3.1 Pavement layers
Figure 1.1 illustrates the case of a heavy-duty pavement with an asphalt surface.

At first glance pavements appear to be unnecessarily complicated. However, everything is there for a reason. The *subgrade* is inescapable of course. *Capping* is simply a subgrade-improvement layer since it is uneconomic to place high-value materials straight onto a weak soil. Capping itself is generally a cheap, locally available material, sometimes simply the subgrade soil treated with lime, cement or some other hydraulic binder.

Moving to the top, the *surface course* (not present as a separate layer in concrete pavements) is a high-quality (and therefore expensive) material, tough enough to withstand direct loading and with surface properties designed to achieve adequate skid resistance. Since it is expensive, it is not generally a thick layer, 20–50 mm being typical.

Somewhere in the middle of the structure, the *base* is the layer which gives the pavement most of its strength. It is usually relatively thick (often 200 mm or more) and therefore has to be as inexpensive as possible within the constraints of required mechanical properties. The result is that large aggregate size tends to be used, whether the layer is an asphalt, a concrete or a granular material. In a concrete, this presents no problem; however, a likely side-effect of large aggregate size in an asphalt or roller-compacted hydraulically-bound base is a relatively uneven finish. This means that it is difficult to achieve a good-quality finished road surface if the surface course is applied directly; hence there is frequently a need for an intermediate regulating layer, the *binder course*. The binder course material is often very similar to the base, but with a smaller aggregate size, which means it can be laid to a typical thickness of 50–80 mm.

Finally, the *sub-base* is much more than just a fill-in layer. The performance of an asphalt or concrete base is critically dependent on the stiffness of the layer immediately beneath, because of its influence on the flexure of the base under traffic load. A firm support will limit such flexure. Sub-bases therefore vary from high-quality granular materials to even stiffer hydraulically-bound layers. A typical thickness is 150 mm; anything much thicker is likely to become uneconomic.

1.1.3.2 Pavement cross-sections

While pavements come in many different guises, there are certain common features, as illustrated in Fig. 1.2. The need to shed water in order to prevent surface ponding means that there will usually be a *crossfall* on the surface, and the imprecision inherent in pavement construction means that 1% is a practical minimum; anything less and there are almost bound to be locations where water will not be properly drained. A crossfall of 2.5% is typical on highways; 1.5% on airfield pavements. There will often be a section of relatively weak construction at the edge of the pavement, where trafficking is not expected to be frequent, known as a *shoulder*. It is basically an extra width of traffickable pavement, suitable for emergency use. For road pavements in urban locations, however, the edge of the pavement is likely to be defined by a *kerb*. The importance of drainage to pavement performance will be emphasised many times in this book and, as Fig. 1.2 shows, *drains* are most commonly located just outside the pavement edge.

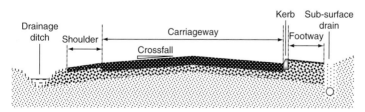

Fig. 1.2 Typical highway cross-section

1.1.4 Financial cost

Pavement engineering is always constrained by cost. Products with excellent performance may appear attractive, but they will only be used if the cost can be justified. Prices fluctuate of course and will continue to do so, and price also depends heavily on geography. Taking the UK as an example, good-quality rock is plentiful in the north and west but not in the south-east, which means that it is much more economically advantageous to utilise river gravels in the south-east than elsewhere. In some parts of the world, bitumen is plentiful and relatively inexpensive; elsewhere cement is more reasonably priced. Anything stated here can therefore only be indicative.

To start at the beginning: soil is effectively free. The natural ground beneath a pavement is there whether wanted or not. Perhaps a modest investment could improve it, for example by installing drainage, or by means of compaction if it is a sufficiently granular soil, or by stabilisation using a hydraulic binder, but the raw material is free.

Taking the price of high-quality unbound crushed rock sub-base as the benchmark, granular materials range in price from about 25% of this for locally extracted sands and gravels, to perhaps 125% for an ultra-tightly controlled crushed rock base.[4] Stabilisation of a native soil using an hydraulic binder will often cost no more than about 50% of the price of a crushed rock sub-base – but of course not every soil is suited to such stabilisation.

Base quality concrete, often known as 'lean concrete', is generally about 200–300% of the cost of crushed rock, with PQC about twice as expensive again, allowing for the complications of joints and reinforcement. Asphalt is of similar cost to PQC.

This of course all means that it is economically desirable to minimise as far as possible the thickness of either asphalt or PQC and to maximise the use made of locally available granular materials, even if their quality is less than one would hope for. In the case of block paving or grouted macadam, with costs up to twice that of asphalt, a very good case has to be made for their use. Similarly, while geosynthetics vary enormously in price (and effectiveness) a top-of-the-range polymer grid is likely to cost the equivalent of about 50 mm of asphalt, again implying that serious thought should be given before specifying such a product.

So, while the engineer is not, in the first instance, concerned directly with cost, it is important to have a feel for relative costs when assessing those options which are worth pursuing. Many solutions may be technically excellent but economically non-viable. The same may be true of environmental cost. The pressure towards the use of environmentally appropriate materials can only increase as humankind makes an ever greater mess of the planet. In pavement construction, this means that 'recyclability' is an important issue. Materials which will be of no further use at the end of their design life, and which will then have to be disposed of, bear a hidden cost, namely an environmental cost.

Fortunately, this isn't the case for the vast majority of pavement materials, but the issue remains as to how best to maximise the value of reused materials. Bitumen, for example, is a relatively expensive component of a pavement and the last thing one should want to do is to bury potentially valuable recycled asphalt planings in the foundation layers, where their valuable properties are not being used. This may satisfy the letter of current advice or legislation but it certainly does not optimise the value of the resource.

1.1.5 Sustainability and the environment

1.1.5.1 Material sources

Pavements, particularly road pavements, play an uneasy and complex part in the environmental equation, just as they play a vital yet complex role in the economic equation. Roads manifestly change the landscape. Some 25–30% of all materials extracted from the ground end up in highway pavements, from which it is obvious that an increase in the life of a road will lead to less demand for the extraction of materials and therefore less blight on the countryside. In purely economic terms, many parts of the world have vast resources of easily accessible rock and there is absolutely no economic pressure not to exploit them; the pressure is all from an environmental and therefore also political angle. However, whether the arguments are economic or environmental, the result is that it falls to the engineer to innovate and design in order to satisfy the aspirations of financiers, environmental experts, governments and ordinary members of the public. The bottom line is that a pavement engineer has to understand his/her materials to appreciate those properties which really are essential as opposed to those which are simply a luxury, and to be able to design for optimum 'value', whatever the changing definition of value might be. Codes may change, as may material costs, taxes, incentives etc. – but the principles of designing and maintaining a ground-bearing structure to carry wheeled vehicles remain the same. This book is concerned with those principles.

1.1.5.2 The energy issue

It is becoming increasingly important in a world of finite resources to do what can be done to minimise the energy which we, as a society, are consuming. There is also, of course, a direct correlation with the quantity of greenhouse gases which is being pumped into the atmosphere. A relevant concept is termed '*embedded energy*'. Every man-made product has a certain embedded energy, being the sum of the energies used to manufacture, transport, process etc. every component of that product. Thus, the embedded energy for PQC, for example, includes that due to aggregate extraction and haulage, also cement production and transportation, together with the energy used in concrete batching, mixing, transporting and paving. To do a really thorough job, one would have to include the energy needed to manufacture and maintain each piece of equipment used at every stage. This is therefore an extremely complicated quantity.

Fortunately, these calculations have been carried out by many researchers, allowing the possibility of quoting ranges of values which are at least approximately correct (see Table 1.1).

Naturally, there is plenty of argument as to what should or should not be included. Bitumen, for example, could be considered a waste product, a by-product of oil refining, and it could be argued that no energy charge should be made other than a very modest one for processing the material to a form suitable for transport and usage. On the other hand, if bitumen is thought of as a primary product of oil refining, then it should bear its share of the energy used in extraction, transportation and refining of crude oil.

Table 1.1 Embedded energies for pavement component materials[5]

	Material	Embedded energy: MJ/t
Ingredients	Sands and gravels	5–10
	Crushed rock aggregate	20–25
	Bitumen	3200–3800
	Portland cement	4500–5000
	Reinforcing steel	23 000–27 000
Mixtures	Hot-mix asphalt	600–800
	Cold-mix asphalt	150–200
	Lean concrete	450–500
	Pavement quality concrete (PQC)	750–1000
	Reinforced concrete	1100–1500
Transportation	All materials (per journey km)	12–20

The result of all this is that it is impossible to be definitive. However, it is certainly possible to draw general conclusions. Both asphalt, especially hot-mix asphalt, and concrete are high-energy products. Anything which can be done to cut back on these materials and increase the engineering value of other, lower-energy, materials will improve the overall energy footprint of a pavement.

However, since no more than about 0.3% of the energy used by developed countries can be attributed to pavement construction (or maintenance),[6] pavement engineers would appear to have limited scope for reducing global energy consumption. But there is another element to the energy equation, namely the issue of transport, responsible for about 36% of all energy consumed in the UK. Many studies have shown that vehicle fuel consumption, and therefore energy usage, differs from pavement to pavement and, summed over a pavement life of several decades, this is potentially a much more significant factor than that of embedded energy. The problem is that the studies do not all agree.[7] Part 3 will address the issue further, but a definitive conclusion cannot yet be drawn.

1.1.6 Summary

These few pages have flitted from topic to topic, introducing some of the key issues involved in pavement engineering and trying to set the subject in its proper context. Most of these issues will be picked up in much more detail in other parts of this book.

Concerning the structure of the book, Parts 2, 3 and 4 will each cover a large topic area, namely 'Materials', 'Design' and 'Maintenance'. The topics are interconnected of course, but the sequence is broadly logical in that *design* should not be attempted without a proper knowledge of the *materials* involved, and *maintenance* design (including full pavement rehabilitation) is really only possible with an understanding of pavement *design* principles.

Within each part, the most appropriate sequence to follow was less clear. Part 2 introduces each of the three principal material types (unbound, hydraulically-bound and bitumen-bound) in turn. Part 3 takes a different line and divides into design aspects (such as 'cracking' and 'durability'), whatever the materials involved. And Part 4 traces a path from minor maintenance to evaluation, rehabilitation design and, finally, pavement management.

This leaves Part 1, which has already opened with a setting of the scene. And this theme will continue. The next section will take a look at the quite different types of pavement that there are and the way that this is likely to impact on design. This is followed by a tour of some practical matters concerning material production, and Part 1 concludes by defining certain basic concepts (e.g. force, stress, strain) with which a pavement engineer has to be concerned.

1.2

Pavement applications

The greater part of this book is concerned with the detailed engineering of a pavement structure. However, it is important to appreciate the differences between different pavement applications, leading to very different design criteria. It is certainly not necessary to apply the same standards to all pavement types. Some are for fast but relatively light traffic; others are for concentrated heavy loads. In some cases surface properties are of key importance; in others not. This section is intended to give a feel for the typical pavement types expected for different applications and the factors which determine the most appropriate choice in each case.

It is not necessary to be concerned with technical details at this stage; the purpose is still to gain a broad appreciation of the subject.

1.2.1 High-speed highways
In general, these will be heavily used routes connecting centres of population. For the users, the purpose is to allow a fast, safe journey with a high level of reliability. The key design requirements are therefore as follows:

> Design requirements:
> - good ride quality
> - safe, skid-resistant surface
> - quiet surface
> - low maintenance

1.2.1.1 Ride quality
A good ride quality at high speed demands an accurate surface level, which in turn demands that the surface is laid using modern paving

equipment. The tolerances can be achieved using either PQC or asphalt, but if PQC is used then joints will usually reduce the ride quality. Non-jointed PQC is possible (continuously reinforced concrete – CRC) but this is an expensive option and therefore suited only to the most heavily trafficked highways.

To achieve the appropriate surface tolerance in asphalt, the surface course has to be placed on an underlying layer (the binder course) which itself is within relatively tight level constraints. Excessive inaccuracy in the surface of the binder course means that the surface course is being asked to accommodate an impossibly large variation. For example, if the surface course varies from 30 mm to 50 mm in thickness and it is placed at a temperature of 110°C then, when the compaction roller begins work some three minutes later, the temperature of the surface of the 'mat' would already vary from about 94 to 102°C (see calculations in Section 1.3.3.3), which makes an appreciable difference in mixture viscosity and therefore in resistance to movement under the roller. In practice, it is necessary to have at least three paver-laid courses in order to ensure the highest standards at top of surface course level.

1.2.1.2 Skid resistance

In general, on a high-speed road skid resistance requirements do not represent an onerous design condition because sight lines are good, there are no sudden stop lines or pedestrian crossings and no sharp bends. However, the high speed does present the possibility of aqua-planing if surface water is trapped between the vehicle tyres and the road surface. This means that the *texture depth* requirement is significant, i.e. either the stones which make contact with the tyres should be set well above the level of material between the stones or the same effect has to be achieved in concrete. Reasonable skid resistance can be obtained, even under water, so long as there is sufficient texture depth.

So long as the texture depth requirement is met, the intrinsic frictional quality of the surface stones or concrete does not have to be exceptionally high in a high-speed road situation. However, it is important that the texture depth does not deteriorate excessively and this means that the surface stones (or concrete protrusions) must have a high abrasion resistance, which usually implies use of a hard igneous rock.

1.2.1.3 Surface noise

There are two quite separate aspects to surface noise. The first is nuisance to the driver; the second is nuisance to an adjacent population.

Both are of course political rather than strictly engineering issues, but the engineer is the one who is able to help solve the political problem. However, the problem of noise is far from straightforward. Different surfaces generate noise in different frequency ranges, concrete tending to higher frequencies, but the nuisance level depends very much on the situation of the listener. Drivers are usually annoyed by high-frequency noise from concrete; as are people close to the road. At a greater distance, the lower frequency and longer wavelength sound will travel 'better' and so will not be attenuated as efficiently as high-frequency noise. Thus, while drivers and close observers tend to prefer low-stiffness voided asphalts because they generate low-frequency noise, this is not necessarily the case for those at a greater distance. Nevertheless, certain general principles can be drawn out:

- Large surface protrusions generate high noise.
- High material stiffness generates high-frequency noise.

The implication is that an asphalt will usually be less annoying than a concrete.

1.2.1.4 Low maintenance

On many intensively-used road networks this is a key influence on design. Maintenance is not just a direct cost for the maintaining authority; it is a severe nuisance to the road user and, more importantly, imposes a considerable indirect cost on the local economy as a consequence. And this introduces the idea of *design reliability*, an important but often neglected concept in pavement design. The point is that there is always a degree of uncertainty in the actual life-span of a pavement no matter how carefully it is designed and constructed. This uncertainty stems from variations in ground condition, differences between materials from different sources (e.g. different rock types), variation in constructed thickness and uncertainty in traffic loading. This then results in a statistical distribution of possible lives and one can speak in terms of a 90% or a 95% reliability, where there is only a 10% or 5% chance of the actual lifespan being less than the stated value. This concept will be pursued more fully in Parts 3 and 4.

For major high-speed highways, the sensible approach is to design to a long life and a high reliability[8] such that disruptive maintenance is kept to a minimum. Resurfacing is accepted by most authorities as a necessity every 10–15 years or so, simply as a result of deteriorating

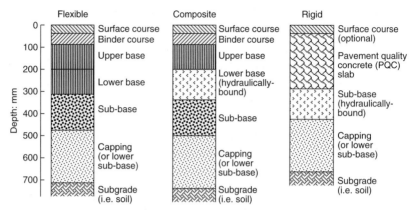

Fig. 1.3 Typical constructions – major high-speed highways

skid resistance, but there is no reason to accept such frequent structural maintenance.

1.2.1.5 Typical constructions

As a result of these design considerations, major high-speed highways tend to have relatively thick construction, as illustrated in Fig. 1.3. The designs shown are intended to be approximately equivalent, although considerable variation is possible using materials of differing qualities. The thicknesses shown are therefore purely illustrative, as is the fact that an asphalt surface course is shown overlying the PQC slab. This reflects current UK policy, dictated mainly by the politics of noise.

1.2.2 Urban roads

Urban roads present a different set of design challenges. Traffic is not usually travelling particularly fast; in fact there will be many locations where stationary or slow-moving traffic is expected. For the driver, there are many more potential hazards to avoid, such as pedestrians, cyclists and parked cars, and there are many reasons why it may be necessary to decelerate suddenly. For the maintaining authority there is the ever-present headache of dealing with the providers of piped services such as clean water, sewerage, electricity, gas and cable television, who regularly need to dig up sections of urban road as they install and then repair their networks. The road surface also tends to be dotted with access chambers fitted with steel access covers, presenting a further cause of uneven ride quality. Since traffic speeds are relatively low, surface quality is hardly critical, but the problem is the disruption caused by digging up sections of road, accompanied by an inevitable reduction in the overall life of the pavement.

Another specific problem is that of buses. Many cities have dedicated or partially dedicated bus lanes, which are excellent from the point of view of public transport provision but which mean that particular sections of the road carry heavy and concentrated loads and are therefore more vulnerable to deterioration, particularly rutting. The design considerations for urban roads can therefore be summarised as follows:

Design requirements:	• maintenance-friendly construction
	• high-skid-resistance surface in places
	• high rut resistance in places
	• low maintenance

1.2.2.1 Maintenance-friendly construction

The easiest approach to this issue is to consider constructions which would *not* be maintenance-friendly. And there are two main matters to address:

1. It should be possible to cut/break the road using standard equipment.
2. Backfill to trenches should not result in a significantly poorer or less stiff construction.

The first requirement suggests that strong PQC should be avoided; similarly reinforced concrete of any strength. Geosynthetics are also sometimes a significant nuisance during excavation, particularly strong polymers. The act of breaking through them tends to damage the material on either side of the excavation.

The second requirement means that the pavement should be of a fairly standard type of construction, not one that relies on any specialist high-strength, high-stiffness material which cannot be reproduced when carrying out a trench repair. In practice, this means that *asphalt* and *granular material* should normally be the main components, although *weak hydraulically-bound base* material is also acceptable. *Block paving* is certainly acceptable but only if the maintaining authority is prepared to commit to carrying out all subsequent restoration work by carefully removing and then replacing the blocks in the area of the work.

21

1.2.2.2 High skid resistance

The principal areas where higher than average skid resistance is typically specified are at pedestrian crossings, junctions and roundabouts. This is generally achieved by means of a special treatment to the surface (of high-friction chippings stuck down with an ultra-tough binder) and so does not affect the design of the underlying pavement, which would be the same as in other areas.

1.2.2.3 Rut resistance

Ruts in asphalt occur under heavy loads and, particularly, when those loads travel slowly. This is because bitumen is still a liquid, even at in-service temperatures, and slow loading allows the bitumen to deform and stones to slip relative to each other. The practical result of this is the rutting which is often visible in bus lanes, at traffic lights, or in bays where heavy goods vehicles load and unload. There are several solutions to this problem (see Fig. 1.4):

- take extreme care to design asphalt mixtures to resist rutting
- use block paving over a hydraulically-bound base
- use PQC
- use grouted macadam.

Asphalt mixture design will be covered in Part 2, and it is true that rut-resistant mixtures can be produced. However, this depends on having the appropriate aggregate and it is not always feasible to make the asphalt strong enough for this very aggressive environment.

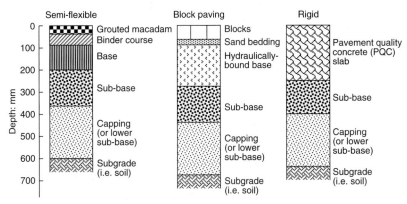

Fig. 1.4 Typical bus lane designs

Block paving has the disadvantage that any rut which develops shows up very clearly indeed. However, if the base has been properly designed and if the sand (or mortar) bedding is not too thick then rutting should never occur. Cost may, however, be an issue.

PQC is an excellent solution so long as the difficulty of future access beneath the concrete does not rule it out.

Grouted macadam has the benefit that it can be 'retro-fitted' to a road with problems. Since it is generally only placed as a surface course of 50 mm or less, it is only necessary to plane out the existing surface and replace with grouted macadam. This saving in time and effort may then offset the high cost of the material itself. It also has advantages over concrete in that joints are not required and there is no dramatic change of construction at the interface with adjacent asphalt.

1.2.2.4 Low maintenance

Having already said that an urban road should be maintenance-friendly since it is always likely to be disturbed by service providers such as water companies, there is also significant pressure on major urban roads not to close any part of them for longer than is absolutely necessary. Rapid maintenance such as surface dressing, slurry sealing or retexturing (see Part 4) is acceptable as disruption is only brief, but major rehabilitation is a serious issue and inevitably takes longer in an urban environment due to the constricted nature of such sites. Major urban roads should therefore be designed to a high reliability. In practice many such roads have evolved over several decades, so the construction may already be that of a rehabilitated pavement, but the principle for future design is the same: reliability should be high.

Of course, this point is critically dependent on the traffic level and the availability of alternative routes. Minor streets effectively come under the next heading, 'estate roads'.

1.2.3 Estate roads

Estate roads and minor city streets are in quite a different category from major urban routes. Their purpose is simply to allow the passage of vehicles to and from individual residential or industrial locations. The flow is small; most loads are light but there will also be occasional heavy goods traffic (deliveries, refuse trucks, fire engines). Speeds are (or should be) low, and ride quality is relatively unimportant. So long as the road is passable and safe, its purpose is fulfilled. This leads to the following design constraints:

> Design requirements:
> - cheap construction
> - should remain passable for many decades
> - must accommodate occasional heavy traffic

1.2.3.1 Cheap construction

Estate roads cannot be justified simply from the number of vehicles using them. They are an expensive necessity rather than a valuable economic asset. They must therefore be cheap. In principle they could be granular pavements, as many access roads are, but for anything other than the most lightly trafficked situation this will give rise to unwanted maintenance costs, so it is usually preferable to apply a bound surface. However, this should be of minimum thickness, usually two courses of asphalt since it is hard to achieve a satisfactory finish with a single course. Concrete slabs, generally around 120–150 mm thick with light reinforcement, are also possible, but experience (and theory) suggests that deterioration may be excessive under the occasional heavy truck loads.

1.2.3.2 Passable for decades

It is this requirement that generally leads to the use of a bound surface. However, it should be noted that 'passable' is quite different from 'in excellent condition'. It should also be noted that there is little restriction on carrying out maintenance (except during antisocial hours) therefore, while it is a cost to be avoided if possible, it can be done if necessary. This means that designs do not have to be to a high reliability. Even 'failure' of parts of the road can still leave the route passable. It is therefore permissible to lower the reliability to as little as 50%[9] and accept that the lower initial cost which this allows will be partially offset by the need for future patching works.

1.2.3.3 Occasional heavy traffic

This requirement means that concrete should only be allowed after careful evaluation of the wheel loads from heavy trucks. Asphalt is a forgiving material and can withstand occasional overloads; concrete cannot.

1.2.4 Rural roads

Rural roads present the challenge of low traffic volumes but, sometimes, relatively high speeds. Alignment constraints also often mean that there are serious safety problems. The design requirements are therefore as follows:

Design requirements: ● adequate ride quality   ● suitably high skid resistance

1.2.4.1 Ride quality

In developed countries, traffic speeds are likely to be in the order of 40–60 mph (60–100 kph), which means that the ride quality has to be sufficient to give safe driving conditions at such speeds. This in turn dictates the use of either an asphalt pavement with multi-layer construction or else PQC. However, the problem with PQC is always cost. The fact that all rural roads take a proportion (sometimes a very high proportion) of heavy axle loads means that a concrete pavement would have to be nearly as thick for a rural road as for a major highway – because of the high sensitivity of concrete to overloading (see Part 2). This leaves *asphalt* as the most likely material for the bound layers, with the option to use hydraulically-bound material in the base if it proves more economic. The lower traffic expected in comparison with a major highway then allows the use of a substantially thinner construction.

If the traffic volume is low enough, rural roads can be almost entirely *granular pavements*, sealed with a *surface dressing* (a thin layer of stones spread over a bituminous spray coat – see Part 4). As deterioration occurs, the surface dressing treatment can then be repeated. Such a pavement will result in a lower safe driving speed, but in many situations this is not a critical issue.

In the so-called 'developing world', granular pavements are the norm in rural settings, with or without a surface dressing treatment. Such pavements are well suited to very low volumes and low to moderate speeds but can accommodate occasional overloading with no greater damage than a slight acceleration in the rate of rut development. However, a fully granular, unsurfaced pavement demands significant maintenance input (regular reprofiling of the surface), and so is really only appropriate for the lowest traffic categories.

1.2.4.2 Skid resistance

Skid resistance is only one factor in maximising the safety of rural roads, alignment being probably of much greater significance. This means that hard decisions have to be taken as to what level of skid resistance is appropriate. It is simply not economic to apply expensive treatments to every sharp bend or junction approach, and the money could usually be much better spent improving the alignment, road markings or signing. However, at the very least, adequate texture depth should be provided to prevent aquaplaning in wet weather.

1.2.5 Pedestrian areas and cycle paths

Once again, the design parameters change. Perhaps unfortunately, the most influential design input for some highway authorities is the need to minimise claims from pedestrians who have tripped over uneven footway surfaces. Nevertheless, and however strange this may seem to those who live in cities where footways are not paved at all, it does make the point that there is little real engineering design involved. *Granular pavements* are perfectly adequate structurally to carry either pedestrian or cycle loading.

The engineering therefore comes in developing cheaper or easier forms of construction. Many *industrial by-products*, for example, lend themselves to use in footways and cycleways since they allow the production of a dense, closed surface despite not having the strength to perform under vehicular traffic. Examples would be certain types of slag, which possess a degree of self-cementing action.[10] *Cold-mix asphalts* are also ideally suited to such applications. These will be explained much more fully in Part 2, but here it should be understood that bituminous binders in cold form can be used to bind many aggregates which would not be suited to hot asphalt production. The result will be a relatively weakly bound material, ideal for footways and cycle track surfaces.

Of course, the traditional medium for paving in a city environment is block (or flag) paving. However, the justification for its use is mainly aesthetic. Blocks are not a cheap paving option, but they can look impressive and lend character to a city centre. Except in locations which will be subject to motor vehicle loading, there is no structural design involved. The blocks are bedded in sand, which is placed over a granular base. The actual laying is a skilled operation and poor workmanship can lead to differential settlement, ponding of rainwater and steps between individual blocks or flags – but there is little the pavement engineer can contribute.

1.2.6 Car, coach and lorry parks

This category of pavement presents its own special problems. The loads this time can be considerable, particularly where trailer feet are allowed to rest directly on the surface; but they are static or slow-moving. Ride quality is not usually an issue, so a degree of deterioration is often acceptable, but most parking area owners would be unhappy if their pavement were to become too much of an eyesore. The challenge for the engineer, therefore, is to come up with solutions which are suitably inexpensive yet provide the operator with an appropriate level of service. The design considerations can be summarised as follows:

Design requirements: • sufficient load-bearing capacity   • maintain an acceptable surface finish

1.2.6.1 Load-bearing capacity

The problem with slow or static loads is that asphalt is not really designed to cope well under such circumstances. If loads are light, as in a car park, then asphalt is a perfectly acceptable solution and the design will not be dissimilar to that for a minor urban road. However, heavy static (or, even worse, ultra-slow-moving) loads impose the most damaging possible conditions on an asphalt. The bitumen has plenty of time to flow, greatly reducing its effectiveness at binding the aggregate particles together and allowing permanent strain to occur, leading to settlement. Trailer feet, usually solid steel rollers, apply a massive stress onto the surface and are highly likely to cause indentations in asphalt-surfaced pavements.

The solutions are similar to those proposed above for bus lanes. *Concrete* is ideal in terms of its deformation resistance but can be expensive, either in actual finance or in construction time, and joints in the concrete can give rise to problems later in the life of the pavement. *Block paving* is often used, but care has to be taken to design the full pavement structure, notably a suitably deformation-resistant base layer, otherwise the whole pavement will deform and the blocks will follow the rest of the pavement down. Of course, as soon as local deformation occurs, rainwater will pond and soak into the subgrade soil at that point – and the condition will become even worse. The third solution, *grouted macadam*, has many advantages, particularly its lack of joints. In effect, grouted macadam is a deformation-resistant asphalt. It will not be able to stop deformation occurring if there is a serious underlying weakness, but at least it will maintain a reasonably water-resistant seal.

1.2.6.2 *Surface finish*

In many applications, the cosmetic appearance of the surface is almost as important as the structural strength of the pavement; hence the popularity of block paving. If the situation demands that a high-quality visual appearance is maintained, then this logically influences the choice of construction. Block paving may be desirable, but the price tag may count against it. Concrete is a risk. While it is intact and the joints are sound, it looks fine; but there are few worse-looking pavements than cracked concrete slabs, spalling at the edges. Asphalt and grouted macadam are much safer in that any blemishes which develop can be remedied without too much difficulty.

It should also be mentioned that numerous unpaved or semi-paved solutions are available, notably reinforced grass surfaces, either using hollow soil-filled concrete blocks or fibre reinforcement in the soil.[11] These give effective and aesthetically pleasing surface finishes, although they are not necessarily cheap.

1.2.7 Ports and heavy industrial pavements

The design criteria for these pavements are similar to those for lorry parks in that slow or stationary loads are expected, although loading details will usually be different. Ports and inland freight terminals generally require container stacking facilities, and container loads are transmitted through small square steel feet, generating very high pressure. A similar situation is found under racking on internal warehouse paving.

Reach-stackers (see Fig. 1.5) apply one of the highest axle loads of any wheeled vehicle, with individual wheel loads of 30 t or more if dynamic effects are taken into account. Fork-lift trucks range from large, high front axle load machines with conventional pneumatic tyres to small, solid rubber-tyred vehicles which, despite the lower

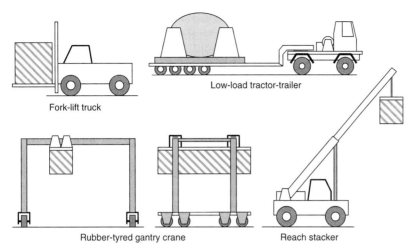

Fig. 1.5 Wheeled vehicles for ports and other industrial areas

total load, can apply high contact pressure through the tyre. Rubber-tyred gantry cranes present another special design case; they run on certain lines only, either side of container stacks, and it is common to design the pavement immediately underneath their lines of travel to be different from that of the surrounding area.

In terms of pavement design, the key requirement is that the surface should not deform excessively, but the allowable deformation will be different for the different design cases. For solid-tyred fork-lift trucks, it is quite important that the surface they operate on is even. Similarly, rubber-tyred gantries cannot accommodate any significant uneven settlement along their lines of travel. Container stack areas, on the other hand, are much more forgiving, and most pneumatic-tyred vehicles can also cope with a certain amount of unevenness. It is unlikely that aesthetics will be given any serious priority, which means that pavement cracking only becomes important if it leads to deformation. In essence therefore:

> Design requirement: ● limit uneven deformation

1.2.7.1 Uneven deformation

In practice, the full range of pavement options, including granular pavements, is used in heavy industrial applications, reflecting the range of equipment for which designs have to be carried out. However, concrete is probably the 'default solution' because of its deformation resistance. Also, since paving is but one of a number of operations being carried out at any industrial development site, there is often no real pressure on construction time, negating one of concrete's main disadvantages, i.e. the time needed to come to full strength.[12]

However, use of concrete always brings with it a danger. A well-designed, well-constructed concrete pavement should have an almost indefinite and trouble-free life, but if a problem does arise, it can be serious. Concrete cracking is no problem in itself, but concrete cracking is most likely to indicate a non-uniform support, which means that settlement may occur in cracked areas and not elsewhere. The conclusion, therefore, is that it is usually worth investing in a high design reliability when using concrete.

Heavy-duty block paving is also common in industrial areas, overlying a substantial hydraulically-bound base. Use of blocks overcomes the need for concrete joints, increasing its economic attraction.

Conventional asphalt is appropriate in many applications, particularly on access roads, lanes between areas of container stacking, or lightly trafficked areas. It has the advantage that construction time is generally much less than for concrete, which in some contracts can be extremely beneficial. Grouted macadam has similar advantages to asphalt and, being practically non-deformable, it can also be used in high or static loading applications.

In conclusion, therefore, industrial pavements require real engineering input. It is essential that the requirements of each particular design situation are properly understood, for which both the magnitude and frequency of the loads and also the acceptable long-term pavement condition need to be known.

1.2.8 Airfield pavements

Aircraft represent yet another form of wheeled transport with their own peculiarities in terms of wheel load, arrangement and speed. The landing gear of an Airbus A380 represents just about the highest concentration of load that a pavement is ever likely to have to accommodate, around 160 t spread over six wheels – and there are four main gears in addition to the nose wheels. Figure 1.6 illustrates typical aircraft wheel arrangements. Such a high concentration of loads means that the stress field developed within the pavement will penetrate much deeper into the subgrade soil than is the case for other pavement types, necessitating extremely thick construction, especially over soft ground sites.

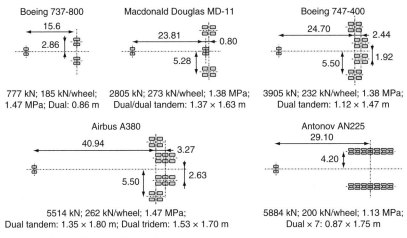

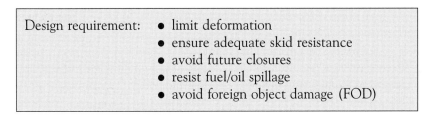

Fig. 1.6 Selected aircraft wheel arrangements (dimensions in metres)

It is a common misconception that the critical loading case occurs in the touchdown zone of a runway, where the wheels impact onto the surface and are accelerated rapidly from zero to a speed of around 150–200 km/h, leaving considerable rubber deposits on the pavement surface. However, the impact is in fact a minor one and most of the load is still being carried by the aerofoil action of the aircraft wings. The critical case is actually when the aircraft is travelling slowly with a full fuel load, whether on the runway, taxiway or apron, and the greatest concentration of loads commonly occurs on taxiways, where variation in the lateral position around the taxiway centreline is minimal.

The principal pavement design requirements are as follows:

Design requirement:	• limit deformation
	• ensure adequate skid resistance
	• avoid future closures
	• resist fuel/oil spillage
	• avoid foreign object damage (FOD)

1.2.8.1 Limiting deformation

A particular problem with deformation of airfield pavements relates to surface water drainage. Aircraft operational requirements limit the crossfall to 1.5% maximum (on major airfields), and water cannot be expected to drain effectively if the slope falls below about 1%, which

31

means that a relatively slight degree of differential settlement can result in ponding. This is undesirable on taxiways, but it is potentially disastrous on runways if an aircraft aquaplanes. The need to avoid ponding means that the overall pavement thickness *must* be adequate to protect the subgrade and avoid deformation at that level.

Particular locations which are always likely to be subject to deformation are aircraft 'stands', since slow-moving and then stationary wheel loads are repeatedly applied to exactly the same points. The slow-moving nature of the load means that asphalt would have plenty of time for viscous flow, which can lead to indentation of the surface. It is therefore usual to use concrete on all heavy aircraft stands, although grouted macadam and block paving represent alternative options.

1.2.8.2 Skid resistance

This is another safety-critical issue, and skid resistance of runways has to be measured regularly, particularly under adverse weather conditions. Runway surfaces therefore have to be suitably textured when constructed. Concrete pavements are usually not a problem; the texture is achieved by grooving (or other similar techniques) while the concrete is still wet (see Section 1.3.2.9). Asphalt pavements, on the other hand, often have insufficient natural texture, which leads to the common practice of sawing grooves in the asphalt surface. Unfortunately, the edge of the groove then represents a weakness if there is any deficiency in the asphalt mixture, and cases of spalling at these edges are not uncommon.[13]

High skid resistance is only required on runways; taxiways and aprons rarely take traffic travelling at more than about 50 kph – other than certain usage by ground vehicles.

1.2.8.3 Avoiding closures

Economically, busy airports cannot afford to close; neither can they afford any reduction in their capacity. This means that the critical parts of an airfield, notably the runways, have to be designed with an eye to possible future maintenance needs. Key factors are as follows:

- Major concrete repairs require time for the concrete to set. This can be as little as a few hours but only if relatively expensive rapid-hardening cements are used.

- Asphalt overlays can be carried out at night in stages, the ends of each night's work being ramped down to provide a sufficiently smooth ride for aircraft.
- Alternatively, work can be carried out at each end of the runway while a reduced operating length is imposed, but there will usually be a section at the centre which cannot be accessed in this way.

It is clearly best if such maintenance needs can be avoided altogether, although the rapid growth of air travel inevitably has made forecasts difficult. It is worth bearing in mind, however, that a small saving in runway materials in the short term may easily be wiped out in whole-life terms by large future maintenance costs. Design reliability should therefore be high.

1.2.8.4 Fuel and oil spillage
Airfield pavements are frequently subjected to spillages, most commonly at aircraft stands, where refuelling takes place. This is a serious bar to the use of asphalt in such locations and further reason why aircraft stands are usually constructed in concrete.

1.2.8.5 Foreign object damage (FOD)
It is critical to aircraft safety that no foreign object is sucked into the engines. The most common such object is a bird, but pavement debris represents another potential hazard. This effectively precludes any surface where stones or other surface material might work loose. Conventional asphalt and concrete (to a sufficiently high specification) are both satisfactory, but the use of rolled chippings (as in surface dressing for example) would not be permitted.

1.2.9 Summary
This section was intended to give a feel for the many and varied types of pavement out there – and the real need for engineering input. Design is always a balance between the competing needs of safety, reliability, cost, aesthetics, maintainability, ride quality etc. The engineer must be able to evaluate where the real priorities lie.

1.3

Practical issues

This book is not a construction manual. Nevertheless, it is important to understand some of the practicalities of material production and pavement construction if sensible decisions are to be taken in design or planning and this section gives a brief overview. The introduction of certain technical matters which will be much more fully explored in later parts of the book is unavoidable, and forward reference will be made where necessary. However, bear in mind that the purpose of this section is not to delve into the physics or mathematics of pavement materials but purely to understand construction practicalities.

1.3.1 Unbound material

1.3.1.1 Natural soils
The natural soil is the most vulnerable element of any pavement; it needs protecting at all costs. Poor construction practice can easily turn a basically sound material into a muddy soup. It is therefore good practice on any site to avoid disturbance to the pavement subgrade, leaving a thin layer of overlying material until the very last moment, thus protecting the subgrade soil from the effects of both the weather and also construction traffic. Only when the contractor is ready to place the first of the pavement layers, usually an unbound granular layer, should the actual top of subgrade be exposed.

1.3.1.2 Granular materials – particle size distribution
Some sands and gravels can be used 'as dug' from the ground, without the need to alter the proportions in any way; however, these materials

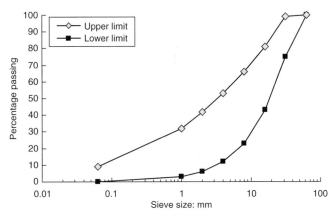

Fig. 1.7 Typical particle size distribution limits for a granular sub-base[14]

are unlikely to be suitable for high-quality sub-base or base materials. The factors affecting the strength of a granular material will be discussed in Part 2 but, unsurprisingly, particle properties and size distribution play major roles in determining the strength of the material as a whole. Maximum particle size is constrained by the thickness of the layer being constructed, since roller compaction is only effective up to a depth of around 250 mm, and materials become very difficult to work if stones larger than about 30% of the layer thickness are present. The particle size distribution is generally specified in terms of upper and lower grading limits (see Fig. 1.7) and these can usually only be met by physically crushing larger rock particles and/or by blending materials from more than one source. The more such processes are required, the more expensive the material becomes.

1.3.1.3 Particle soundness

Particles of granular pavement layers do not have to be exceptionally strong since the behaviour of the layer as a whole is largely a function of inter-particle effects at contacts. Nevertheless, particles cannot be allowed to crumble to dust. It is therefore usual to place limits on their strength and durability. Tests exist for crushing strength,[15] abrasion resistance,[16] frost damage[17] and chemical weathering[18] – all intended to ensure durability. Unfortunately, acceptable limits have often been set historically purely in order to exclude certain materials rather than for scientifically sound reasons, and this means that otherwise excellent secondary or recycled materials can fall foul of such limits.

35

1.3.1.4 Particle shape

Particle shape can be specified in various ways, using words such as 'angular' or by demanding a certain minimum percentage of crushed faces. Many specifications also place limits on the 'flakiness' and 'elongation' of particles, determined from the ratio of the minimum and maximum dimensions respectively to the mid-size dimension.

The shape of a crushed particle is a function of the equipment used to carry out the crushing and the nature of the parent rock. In general, a high shear strength mixture is achieved with highly angular stones. Individual stones can then lock together effectively within a pavement layer and inhibit movement of one particle relative to another. The restrictions on flakiness and elongation are included since experience is that, with a high proportion of such particles, handling difficulties can arise, accompanied by segregation of large particles from small; however, debate continues on the need or otherwise for such limits since many flaky or elongated materials have been found to perform well in practice.[19]

1.3.1.5 Water content

All unbound materials are sensitive to water. If the amount of water is relatively low, it will tend to accumulate at contact points between particles because of surface tension effects at the air–water interface (see Part 2 for details). This results in a difference in pressure between the atmospheric pressure of the air and the pressure within the water, the water pressure being slightly lower, and the effect is known as *negative pore pressure* or *suction*. This will induce a small additional compressive force between particles (increasing what is known as *effective stress*), making it harder for one particle to slip over another and, once in the pavement, this is a highly *desirable* state. Unfortunately, it is a highly *undesirable* state during compaction since it makes it harder to rearrange the particles into a dense packing.

If the water content is increased, suction is reduced as some of the voids become totally filled with water. These water-filled voids then have the potential to develop *positive pore pressure* since, when load is applied, the water will resist any reduction in the volume of the void. Positive pore pressure reduces the compressive forces at particle contacts (reducing effective stress) and therefore makes it easier for one particle to slip over another. In an in-service pavement this is a most *undesirable* condition since easier inter-particle movement means lower strength and stiffness. However, during compaction it is most *desirable* since particle rearrangement becomes much easier. Figure 1.8

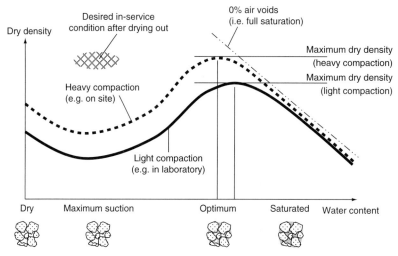

Fig. 1.8 The effect of water content on achieved density

shows schematically the influence of water content on the dry density achieved (i.e. the density of the aggregate alone) during compaction and the optimum water content is the condition in which compaction is easiest and the highest densities are reached. At even higher water contents, there is simply no room for all the water in the mixture without a reduction in density. As Part 2 will illustrate, maximising density is critical in maximising material strength and reducing deformation.

A proper appreciation of these water-related effects is crucial if a high-quality granular layer is to be achieved and it means that the following procedure is needed:

- Mix material at optimum water content (or slightly above to allow for evaporation during handling).
- Compact at optimum water content.
- Allow to dry out as drainage and evaporation take place, maximising suction.

In general, the pavement industry understands the need to compact at optimum water content, but the need to allow the material to dry is less well appreciated – and excess water can lead to failure of an over-lying material even under the action of a roller. It means that it should *NOT* be acceptable to place an overlying bound layer immediately after heavy rain when the granular layer is near saturation since: (i) there is a danger of damage under the roller; and (ii) the high water content is likely to remain for the long term because the overlying layer cuts off

37

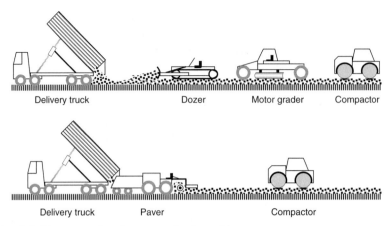

Fig. 1.9 Equipment for placement of unbound layers

the evaporation route. The problem is that it is not always easy to build this restriction into a watertight (excuse the pun) specification[20] and engineering understanding is required by all parties to a construction contract; there are no winners when a substandard product results.

1.3.1.6 Placement and compaction

The method of placement depends on the level control required. Granular material can be tipped and spread with a blade; the finish can then be improved by means of a grader – a machine with a blade set at an angle to the direction of travel. However, for granular bases where level control is essential to avoid problems achieving tolerances in overlying bituminous layers, an asphalt paver can also be used. Figure 1.9 illustrates.

Compaction is achieved by repeated stressing of the layer, usually by means of a roller. Vibratory compactors allow very rapid load repetition, leading to rapid densification. However, the stress level applied is important and this places a limit on the thickness of layer which can be effectively compacted by any given equipment. In general, 250 mm is a realistic limit; anything higher and the bottom of the layer will tend to be under-compacted.[21]

1.3.2 Hydraulically-bound material

1.3.2.1 Particle shape and size distribution

Hydraulically-bound materials do not, in the long term, rely significantly on particle-to-particle interaction for their engineering properties and so the shape and size distribution are less critical than is the case for unbound material.[22] The principal exception is the case of slow-setting hydraulically-bound materials, which rely on particle-to-particle contacts for stability during the early days and weeks of life, particularly during the construction phase of a project.

In general it is undesirable for there to be a high void content, since water can attack the hardened material if it can gain access through voids. There should therefore always be enough fine material in the mixture to ensure that large voids do not occur. Broadly speaking, the denser the mix the higher its resulting strength will be, and strength is the property which really matters. However, dense mixtures can be achieved using a wide range of particle sizes; maximum size is typically 40 mm or less and is constrained to no more than around 30% of the layer thickness to ensure mixture workability.

1.3.2.2 Water content

If water content is critical for unbound materials, it is even more so for hydraulically-bound mixtures. The primary issue is that of ensuring that there is just the right amount of water for the *hydraulic reaction* to take place, and this depends on the binder content and also the type of binder or cocktail of binders being used. Too little water and not all the binder will be activated, resulting in reduced strength of material; too much water and some will remain as free water even after the reaction has taken place – water which will evaporate leaving air voids and a seriously weakened mixture. Thus, for each mixture and binder content there is an optimum water content to maximise the hydraulic reaction.

However, there is a secondary issue and that is the water necessary for *compaction*. In the case of wet concrete, there must be enough water to ensure workability under vibrator action; for drier mixtures, compacted by roller in exactly the same way as unbound materials, there will be an optimum water content related to a maximum achievable density. The trick is to ensure that the two optima (one for hydraulic reaction, the other for compaction) are similar, which places limits on the binder content that can be used with a given aggregate type and gradation. For many materials this restricts dry-mix hydraulically-bound materials to medium-strength applications such as sub-bases and bases, although high-strength roller-compacted concrete is possible with certain aggregates. Part 2 will discuss these issues in more detail.

The problem is further complicated if the mixture is to be placed via a slip-form paver, a technology which demands workability between strict limits (see Section 1.3.2.4). This is because the material has to be self-supporting once the side forms of the paver have passed, i.e. only about a minute after the material is first fed into the machine, which means that it has to be relatively dry. This places limits on the strength range possible.

1.3.2.3 Mixing and batching

Hydraulically-bound materials require careful proportioning and mixing. The usual technique is to mix in batches, with a certain measured volume of water and a certain weight of hydraulic binder such as Portland cement. Mixing takes about 30 s and, on completion of the mixing, the material is dropped into the back of a waiting wagon and transported to site. For wet concrete (usually PQC), it is also common to use ready-mix suppliers, in which case the concrete is delivered in mixing trucks.

An alternative to batch mixing is to mix continuously in a drum mixer. A controlled feed of aggregate and binder is fed into one end of the drum, together with a measured flow of water; the rotation of the drum then mixes the materials together while baffles on the inside of the drum draw the mixture to the far end and out, whence it can be fed directly into a waiting wagon. The advantage is that higher productivity can be achieved, but the technique is only really suited to relatively dry mixes.

1.3.2.4 Placement and compaction

Dry concrete is designed to be roller-compacted, and placement and compaction techniques are exactly the same as for unbound materials. The same restrictions on layer thickness apply because of the need to achieve density, an even more critical matter for hydraulically-bound materials than for unbound.

However, wet concrete is a different matter entirely. Traditionally, concrete has been laid in bays between strips of formwork, often in a chessboard pattern, so that half the bays (equivalent to the red squares on a chessboard) are formed first, and the other half (the white squares) are then infilled. The concrete is wet and flows easily, hence the need for formwork. It is not stable enough for roller-compaction and so vibrating pokers are used, often together with a vibrating screed. This

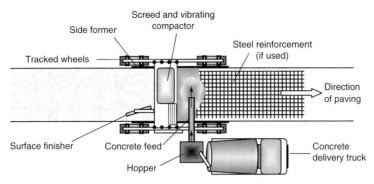

Fig. 1.10 Plan view of slip-form concrete paving

brings the larger air bubbles to the surface and makes sure that the concrete flows around any obstruction such as steel reinforcement bars.

For road construction, where a long thin length is required, the traditional approach has been to set up a so-called 'concrete train', a series of pieces of equipment which run on side rails, also used as side formers for the concrete. This allows a continuous high-efficiency pattern of work and a high-quality well-regulated finish to the pavement.

However, for really high productivity, slip-forming is the technique to use (see Fig. 1.10). A slip-form paver is not unlike an asphalt paver in that it is a relatively short piece of equipment that spreads the material across the paving width and applies compaction by means of a vibrating screed. Side formers are attached to the paver and so move continuously such that the formed concrete slab has to be able to support itself almost as soon as it is formed.

1.3.2.5 In situ stabilisation

All hydraulic binders lend themselves to in situ stabilisation work. This is the process whereby an existing material, either a natural soil or a placed material, is mixed in-place with an added binder (together with water if necessary). The most common use is to improve the quality of a soil, thereby reducing the thickness of overlying pavement construction required, but it is quite possible to carry out in-place mixing of other pavement layers. The machinery needed is basically an adaptation of the agricultural rotovator, plant which is capable of mixing to the required depth, sometimes up to 350 mm. However, it is an inescapable fact that the process cannot be controlled as well as plant mixing. The distribution of binder and water is unlikely to be uniform, and the result is a layer which, though it may be fit for purpose, is certainly more varied than an equivalent plant-mixed material. This must be borne in mind in the pavement design.

1.3.2.6 Curing

A particularly important issue for all hydraulically-bound materials is 'curing' – the process of strength gain. The chemical reactions which lead to cementing action take time, generate heat and cause shrinkage of the cementitious mortar, and these facts pose the danger of *shrinkage cracking*. The problems are as follows:

- The rate of set of the mortar is temperature and water-supply dependent.
- There is commonly a temperature differential through the depth of the slab since setting of the body of the material generates heat.
- Heat generation can also mean that the temperature at the point of set is high, which will result in significant thermal shrinkage as the slab cools.
- Unless special measures are taken, the upper surface of the slab will dry quickest, especially if exposed to sunshine or wind.

If the body of the slab is at a much higher temperature than the surface, then it will tend to set first. The upper part will then try to set and, as it does so, to shrink. This shrinkage will be restrained by the already set material at depth and the result will be shallow cracking.

If, however, the surface is allowed to dry out quickly, it will be the first to set. This will then restrain the rest of the material as it tries to shrink and the result will be shrinkage cracks through the body of the material, and these will quickly propagate to the surface. This is a much more damaging situation since the cracks will penetrate right through the slab.

To counter these problems, two actions are desirable. The first and most important is that the surface must not be allowed to dry out prematurely and this is achieved either by physically keeping the surface wet (e.g. by means of a damp sheet of fabric), or by sealing in the moisture using bitumen or a chemical spray. The second action is to prevent the upper part from cooling much more rapidly than the rest, although this may not be necessary if the weather conditions are favourable. 'Concrete blankets' of various designs are available.

It should be appreciated that curing problems really only become an issue in relatively rapid-setting materials such as Portland cement concretes. Slow-setting materials simply do not generate significant heat of hydration and so the danger of differential temperature gradients disappears. Also, if any internal damage takes place, there will still be plenty of unused binder available to 'heal' any minor cracks which occur. In high-strength concretes, delayed set can be achieved by the use of additives such as fly ash. For base or sub-base mixes, it is often acceptable to use very slow-setting mixtures, for example incorporating blast-furnace slag, fly ash or lime.

1.3.2.7 Reinforcement

Reinforcement is generally only used in PQC – and sometimes not even there; a perfectly satisfactory concrete pavement can be constructed unreinforced, relying on nothing more than the tensile strength of the concrete to prevent cracks from opening. However, reinforcement gives extra tensile strength. It does not stop cracks from forming but it does prevent them from opening, which can slow down the process of deterioration in surface condition considerably. In industrial pavements, for instance, it is common to provide a light mesh of reinforcing steel as an insurance policy, in case unexpected pavement cracking occurs. In highway pavements, where loads are often more certain and which are usually designed not to crack at all, it is common to omit the reinforcement because of the benefit in terms of ease of construction.

In general, reinforcement does not overcome the need for joints, although the added tensile strength is often used to extend the distance between them. However, if enough reinforcement is added (about 0.7% of the cross-sectional area – see Part 3) then it is actually possible to provide a continuous jointless pavement (continuously reinforced concrete – CRC), at least in one direction, because the stresses generated by thermal contraction of the concrete are insufficient to fracture the steel. This is an attractive proposition since joints are invariably a nuisance to maintain, but it does of course add considerably to the cost of the pavement and so is not usual except for the most heavily trafficked highway applications.

A final option, frequently used in internal pavement applications (in warehouses for instance), is to mix *steel fibres* into the concrete, thus forming a continuous randomly orientated reinforcement within the material.[23] The added tensile toughness often allows joints to be either omitted or else very widely spaced. However, external applications, subject to much greater and more rapid temperature variation, render fibre reinforcement less useful.

1.3.2.8 Joints

In practice, almost all PQC pavements have joints. Even CRC pavements have joints in the longitudinal direction. Wherever there is a tendency for significant expansion and contraction or warping, the brittle nature of concrete dictates the use of joints. Without joints, the concrete would be so highly stressed as a consequence of temperature variation, that it would crack anyway, so the obvious course of action is to make sure that these cracks are pre-provided in the form of straight, well-controlled joints.

Joints come in three basic types (see Fig. 1.11), namely *expansion*, *contraction* and *warping*, allowing these three types of pavement deformation to take place. They all place a burden on the construction process since, whatever else is provided, it is necessary somehow to ensure that a straight crack is formed at the chosen location. Since the pavement will crack anyway as it shrinks due to cement hydration and then due to thermal effects, the trick is to persuade it to crack where the designer wants, and this is achieved by making sure that it is significantly weaker along the line of the desired joint than it is elsewhere in the body of the material. Figure 1.11 illustrates possible techniques.[24]

In the case of an expansion joint, a further complication arises in that a compressible 'board' of material has to be incorporated in order to allow the concrete either side of the joint to expand, and it is not

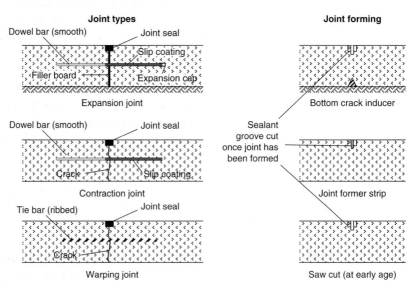

Fig. 1.11 *Joints in concrete pavements*

straightforward to fix such a board sufficiently well to remain in place during concrete placement.

The other major issue is that a joint represents a serious weakness in the pavement. In cold weather, when the concrete shrinks and the joints open up, there will be a loss of continuity across the joint; the concrete slab each side will behave as if it had an unsupported edge. The way around this is to provide *dowel bars* (for expansion and contraction joints) and *tie bars* (for warping joints) – see Fig. 1.11 – which means that these bars either have to be inserted into the wet concrete or they have to be accurately and securely fixed in place beforehand. Both are disruptive processes and represent potential sources of construction defects. Dowel bars in particular will fail to perform well if they are misaligned more than a fraction.[25] The incentive to avoid joints wherever possible is therefore a strong one.[26]

Finally, joints need to be sealed, otherwise they are simply easy passages for water to access the often moisture-susceptible subgrade soil. This requires the formation of a groove and the application of a sealant. Furthermore, it often necessitates regular maintenance of the seal, since even the most advanced sealant materials have a finite life in such an aggressive environment.

1.3.2.9 Surface finish

The final complication when constructing a concrete pavement is the surface finish. Whereas an asphalt can be designed such that its natural surface gives adequate skid resistance without any special treatment, this is not generally the case for concrete, which would usually be very smooth indeed if no special measures were taken. The texture depth which is so important in the provision of wet skidding resistance has to be specially formed in concrete and Fig. 1.12 shows the options available.

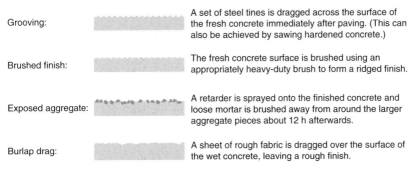

Grooving:		A set of steel tines is dragged across the surface of the fresh concrete immediately after paving. (This can also be achieved by sawing hardened concrete.)
Brushed finish:		The fresh concrete surface is brushed using an appropriately heavy-duty brush to form a ridged finish.
Exposed aggregate:		A retarder is sprayed onto the finished concrete and loose mortar is brushed away from around the larger aggregate pieces about 12 h afterwards.
Burlap drag:		A sheet of rough fabric is dragged over the surface of the wet concrete, leaving a rough finish.

Fig. 1.12 Concrete surface finish options

Surface finish is undeniably one of the major issues affecting the popularity of concrete-surfaced pavements. Even a relatively smooth concrete induces quite high tyre noise, and a high texture depth finish such as that produced by grooving can lead to a rather unpleasant ride quality. Exposed aggregate definitely offers the most favourable combination of skid resistance and ride quality, but at a higher price.

1.3.3 Asphalt

Bitumen is quite different from the hydraulic binders, and the technology of asphalt production is very different from that of cementitious materials. The standard process demands that hot binder is mixed with aggregate in a water-free environment, which effectively means that the stones have to be pre-heated to drive off any moisture present. The exact temperature required for mixing depends on the properties of the particular bitumen being used, but the range is from about 140 to 180°C, which means that asphalt production is a highly energy-intensive process. The asphalt then has to be transported to the site, paved and compacted, for which the temperature should still be greater than about 90°C if proper compaction is to be achieved. The need to maintain temperature tends to shape asphalt production technology.

The alternative is 'cold-mix', a form of asphalt which allows the use of non-heated aggregate. This means that the bitumen has to be in one of two special forms, either *foamed* or as an *emulsion*, and these will be described in Part 2.

1.3.3.1 Particle shape and size distribution

The strength, stiffness and deformation resistance of an asphalt come from a combination of the binder used and the aggregate. For high stability, i.e. low deformation under load and therefore good rut resistance, the criteria are fairly similar to those applying to an unbound material, which means that there will be tight limits on particle size distribution to ensure good interlock between stones. Maximum particle size is once again limited by workability requirements, this time to around 35–40% of layer thickness. Unsurprisingly, the shape of the particles is also important, angular particles giving greater resistance to deformation. Basically, bitumen is not capable of preventing a steady 'creep' from taking place within the asphalt under the action of millions of repeated loads; this can only be stopped by ensuring that the aggregate particles interact and 'lock up'.

1.3.3.2 Mixing and batching

There are two basic types of mixing plant, known as 'batch mixers' and 'drum mixers'. In both types (except in the case of cold-mix) the aggregate has to be proportioned by weighing amounts from different storage hoppers and then fed into a drying chamber where it is super-heated to drive off all moisture. In batch mixers, the dried aggregates are fed through a set of sieves into hot-storage bins, from which they are dropped (in exactly measured proportions) into the mixing chamber, together with the appropriate volume of hot bitumen. The reason for the second stage of proportioning, from the hot-storage bins, is that the initial proportioning was of moist aggregate and may therefore not have been precisely correct. Once mixed, typically after about 30 s, the mixture is dropped into the back of a waiting truck and taken to site.

As in the case of hydraulically-bound material, a continuous drum mixer has the advantage that higher productivity is possible. Drum mixers rely on accurate proportioning of the moist aggregate, with due allowance for the likely differences in moisture content of each size fraction, since the bitumen is fed directly into the drying chamber (which takes the form of an inclined rotating drum). The drying chamber therefore doubles as the mixing chamber and the hot mixture is fed out continuously from the drum to a hot storage hopper before being dropped into the back of a waiting truck. Figure 1.13 illustrates the principles of the two mixer types.

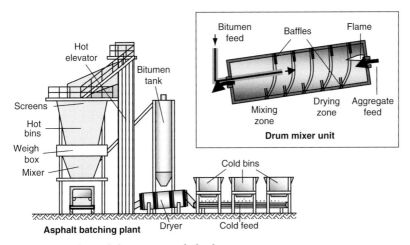

Fig. 1.13 Batch- and drum-type asphalt plants

In contrast to the energy-intensive business of hot-mix asphalt production, cold-mix technology removes the need for heating of the aggregate during production since water is an essential ingredient in the mixture. This means that any mixing plant suited to hydraulically-bound mixtures will, with minor adaptation, also be suitable for cold-mix asphalt.

1.3.3.3 Placement and compaction

The next task is to transport the asphalt mixture to the site – which presents its own challenges. Basically, the mixture has to arrive on site at a suitably high temperature (for hot-mix asphalt) and in a non-segregated state. This means the following conditions must be met:

- Trucks for transport of hot-mix asphalt have to be well insulated and covered.
- The journey must not be too long or cooling, segregation or, in the case of cold-mix, premature setting may result.
- In some cases cellulose fibres have to be added to the mixture to prevent 'binder drainage', i.e. the phenomenon of bitumen flowing to the bottom of the mixture under gravity.

The mixture is then paved by means of an asphalt paver (see Fig. 1.14). This results in an even layer of material placed to a controlled level and, in modern machines, with a significant degree of compaction already induced by the vibrating screed. However, to achieve full compaction, the 'mat' of asphalt has to be rolled (before it has cooled excessively) and there are various different types of roller available, namely:

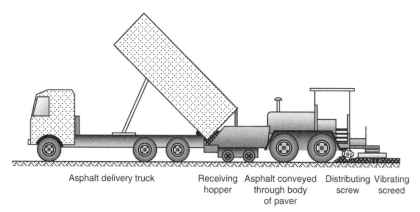

| Asphalt delivery truck | Receiving hopper | Asphalt conveyed through body of paver | Distributing screw | Vibrating screed |

Fig. 1.14 Asphalt paving

- vibratory steel-drum rollers; these induce large numbers of cyclic load applications into the mixture, encouraging densification but also resulting in some loosening of surface material behind the roller;
- dead-weight pneumatic-tyred rollers; these impart many fewer load applications but at a higher load level and avoid the problem of loosening of surface material;
- dead-weight steel-drum rollers (can be vibratory rollers with vibration mode switched off); these are principally used to compact the surface layer, particularly as a finishing process after using vibratory compaction.

Compaction is critical to asphalt performance, just as it is for unbound and hydraulically-bound materials. If the mat is too cool, then it will tend to form surface cracks beside and behind the roller; if it is too hot then it will deform too much and it will be difficult to achieve the required level tolerances. A skilled roller operator is a very valuable member of staff indeed. However, no operator, however skilled, can achieve the impossible and the mathematics of asphalt mat cooling, detailed in Calculation Sheet 1.1 below, demand that the material is not placed either too thin or too thick. It is no good if the operator has to wait so long for the main body of the mat to reach its ideal rolling temperature that the top and bottom have already cooled and can no longer be densified. In fact, the base of the layer represents a problem which simply has to be accepted, since the almost immediate heat transfer between the hot asphalt and the colder substrate inevitably results in very rapid cooling indeed. Figure 1.15 presents predictions of asphalt mat temperature against time for

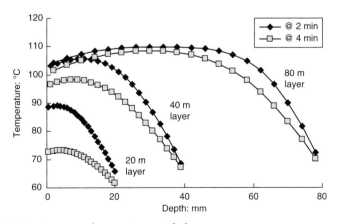

Fig. 1.15 Temperature changes in an asphalt mat

different mat thicknesses assuming a 110°C delivery temperature, using the methodology outlined in Calculation Sheet 1.1.

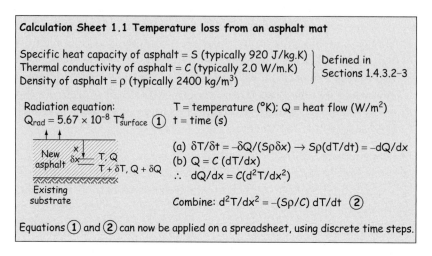

The practicalities of compaction mean that it is unwise to place hot-mix asphalt in layers of over about 120 mm thick. The lower limit on thickness is a function of aggregate particle size and a limit of 2.5 times the maximum particle size is often used. Whatever the particle size, however, any layer under about 25 mm in thickness is clearly going to be difficult to compact due to its rapid heat loss.

1.3.3.4 Inter-layer bond

Asphalt pavement performance relies on there being a good bond between individual asphalt layers; if not, then upper layers can detach, crack and eventually give rise to potholes. It is therefore important to at least make sure that there is nothing present which might inhibit the development of such a bond, in particular water or dirt. However, to achieve a higher level of assurance, it is necessary to physically add a bonding agent, i.e. a 'tack coat' or 'bond coat'. This comprises a thin (generally about 0.3 litres/m²) layer of bitumen sprayed onto the surface shortly before placing the upper lift of asphalt.[27]

1.3.3.5 Asphalt reinforcement

This short paragraph is included simply to warn the reader that special care is needed where reinforcing products (geogrids, geotextiles) are used in asphalt. In theory, there should be no disruption to asphalt paving and no special measures should be needed. However, experience suggests that the fixing of the reinforcement to the layer beneath, for which many techniques have been devised, is critical. If it is well fixed then no problems should occur; if not, then the reinforcement product will tend to move around under the action of the paver and the likelihood is that this will result in voiding at the base of the layer. If this happens, then any benefit which the reinforcement might have given is more than offset by the danger of deterioration due to high void content, particularly if water is able to accumulate at the level of the reinforcement.

1.3.3.6 Surface finish

In general an asphalt surface is well suited to vehicle use. It absorbs more energy than concrete, which makes for a smoother ride, and modern pavers are quite capable of obtaining the required longitudinal profile. However, the requirement for skid resistance demands certain actions – depending on usage of course – and there are also desirable features such as spray retarding and noise absorption which also affect the choice of surface application technique. Figure 1.16 illustrates conceptually the different methods used.

The material depicted as *bituminous macadam* in Fig. 1.16 is illustrative of a wide range of different mixtures, all having the property that they need no further treatment in order to form the finished pavement surface. In fact, options range from dense mixtures (having broad aggregate gradation) often known as *asphalt concrete*, through *stone mastic asphalt* (with a slightly coarser gradation) to *porous asphalt*

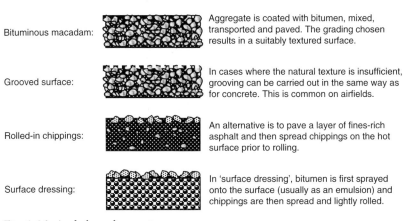

Bituminous macadam:	Aggregate is coated with bitumen, mixed, transported and paved. The grading chosen results in a suitably textured surface.
Grooved surface:	In cases where the natural texture is insufficient, grooving can be carried out in the same way as for concrete. This is common on airfields.
Rolled-in chippings:	An alternative is to pave a layer of fines-rich asphalt and then spread chippings on the hot surface prior to rolling.
Surface dressing:	In 'surface dressing', bitumen is first sprayed onto the surface (usually as an emulsion) and chippings are then spread and lightly rolled.

Fig. 1.16 Asphalt surface options

(almost single-sized). Part 2 describes the materials while Part 3 includes a section on surface design.

1.3.4 Summary

This section should have given the reader a reasonable understanding of the art of the possible as far as pavements are concerned. The limitations of plant and equipment represent one of the key constraints affecting pavement design. As in all branches of engineering, it is important to bridge the gap between the design theorist and the practitioner.

1.4

Basic engineering concepts

This section is included for those who feel they need reminding of concepts studied years ago and long since forgotten under the weight of practical engineering. It will introduce various properties, quantities and concepts, all relevant to the methods presented in the remainder of this book.

1.4.1 Basic quantities

As in any field, civil engineering is awash with technical and not so technical terms, and the exact meaning of each is sometimes far from clear. The following paragraphs give definitions for key basic quantities, most of which the reader will probably know perfectly well.

1.4.1.1 Mass

Every object has a *mass*, measured in kilograms (or tonnes; $1000\,\text{kg} = 1\,\text{t}$). Mass has no particular direction.

1.4.1.2 Weight

The *weight* of an object refers specifically to the downward effect of a *mass* due to the action of the earth's gravity. Gravity is expressed as an acceleration ($9.81\,\text{m/s}^2$), being the rate at which an object would accelerate downwards towards the centre of the earth in the absence of any resistance.

Weight is measured in newtons (N). It is defined as the mass of an object multiplied by the acceleration due to gravity. On the surface of the earth, therefore, 1 kg of *mass* has a *weight* of 9.81 N.

1.4.1.3 Density, unit weight and specific gravity

The *density* of a material is the mass per unit volume (kg/m^3). For example, water has a density of 1000 kg/m^3, while most rocks are between 2500 and 3000 kg/m^3. Soils, being combinations of rock particles, water and air, tend to have densities in the range 1500–2000 kg/m^3, while crushed rock pavement layers are usually around 2200 kg/m^3. Asphalt and concrete are typically around 2400 kg/m^3.

In civil engineering, where most materials are static and the effect of density is to generate weight due to gravity, it is often convenient to work in terms of *unit weight* rather than density. This is defined as the weight per unit volume and is expressed in N/m^3, or more usually kN/m^3. Thus, pavement layers tend to have unit weights in the range 18–24 kN/m^3.

Finally, *specific gravity* is simply a convenient relative measure. Water is assigned a specific gravity of 1; other materials have a higher or lower specific gravity according to the ratio of their densities to that of water. Thus, bitumen, for example, being marginally denser than water, has a specific gravity of 1.02–1.03.

1.4.1.4 Force and load

The weight of an object under gravity is an example of a *force*. More generally, however, a force can be generated in numerous different ways (e.g. braking, acceleration, impact). Like weight, force is measured in newtons (N), or more commonly kN.

Load is also a force. It is usually applied in the same way as weight, but can also be used to describe any force which 'loads' an object (or a pavement for that matter).

1.4.1.5 Stress and pressure

These two words have exactly the same meaning in engineering terms, although *stress* is most commonly used when dealing with solids, whereas *pressure* usually relates to liquids and gases. They are both defined as force divided by area, giving units of N/m^2, also known as pascals (Pa). Thus, the load from a wheel can be expressed directly in newtons, but it is also relevant to know the intensity of that load on the surface, and this is given by the contact stress, i.e. the load divided by the contact area. This will be approximately equal to the air pressure within the tyre – although the complexities of tyre wall behaviour mean that it is a little more complicated than this in reality.

Thus, the vertical contact stress (and tyre pressure) of a typical heavy goods vehicle wheel are both around 600 kPa. Because of the way the pavement spreads the load, the vertical stress at the top of the subgrade may be no more than about 10 kPa.

1.4.1.6 Strain

Strain is often the consequence of stress. Strain describes the degree to which a material deforms, and it is defined as the change in a dimension divided by the original magnitude of that dimension. Thus, if a 100 mm thick layer of asphalt compresses to 99 mm, the strain is $(100 - 99)/100$, i.e. 0.01. It has no units since it is a relative change. Where strains are large, they are often expressed as percentages (1% in this example). However, for the very small strains generated within a pavement under load, the unit is usually microstrain ($\mu\varepsilon$); $1\,\mu\varepsilon$ is a strain of 10^{-6} (a change of one millionth in the original dimension).

1.4.2 Mechanical properties

The following paragraphs identify and explain the important engineering properties referred to throughout the remainder of the book.

1.4.2.1 Stiffness

Stiffness is a particularly loose term. However, it is in common usage among engineers and so has to be introduced. At its most basic, it refers to a ratio of load to deformation. This could be, for example, the ratio of a wheel load to a pavement deformation. It could equally refer to the load-to-deformation ratio of a vehicle suspension spring.

However, stiffness is also used much more generally to describe the resistance of a material to stress, whether it is the bending stiffness of a pavement layer, the shear stiffness of a bitumen or the load transfer stiffness across a concrete joint. Because it is such a loose term (and will be used as such in this book), it will not be given a specific definition.

1.4.2.2 Elastic modulus (or elastic stiffness)

This is the most common measure of *stiffness* used by engineers. It is the ratio of applied *stress* to induced *strain*. Thus if a block of concrete is subjected to a stress of 1 MPa (1 megapascal or 10^6 Pa) and it develops a strain (in the direction of the stress) of $50\,\mu\varepsilon$, it would have an *elastic modulus* of $10^{6}/(50 \times 10^{-6})$, which is 20×10^{9} Pa or 20 GPa (gigapascals).

This is an extremely useful concept, but it assumes that the behaviour of the material concerned is *linear*; that means that if the stress is doubled then so is the strain. For concrete and other intact hydraulically-bound materials this is approximately true, within the normal working range; similarly for steel. However, unbound material is significantly non-linear while asphalt stiffness varies with temperature and loading rate, which means these materials cannot be said to possess a single elastic modulus value. That does not stop engineers using the concept for both unbound material and asphalt – but it means they use a different term.

1.4.2.3 Stiffness modulus and resilient modulus

These terms are used to indicate that the measure used, though still *stress* divided by *strain*, does not really imply a single linear elastic property. Asphalt has a viscous (temperature-dependent) component to its behaviour and the rather general term *stiffness modulus* is therefore used – but, at a given temperature and loading rate, the definition is exactly the same as that for elastic modulus.

The term *resilient modulus* is reserved for soils and other unbound materials. It is used to separate out the component of behaviour which is approximately elastic (though still non-linear and therefore stress-dependent) from the plastic component, where strains are non-recoverable. However, under a given set of stress conditions, the definition of resilient modulus is still exactly the same as that of elastic modulus, i.e. stress divided by strain.

1.4.2.4 Poisson's ratio, shear modulus and bulk modulus

Up until this point, it has been assumed that stress and strain act in a single direction. However, in real life, the fact that the world is three-dimensional cannot be ignored and the stresses and strains in a pavement occur in all directions.

For many purposes, the most convenient way of dealing with the interaction between effects in different directions is by means of the quantity known as *Poisson's ratio*. Figure 1.17 gives the definition. Poisson's ratio controls the degree to which a material compresses under load. In an incompressible material, it has a value of 0.5. Clays

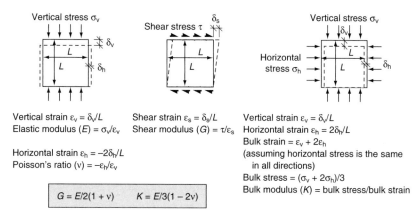

Fig. 1.17 Measures of stiffness

at high levels of saturation are nearly incompressible and so have Poisson's ratio values of 0.45 or more; granular materials tend to have a much higher air void content, giving a lower Poisson's ratio, typically 0.3–0.35, and values for asphalt tend to be similar. Hydraulically-bound materials usually have the lowest values of all pavement materials, often in the 0.15–0.2 range.

The other quantities, *shear modulus* and *bulk modulus*, are also defined in Fig. 1.17. They are directly related to elastic modulus and Poisson's ratio – through formulae given in the figure – but it is sometimes convenient to work in terms of shear or bulk properties for particular problems.

Note that the underlying assumption here is *linear elasticity*. These quantities can still be used for non-linear or temperature-dependent materials, but it has to be remembered that they will no longer be absolute and unchanging properties although they may be valid for a certain set of conditions. Unbound materials in particular can display an enormous range of Poisson's ratio values depending on stress conditions, even values well above 0.5, meaning that the material dilates as it strains.

1.4.2.5 Modulus of subgrade reaction

This is not really a material property, but it makes sense to introduce it here because it is easy to confuse with the stiffness modulus or resilient modulus of the subgrade material. The *modulus of subgrade reaction* is defined as the ratio of an applied vertical stress (at top of subgrade level) to the resulting vertical deflection. This is convenient for two reasons:

1. It can be measured directly by means of a plate loading test.
2. It fits nicely into a widely-used computational approach for stress in concrete pavements – introduced in Part 3.

Unfortunately, although convenient, this is not a fundamentally correct way to describe a pavement foundation. Calculation Sheet 1.2 presents an approximate method for estimating modulus of subgrade reaction from stiffness modulus. Notice the use of a load spread angle; for this a default value of 35° is recommended, since this gives surface deflections equal to those obtained theoretically for the case of a uniform elastic 'half-space' under a circular load. Taking an upper subgrade thickness of 1 m, and the standard case of a 762 mm (30 in.) diameter plate test, the equation in Calculation Sheet 1.2 (with a 35° load spread angle) gives values of modulus of subgrade reaction in MN/m^3 between 54% and 84% of the stiffness modulus in MPa – typical of quoted ratios.[28] However, the results are highly sensitive to the diameter of the loaded area. If a real pavement were to spread each wheel load over a 1 m diameter loaded area, these percentages would become 71% and 122%; on the other hand a more flexible structure, spreading the wheel load over a 0.5 m diameter area, gives only 36–48%. Care is therefore needed when working with a modulus of subgrade reaction.

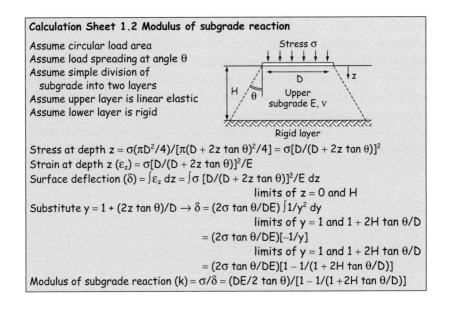

Calculation Sheet 1.2 Modulus of subgrade reaction

Assume circular load area
Assume load spreading at angle θ
Assume simple division of subgrade into two layers
Assume upper layer is linear elastic
Assume lower layer is rigid

Stress at depth z = $\sigma(\pi D^2/4)/[\pi(D + 2z \tan \theta)^2/4] = \sigma[D/(D + 2z \tan \theta)]^2$
Strain at depth z (ε_z) = $\sigma[D/(D + 2z \tan \theta)]^2/E$
Surface deflection (δ) = $\int \varepsilon_z \, dz = \int \sigma [D/(D + 2z \tan \theta)]^2/E \, dz$
$\qquad\qquad\qquad\qquad\qquad$ limits of z = 0 and H
Substitute y = $1 + (2z \tan \theta)/D \rightarrow \delta = (2\sigma \tan \theta/DE) \int 1/y^2 \, dy$
$\qquad\qquad\qquad\qquad\qquad$ limits of y = 1 and 1 + 2H tan θ/D
$\qquad\qquad\qquad\qquad\qquad$ = $(2\sigma \tan \theta/DE)[-1/y]$
$\qquad\qquad\qquad\qquad\qquad$ limits of y = 1 and 1 + 2H tan θ/D
$\qquad\qquad\qquad\qquad\qquad$ = $(2\sigma \tan \theta/DE)[1 - 1/(1 + 2H \tan \theta/D)]$
Modulus of subgrade reaction (k) = σ/δ = $(DE/2 \tan \theta)/[1 - 1/(1 + 2H \tan \theta/D)]$

1.4.2.6 *Viscosity and kinematic viscosity*

Viscosity is a property displayed by a liquid such as water or bitumen. It is defined as the ratio of an applied stress to the resulting strain rate (*strain* per second), and so has units of pascal seconds (Pa.s). In effect it parallels the concept of elastic stiffness in a solid. If related to a single direction, the property might be more properly termed *axial viscosity*; Poisson's ratio is usually 0.5 since liquids are generally incompressible, which means that *shear viscosity* is one third of axial viscosity and *bulk viscosity* is infinite – following the interrelationships presented in Fig. 1.17. The viscosity of water at 20°C is around 10^{-3} Pa.s; that of bitumen ranges from about 10^3 Pa.s at 40°C to as much as 10^7 Pa.s at 0°C.

It is often convenient in engineering problems to work with a quantity known as *kinematic viscosity*, which is defined simply enough as the viscosity divided by the density. The resulting fundamental unit is m^2/s, but the value is more usually quoted in 'centistokes', a centistoke being a mm^2/s, giving a kinematic viscosity of water of approximately 1 centistoke.

1.4.3 Thermal properties

While the mechanical properties of pavement materials are the most influential, determining the response to traffic load, stresses and strains can also be generated by changes in temperature, which means that the thermal properties also have to be understood.

1.4.3.1 *Coefficient of thermal expansion*

Every material tends to change its volume slightly with temperature, which can cause problems in a continuous stretch of pavement. The extent to which this occurs is governed by the *coefficient of thermal expansion*, which is defined as the proportional change in a given linear dimension due to a 1°C rise in temperature. For rocks, this tends to be in the range 0.6–1.4×10^{-5}/°C, and since rock (or rock derivative, i.e. slag, minestone, demolition waste) is usually the major component of pavement materials, this means that the same range is found for hydraulically-bound materials (and steel). Asphalts tend to have a slightly higher value, typically 1.8×10^{-5}/°C, because of the much higher thermal expansion potential of bitumen. Use of limestone aggregate minimises thermal expansion; use of gravel aggregate usually maximises it.

1.4.3.2 Thermal conductivity

If thermal expansion is a significant issue, then this means that the temperature at any depth in a pavement at a given time is also important, and this will depend on the efficiency with which the different pavement materials allow heat energy to travel. The relevant property is *thermal conductivity*; it describes the flow of energy (in joules per second, or watts) caused by a 1 K (i.e. 1 degree Kelvin; = 1°C) temperature difference across a 1 m length of material, 1 m² in cross-section. The units are therefore W/mK. Typical values range from 0.25 W/mK for dry soils to around 2 W/mK for asphalt or concrete.

1.4.3.3 Specific heat capacity

This is the final property required in any prediction of temperature changes within a pavement. It describes how much energy is required to heat up a given mass of material by 1 K. The units are therefore J/kgK, with typical values for pavement materials in the range 800–1000 J/kgK, a little higher for wet soils.

1.5

Conclusion to Part 1

Whatever complex computations are carried out by researchers in pursuit of a purer understanding of material behaviour, pavement engineering is still essentially a *practical* subject. No matter the extent to which scientific principles and mathematical processes are introduced, it is useless trying to produce sensible designs for materials, pavement construction or rehabilitation without an understanding of practical and economic issues. This chapter has addressed some of these issues. There is, of course, no substitute for experience. No amount of description of matters such as asphalt compaction and concrete curing can possibly replace the learning achieved through direct observation. No amount of advice on what sort of pavement to use in different circumstances can possibly develop the wisdom that comes through having to put such choices into practice. So, while it is hoped that the advice and explanation offered in this chapter may prove a useful starting-point, it is only a start.

Notes

1. Cement technology is a vast subject in its own right and involves several different chemical reactions. The most important are the conversion of tricalcium silicate (c. 50% of Portland cement) and dicalcium silicate (c. 25%) into hydrates (forming strong solids) by reaction with water, also generating calcium hydroxide and heat. The first reaction is rapid; the second is slower. The reader should refer to specialist literature for details.

2. There are countless stories as to when bituminous products were first used on roads, such as the accidental spillage of tar outside Derby iron works in 1901. Mastics including natural asphalt had been used on footways since the 1830s, but were not stable enough for roads. The first usages of tar-bound stone occurred in the US and Europe at approximately similar dates, around 1900–1901. Lay (1990) gives further information.

3. Grouted macadam is known as 'resin-modified pavement' in the US and is also sometimes known as 'semi-flexible' material.

4. The price of granular materials is often largely determined by haulage (or shipping) distance. In general it is uneconomic to transport such materials further than about 40 km by land.

5. Derived from Stripple (2001).

6. This figure is derived from UK data. Current UK energy usage is running at about 7.6×10^{18} J per year (170 million tonnes of oil equivalent). Total production is some 48% higher than this, but much is lost before reaching the consumer. The energy used in pavement construction (not including major earthworks, tunnels and bridges) is probably around 2×10^{16} J per year, extrapolated from asphalt consumption figures.

7. There is full agreement that a rough texture leads to high rolling resistance and therefore high fuel consumption (e.g. Yap, 1987). However, there are also studies that suggest that a stiff pavement (notably a concrete surface) will reduce energy losses and lower fuel consumption (e.g. Zaniewski, 1982).

8. The latest recommendations from the US (AASHTO, 2007b) suggest that a reliability of 85–97% should be used on the most heavily trafficked roads, falling to 50–75% for minor roads. In the UK, 85% reliability has been adopted for major roads for a number of years.

9. See AASHTO, 2007b.

10. Examples of industrial by-products used in pavement construction are mining waste (e.g. from coal or china clay extraction) and slags (from various metal extraction processes, notably iron). Suitable recycled materials are construction and demolition waste, notably crushed concrete, and recycled asphalt planings (RAP).

11. Both fine polymer fibres and mesh elements have proved effective at significantly increasing the strength of sandy/silty soils. The chief difficulty (and therefore expense) lies in the mixing process.

12. There is considerable variety in the types of concrete used in port pavements. Strengths range from 10 to 40 MPa (compressive); both wet-formed and roller compacted placement techniques are common. Guidance is given in Knapton and Meletiou (1996).

13. Because of the high stresses at the edges of the grooves, grooving is only suited to the strongest mixes.

14. These gradations are taken from the current UK Highways Agency specifications (Highways Agency, 2007).

15. The standard particle strength test in the UK was known as the '10% fines' test (a measure of the stress required to induce a 10% increase in fines in a sample of a designated size); however, this has now been discarded in favour of the tests mentioned in note 16.

16. The best known are 'Los Angeles abrasion' (CEN, 1998a; AASHTO, 2002a; ASTM, 2003 and 2006b) and 'Micro-Deval' (CEN, 1996; AASHTO, 2006c; ASTM, 2006e), both of which consist of 'shaking' a batch of material and observing degradation.

17. AASHTO (2007a) is an example of a freeze–thaw soundness specification. Frost heave tests are described in Croney and Jacobs (1967) and ASTM (2007).

18. AASHTO (1999) and CEN (1998b) describe tests using magnesium or sodium sulphate to evaluate resistance to chemical weathering.

19. There is no limit for flakiness or elongation in current UK standards for unbound pavement materials.

20. The stage at which pavement drainage is installed is significant here. It is always preferable to have finished drainage installation before pavement construction. UK Highways Agency standard IAN73 (Highways Agency, 2006c) seeks to ensure quality by insisting on dynamic plate testing (see Part 2) immediately prior to placement of an overlying layer.

21. The usual UK limit (Highways Agency, 2007) for compaction of unbound materials is 225 mm.

22. For example, it is common to blend large aggregate with sand in a concrete mixture. The resulting rather discontinuous gradation would not be suitable for an unbound layer but gives excellent concrete. Similarly, rounded gravel, though highly undesirable in unbound materials, is perfectly suitable in a concrete.

23. The UK Concrete Society report TR34 (Concrete Society, 2003) is an example of a design method which includes fibre reinforcement as an option.

24. If a bottom crack-inducer is used, this would normally be in conjunction with a surface saw cut. While this is practically certain to induce a crack, any misalignment between crack-inducer and saw cut may result in the crack missing the saw cut.

25. The UK Highways Agency (2007) places an absolute limit on dowel bar misalignment of 6 mm over a 300 mm length.

26. It is, of course, quite possible not to use dowel bars at joints, so long as the slab is thick enough and strong enough. British Airports Authority is an example of a pavement authority which prefers not to use dowels.

27. The need or otherwise for inter-layer bond and how to specify and achieve it are still subject to debate. In many specifications, reliance on surface cleanliness is considered sufficient; at the other extreme (Stöckert, 2001), bond strength is specified and measurements are carried out on specimens cored from the pavement.

28. British Airports Authority (1993) quotes a direct relationship between the modulus of subgrade reaction, k (in MN/m^3), and an equivalent foundation modulus, E (in MPa), as follows: $k = (E/4.97)^{1.292}$

Part 2
Materials

2.1

Unbound material

It is easy for pavement engineers to get lost in a world of asphalt and surface issues and to forget that the most fundamental element in any pavement is the ground upon which it is built – and that ground will be an *unbound* material. It is a class of material that is all around us, which we come into contact with on a daily basis, but which is very poorly understood from the point of view of its mechanical properties. Yet a reasonable level of understanding is not hard to achieve. The defining feature of an unbound material is that is has no binder. This means that it has a tensile strength of zero. Whatever is asked of such a material, it cannot possibly be asked to take any tension.

2.1.1 Shear strength
Unbound materials cannot withstand tension – but they can withstand shear. It is meaningless to talk of tensile failure of an unbound material since there is nothing to fail; failure in unbound material is always *shear* failure. Deformation in an unbound layer of a pavement is always associated with failure along shear planes.

2.1.1.1 Inter-particle slip
Significant shear strain in an unbound material can only occur if slip takes place between particles. Figure 2.1 illustrates the point.

In order to achieve shear strain within the body of the material, some at least of the individual particles have to translate and rotate into new positions, and this can only occur through stones sliding against one another. This of course is resisted by *friction*, and the resistance to strain might therefore be expected to relate to the frictional qualities

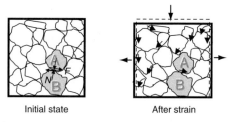

| Initial state | After strain |

Fig. 2.1 The mechanism of shear in an unbound material

of the aggregate surface. Furthermore, the *shape* of the particles is clearly also important. A rounded particle is obviously easier to slip past than an angular one, whatever its frictional properties.

As in any frictional problem, it is the ratio of shear force to normal force that controls whether slip occurs. For example, particle A in Fig. 2.1 could never slip along the face of particle B unless the shear force F was enough to overcome the normal force N. This frictional property can either be expressed as a coefficient of friction μ or an angle of friction θ:

At slip: $F = \mu N = \tan \theta \times N$

For crushed rock particles, θ is typically around 30–35°; rather less for smooth river gravels.

2.1.1.2 Angle of internal friction

Just as the slip between individual particles is controlled by the friction at stone-to-stone contacts, so shear failure of an unbound granular matrix can be thought of in a similar fashion. Stone-to-stone friction, particle shape and also particle size distribution all contribute to resisting the development of a shear plane. The actual movements of particles will be a complex combination of slip, rotation and sideways displacement, but the overall effect (illustrated in Fig. 2.2) will be that the shear stress τ to cause failure on a given plane will be a function of the normal stress σ across that plane – just as in any frictional system – and this relationship can be described by the angle of internal friction ϕ.

At shear failure: $\tan \phi = \tau / \sigma$

The situation shown in Fig. 2.2 may be readily understandable, but it represents a highly constrained and artificial state for the material,

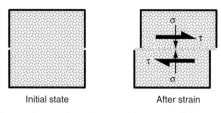

Initial state   After strain

Fig. 2.2 Shear failure of an unbound granular material

a state in which the failure plane is predetermined. More generally, however, failure will take place on any plane where the τ/σ ratio exceeds its limiting value. For example, Fig. 2.3 shows the change in stress state at a point within a material in the form of 'Mohr circles'[1] of increasing magnitude, together with a line representing the limiting τ/σ ratio. The Mohr circle construction (refer to Calculation Sheet 2.1) describes the stress state in every direction on a given plane, and any point on the circle which touches the line of limiting τ/σ ratio represents the onset of shear failure in a particular direction. In Fig. 2.3, shear failure planes would be inclined at an angle of $\alpha/2$ to the vertical – following the mathematical explanation in Calculation Sheet 2.1.

Please do not confuse the angle of internal friction ϕ with the angle of friction relating to stone-to-stone contact θ. The angle θ is a fundamental property of the surface of the aggregate particles while ϕ is a composite, with contributions from stone-to-stone friction, particle shape and particle size distribution. While θ has a relatively narrow range of possible values, between about 25 and 40°, ϕ can range from around 20° for some single-sized silts to as much as 60° for broadly graded, angular aggregate.

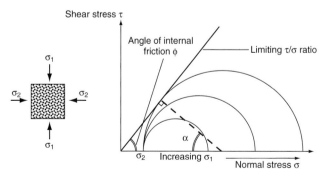

Fig. 2.3 The shear failure state on a Mohr circle diagram

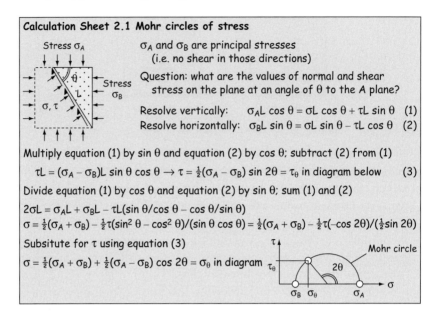

Calculation Sheet 2.1 Mohr circles of stress

Stress σ_A

σ_A and σ_B are principal stresses (i.e. no shear in those directions)

Stress σ_B

Question: what are the values of normal and shear stress on the plane at an angle of θ to the A plane?

σ, τ

Resolve vertically: $\quad \sigma_A L \cos\theta = \sigma L \cos\theta + \tau L \sin\theta$ (1)

Resolve horizontally: $\quad \sigma_B L \sin\theta = \sigma L \sin\theta - \tau L \cos\theta$ (2)

Multiply equation (1) by $\sin\theta$ and equation (2) by $\cos\theta$; subtract (2) from (1)

$\tau L = (\sigma_A - \sigma_B) L \sin\theta \cos\theta \rightarrow \tau = \frac{1}{2}(\sigma_A - \sigma_B)\sin 2\theta = \tau_\theta$ in diagram below (3)

Divide equation (1) by $\cos\theta$ and equation (2) by $\sin\theta$; sum (1) and (2)

$2\sigma L = \sigma_A L + \sigma_B L - \tau L(\sin\theta/\cos\theta - \cos\theta/\sin\theta)$

$\sigma = \frac{1}{2}(\sigma_A + \sigma_B) - \frac{1}{2}\tau(\sin^2\theta - \cos^2\theta)/(\sin\theta\cos\theta) = \frac{1}{2}(\sigma_A + \sigma_B) - \frac{1}{2}\tau(-\cos 2\theta)/(\frac{1}{2}\sin 2\theta)$

Subsitute for τ using equation (3)

$\sigma = \frac{1}{2}(\sigma_A + \sigma_B) + \frac{1}{2}(\sigma_A - \sigma_B)\cos 2\theta = \sigma_\theta$ in diagram

Mohr circle

2.1.1.3 Stress ratio at failure

In many applications it is convenient to think in terms of a limiting ratio of two orthogonal stresses σ_1 and σ_2, as in Fig. 2.3. This is related to the angle of internal friction ϕ by the geometry of the Mohr circle diagram since the sine of ϕ is the ratio of the radius of the Mohr circle to the distance of the centre of the Mohr circle from the origin, i.e.:

$$\sin\phi = \tfrac{1}{2}(\sigma_1 - \sigma_2)/\tfrac{1}{2}(\sigma_1 + \sigma_2)$$

Rearranging:

$$\sigma_1 = \sigma_2(1 + \sin\phi)/(1 - \sin\phi)$$

Good-quality crushed stone base should have a value of over 10 for the σ_1/σ_2 ratio (equating to a ϕ value of over 55°).

2.1.1.4 Interlock

The characterisation of shear strength by means of angle of internal friction ϕ is approximately correct for most granular materials other than those with a clay content (see next section) – but only approximately. The way that angular particles interact creates what has been termed the 'dry stone wall' effect.[2] Referring back to the diagram on the left of Fig. 2.3, it is possible to withstand a moderate level of stress σ_1

even if σ_2 is zero. The effect this has on the failure characteristic when plotted on a Mohr circle diagram is to raise it slightly, giving an intercept on the τ axis. This intercept is akin to the effect of water in clay soil, for which the term 'cohesion' and symbol c are used. In this case, the property is certainly not cohesion, but the term 'apparent cohesion' is still often applied. The effect on the stress state at failure is as follows:

$$\sigma_1 = [\sigma_2(1 + \sin\phi) + 2c\cos\phi]/(1 - \sin\phi)$$

The value of the interlock (or apparent cohesion) intercept is rarely more than a few kilopascals, perhaps as much as 20 kPa in a broadly-graded crushed rock.[3] In a single-sized material it is unlikely to be more than about 5 kPa, but even this modest quantity can be highly influential in determining performance, particularly in unsurfaced pavements. After all, 5 kPa is equivalent to the stress from a 250 mm thickness of overburden.

2.1.1.5 Cohesion

True geotechnical engineers will often claim that cohesion does not exist – but in the world of the practical pavement engineer it certainly does.[4] For a start, soils generally exhibit a suction depending on their moisture state (see Section 2.1.4.5), the measurable effect of which is a cohesion. An additional cohesive effect is created by the need for water to flow between very small pore spaces as a soil deforms. Inevitably, as deformation takes place and particles rearrange themselves, some void spaces will want to expand while others will want to contract. If many or all of these voids are filled with water, this means that water has to flow from one void to another and this will be resisted because of the viscosity of water and the extreme narrowness of some of the gaps available. The effect is loading rate dependent and would disappear if the material was given enough time for the water to flow and for pressures to dissipate. However, for most pavement engineering purposes, loading is much too quick for the small pores present in many soils, and pore pressure dissipation is therefore limited – which means that cohesion, even if it is termed 'apparent' cohesion, is a very real property.

For most clays under short-term (i.e. *undrained*) loading, cohesion is the dominant component of shear strength and it operates equally at all levels of confinement, i.e. all levels of normal stress. An element of soil which is saturated will be incompressible. Thus, confining stress will be

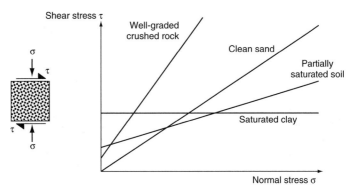

Fig. 2.4 Forms of shear strength characteristic – undrained conditions

quite unable to cause strain in the soil skeleton, which therefore cannot increase its contribution to carrying that stress; it simply increases pressure in the water. And if there is no change in the forces between soil particles, there will be no change in the shear stress at failure. The result is a horizontal failure characteristic, as shown in Fig. 2.4.

Not surprisingly, partially saturated soils have short-term (undrained) failure characteristics somewhere between that of a saturated clay and that of a dry granular material – see Fig. 2.4. Many voids will still be full of water, which means that cohesion will therefore still exist. On the other hand, when confining stress is added, the presence of air voids means that the material is no longer incompressible and that some of the increased stress will be taken by the soil skeleton. This will give an apparent angle of friction, much less than the value would have been under dry conditions because a high percentage of normal stress is still being transmitted directly to the pore water.

Please note that the behaviour described here only applies under conditions which can be considered undrained. That certainly applies under moving vehicle loading, but it does not apply to long-term geotechnical problems such as embankment stability or sub-soil compressibility.

2.1.1.6 The effect of particle and mixture properties

Figure 2.4 has illustrated the typical forms of the shear strength characteristic for different unbound materials. However, these are merely generic observations and there are a number of parameters which contribute strongly to the exact values applying, as follows:

- particle shape and angularity
- particle size

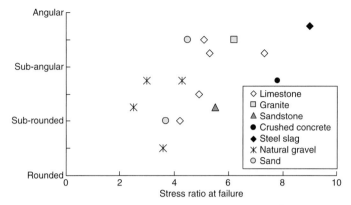

Fig. 2.5 The influence of particle angularity on shear strength[5]

- particle size distribution
- particle packing
- water content.

A further issue is the strength of individual particles, but in practice this is rarely significant as regards the shear strength of pavement materials.[6] The frictional properties of the surface of particles are also relatively unimportant, as is the stiffness of the parent material from which the particles derive.

Particle shape and angularity
From previous paragraphs it will already be clear that an angular material will tend to have a high angle of internal friction (and therefore a high stress ratio at failure). This is illustrated in Fig. 2.5 for a range of non-cohesive pavement materials.

Angularity is not a property which is readily quantified. Most methodologies rely on description and visual categorisation, as in Fig. 2.5; counting of apexes or faces is possible, but this takes no real account of the sharpness of the edges between faces and therefore cannot be relied upon to give a clear measure.

Particle size
There seems little reason to expect particle size to affect the angle of internal friction of an aggregate, so long as particle shape is unchanged. If the well-known Hertzian contact law[7] between spherical particles is assumed to apply, the size effect should be zero. However, experience

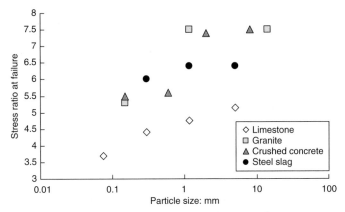

Fig. 2.6 The influence of particle size on aggregate strength[8]

is that aggregates with larger particles tend to display a larger angle of internal friction, as illustrated in Fig. 2.6 for the case of single-sized materials, and this strongly suggests that the Hertzian law, in which compression at particle contacts is proportional to force to a power of two thirds, requires modifying for real aggregates. The effect shown in Fig. 2.6 implies that the real compression at particle contacts is very approximately proportional to force to the power of a half. There may also be effects due to:

- increased interlock with larger particle sizes – often mistaken for true angle of internal friction
- a finite number of particles on each potential failure plane – less particles and the chances of localised weaknesses are reduced.

Particle size distribution
It is entirely unsurprising that a broadly graded aggregate tends to have a higher angle of internal friction than a single-sized material. Basically, the increased number of particle contacts which a broad gradation allows makes the development of a failure plane more difficult, increasing strength. This is illustrated in Fig. 2.7 for aggregates having the same maximum particle size but different size distributions. The measure used for particle size distribution in Fig. 2.7 is *uniformity coefficient*, defined as the ratio of the sieve size through which 60% of the material passes to that through which just 10% passes.

However, there is a limit, an optimum beyond which there is no gain in broadening the size distribution – a uniformity coefficient of around

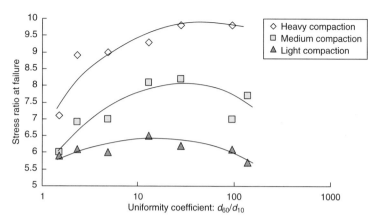

Fig. 2.7 The influence of particle size distribution on aggregate strength[9]

40 for the 'heavy compaction' case illustrated in Fig. 2.7. The point is that if too many small-size particles are included into a mixture, then they will dominate behaviour and the larger particles will become detached from one another. For optimised aggregate strength, there needs to be exactly the right number of particles of each size to fill the voids between larger particles, developing a maximum number of particle contacts, and experience suggests that this is achieved by using a so-called *Fuller curve*.[10] Fuller curves obey the following formula:

$$\% \text{ passing sieve size } d = 100(d/d_{max})^n$$

The key parameter is clearly the exponent n, and it is generally found that the most efficient packing is given when $n \approx 0.4$–0.5 (uniformity coefficient 36–88). This will depend on the particle shape of course and so can only be taken as an approximate guideline. However, Fig. 2.8 shows the Fuller curve series in comparison with the current UK speci-fication for high-quality unbound road sub-base,[11] and it is clear that exponents between 0.3 and 0.8 approximately cover the specified range.

Particle packing
Obviously particle size distribution is an important factor controlling the efficiency of particle packing. However, packing also depends on the degree of compaction (or consolidation). An aggregate following the $n = 0.4$ Fuller gradation will pack well even if simply tipped out of a wagon – but it will pack substantially better if it is compacted. The effect of compaction on shear strength was illustrated in Fig. 2.7.

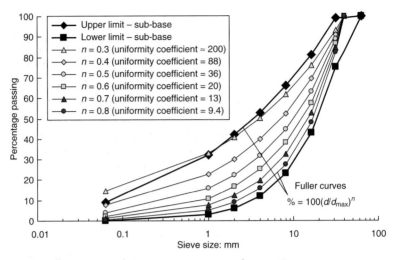

Fig. 2.8 Fuller curve gradations; maximum particle size 40 mm

Compaction will therefore be a key requirement for any unbound pavement layer. It will usually be specified in terms of percentage relative to a controlled laboratory procedure.[12]

Water content
This is a complex issue. Part 1 has already explained the practicalities, whereby a relatively high water content has to be used during compaction in order to achieve optimised particle packing, but that the material should then be allowed to dry out in order to generate the best possible in-service properties. Section 2.1.4 will examine the subject in more detail. Here it should simply be noted that a high water content is usually associated with a low unbound material shear strength, but that this may be due to two effects:

1. Void spaces which become filled with water have the potential to develop positive pore water pressure under applied load. This reduces the normal forces between aggregate particles, making inter-particle slip easier. Thus, the greater the proportion of voids that are filled with water, the lower the shear strength will be.
2. In materials which are already saturated – generally clays – an increased water content simply means greater spaces between particles and therefore less contact points. This too reduces shear strength.

2.1.1.7 Shear strength tests

The principal laboratory test is the *triaxial* test (Fig. 2.9). Cylindrical clay specimens can be cut during borehole excavation. More usually, the specimen has to be compacted into a cylindrical mould (using a specified compaction procedure). In either case, the specimen must be surrounded by a membrane (typically latex rubber or polythene) which is sealed to the top and bottom loading platens. The whole arrangement is then contained in a sealed cell, which is pressurised to a desired stress level. This stress, known as the *confining stress*, acts in all directions on the specimen. The test then consists of applying an additional stress to the top platen, known as the *deviator stress*, increasing it until the point of failure. Figure 2.9 illustrates use of the triaxial test to determine shear strength parameters c and ϕ.

Various types of *shear box* test (using the principle illustrated in Fig. 2.2) are also available, but the stress conditions are generally much less uniform than those in the triaxial test, giving the result less validity.

For in situ determination of shear strength, the *shear vane* (see Fig. 2.10) can be used in clays up to a certain strength. This is a quick and convenient test, ideal for testing the properties of soil exposed during a trial pit investigation. The device is thrust into an exposed clay face or into the base of the excavation and the operator then applies a steadily increasing torque until the vane begins to rotate. This point may be taken as indicating shear failure on a circular plane.

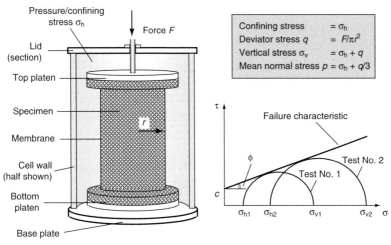

Fig. 2.9 *The triaxial test for shear strength determination*

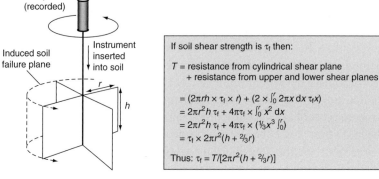

If soil shear strength is τ_f then:

T = resistance from cylindrical shear plane
+ resistance from upper and lower shear planes

$$= (2\pi rh \times \tau_f \times r) + (2 \times \int_0^r 2\pi x\, dx\, \tau_f x)$$
$$= 2\pi r^2 h\, \tau_f + 4\pi\tau_f \times \int_0^r x^2\, dx$$
$$= 2\pi r^2 h\, \tau_f + 4\pi\tau_f \times (\tfrac{1}{3}x^3\, \big|_0^r)$$
$$= \tau_f \times 2\pi r^2(h + \tfrac{2}{3}r)$$

Thus: $\tau_f = T/[2\pi r^2(h + \tfrac{2}{3}r)]$

Fig. 2.10 The shear vane test

2.1.1.8 Typical shear strength values

This section is included in order to allow an appreciation of any data which the reader may obtain. There is no such thing as a typical material and the numbers given here should never be assumed in actual design. However, so long as this is understood, it is always useful to put data into context.

Clays
The weakest materials likely to be encountered are peats and recently deposited alluvial clays. Water contents (water mass as a percentage of solid mass) can be as high as 300 or 400%, i.e. the great majority of the volume is actually water. Cohesion values can be as little as 10 MPa, with a zero angle of internal friction (under short-term loading of course). Unfortunately, these soils tend to lie in wide, flat locations which would otherwise be ideal for construction of cities, airports, ports etc. Inevitably, any added vertical load will compress the soil significantly (often achieved deliberately by pre-loading) and cohesion would therefore be expected to increase, perhaps to 15–20 MPa.

Peats lie at one extreme of a massive range of clays of differing strengths, through soft glacial deposits, to firm and then stiff layers. Cohesion is often in the 50–100 MPa range but, for the strongest materials, much higher values are possible.

All clays are sensitive to moisture. It is not the purpose of this book to pursue clay mineralogy any further, but the reader should be aware that so-called low-plasticity clays (see Section 2.1.4.6) are particularly vulnerable to wetting up during the in-service life of a pavement.

A strength of well over 50 MPa under normal equilibrium moisture conditions may reduce to much lower values with just a few percentage points change of water content.

Sands etc.

In contrast to a clay, a pure sand will have a negligible value of cohesion and the strength will be provided entirely by the angle of internal friction. A value of around 30° is typical. A fine sand or silt will often have a slightly lower value, between 20 and 30°. However, in many cases natural sands and silts include a clay content and this will supply a cohesion of a few kilopascals, something which dramatically changes the nature of the material. Pure sands, such as wind-blown desert deposits, flow easily and are therefore intrinsically unstable; if even a small cohesion is present, stability increases greatly.

Gravels

Naturally occurring gravels are commonly used in lower pavement construction layers. In most cases, the materials are a mix of gravel, sand, silt and often clay, and the angle of internal friction is frequently in the 40–45° range. This angle is chiefly dependent on the angularity of the particles; a predominance of rounded stones results in a relatively lower angle. As with sands, a small clay content, providing a degree of cohesion, greatly increases the stability of the layer – but also its susceptibility to water content changes.

Crushed rock etc.

Crushed rock is the premier pavement construction aggregate. Particles are angular (although different rock types result in significantly different typical shapes) and the faces are often rough. This, together with the fact that a broad range of particle sizes is commonly present, means that there will usually be some 'interlock' (apparent cohesion); 10–20 kPa is probably typical. The angle of internal friction is usually in the 50–60° range.

Although rock is the traditional source for high-quality granular layers, there are several secondary materials, i.e. materials from industrial processes, as well as various waste products, which make perfectly acceptable aggregate when crushed. Steel slag, concrete from demolition waste, various arisings from mining operations – all

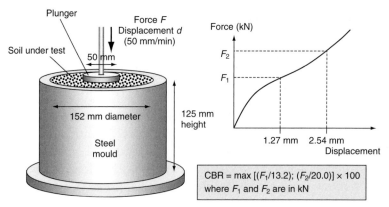

Fig. 2.11 The California bearing ratio (CBR) test

such materials can logically be considered for aggregate for pavement construction. Assuming that their chemical composition does not exclude them and that the particles themselves are strong enough not to fragment excessively, the principal factors affecting shear strength will be exactly the same as for crushed rocks, i.e. particle shape, particle size distribution and surface roughness.

2.1.1.9 The California bearing ratio

While shear strength is a measure with fundamental meaning, shear strength tests are not always convenient to carry out. The California bearing ratio (CBR) was developed by the California State Highways Department in the 1930s as an index test for soils, specifically for the purpose of pavement design, since it uses relatively low-technology equipment and gives a general indication of soil shear strength, and it is still in common use worldwide.[13] However, it is important to remember that it is an *empirical* measure and has no absolute and fundamental meaning. It has been described, not unreasonably, as an instrumented 'heel of the boot'. Figure 2.11 details the standard test and Calculation Sheet 2.2 derives an approximate relationship with soil shear strength parameters.

Note that Calculation Sheet 2.2 ignores the confining effect of the side walls of the mould, and therefore describes an in situ test. This can be carried out by jacking against a restraint such as the underside of a vehicle and, without the confinement of the mould, a lower value is generally found. The actual effect of wall confinement will be similar to that of an overburden. It is also common to add a further

---

Calculation Sheet 2.2 Relating CBR to c and ϕ

The CBR test is effectively a bearing capacity failure problem with a circular loaded area. The equation for this is:

$$q_f = 1.3cN_c + 1.2p_oN_q + 0.3\gamma dN_\gamma$$

where q_f = stress to cause failure; c = cohesion; p_o = overburden stress; γ = unit weight; r, d = radius and diameter of loading platen; N_c, N_q, N_γ are bearing capacity parameters for which the following approximations are suggested:[14]

$$N_c = 5.5 + 0.32\phi + 3 \times 10^{-5}\phi^4$$
$$N_q = 1.0 + 0.12\phi + 9 \times 10^{-3}\phi^2 + 9 \times 10^{-12}\phi^8$$
$$N_\gamma = 6 \times 10^{-4}\phi^3 + 2.33 \times 10^{-21}\phi^{14}$$

where ϕ = angle of internal friction (degrees).

Assume that bearing capacity failure approximately equates to a displacement of 1.27 mm, the corresponding 100% CBR load for which is 13.2 kN (see Figure 2.11).

Therefore: $$CBR \approx 100\pi r^2 q_f/13.2$$

---

surcharge to the surface of the soil immediately around the plunger, simulating the effect of confinement beneath a pavement construction, and both wall confinement and surcharging have a particularly marked influence on measured CBR in the case of sandy soils with low cohesion.

Despite the non-fundamental nature of the CBR, its convenience and relationship to readily observable behaviour on site has meant that the test continues to be used and that pavements continue to be designed on the basis of a 'design CBR'. In many cases a 'soaked CBR' is specified, a measure of the properties of a material in a wet condition, and procedures exist in several specifications for carrying out the soaking, a four-day soaking period being typical.[15]

2.1.1.10 Plate loading tests

The problem with an in situ CBR test is that the loaded area is very small, just 50 mm diameter, and many pavement foundation layers have particles large enough to induce serious error in such a test.[16] The logical answer, therefore, is to increase the size of the loading plate. This provides a more uniform distribution of stress, but it also provides a deeper zone of stress, usually including effects from more than one layer. The plate loading test cannot therefore be seen as a material test but rather a composite foundation (or part-foundation) test. Furthermore, the larger the plate, the less the test can be considered a strength test and the greater the influence of material stiffness (see Section 2.1.2), since practical considerations dictate that the deflection induced is rarely more than a very few millimetres, representing a relatively small strain.

The quantity which results directly from a plate loading test is the 'modulus of subgrade reaction' and is given the symbol k – refer to Part 1 (Section 1.4.2.5). It is defined as the pressure required to induce unit deflection, and so has units of MN/m^3. The traditional plate diameter is 762 mm (30 in.), giving a k_{762} value. If alternative plate sizes are used then the k value will, in general, be different because of the different contributions made by the different layers within the foundation. The UK Highways Agency suggests a method of conversion between plate sizes,[17] but this can be considered as no more than approximate and assumes conventional highway foundation materials. The same document also proposes a conversion between k and CBR,[18] although this is clearly more approximate still because of the quite different loading systems; it is not advised for anything other than a very rough assessment and should preferably not be included in a specification.

2.1.1.11 Cone penetrometers

Cone penetrometers are instruments which measure the force as a steel cone is inserted into a soil. This induces shear failure in the surrounding material, and the insertion force should therefore relate to material shear strength. There are several different sizes of cone penetrometer on the market from pocket-size to large, mechanically assisted, and each has to be carefully calibrated. The number which results (either shear strength or CBR) will only be approximate; nevertheless the technique is extremely practical for in situ work.

2.1.2 Stiffness

In engineering terms, stiffness means the ratio of applied stress to induced strain. In a linear elastic material, this is a single and fundamental property, and many engineering materials can be considered linear elastic. However, an unbound material is highly complex and certainly *non-linear*. This means that the ratio of applied stress to induced strain varies depending on the stress conditions applying. Numerous PhD studies have been carried out on this subject, which reveals in itself the fact that the behaviour is still not completely understood. Here, the principal factors applying will be introduced, together with a couple of approximate methods to describe such behaviour.

2.1.2.1 The mechanism of unbound material strain

The stiffness of an unbound material is quite different from that of the particles from which it is made up. Rock may be considered as an approximately linear elastic material with a stiffness modulus commonly between 100 and 200 GPa; unbound materials rarely develop more than 1 GPa, even under the most favourable stress conditions. The fact is, of course, that the stiffness of an unbound material is governed by inter-particle behaviour, notably frictional slip between particles (see Section 2.1.1.1). Figure 2.12 illustrates what happens throughout an unbound material when it strains (in response to applied stress). In this example, there is no change in the relative positions of particles E, F, C and D and so no slip. At the A–C contact, there is rotation, which means the exact point of contact moves – but there is still no slip. However, as B is pushed to the left it slips against D, and it also rotates and slips against A.

The material will naturally try to avoid slip wherever it can. Particles will take the path of least resistance and this means that the number of slip points will be minimised as far as possible. However, it is clearly not possible to avoid them entirely. If a particle manages to rotate against one neighbour (A against C in Fig. 2.12), this will usually require slip against another neighbour (A against B in Fig. 2.12).

There is also one other very important factor to consider. Individual particles may be very stiff – but they are not rigid. Furthermore the size of the contact area is extremely small, which means the contact stress can be extremely high. This causes elastic compression at the contacts, and the magnitude of this compression affects the ease with which one particle can move relative to another. For example, relatively large compression at the A–C contact in Fig. 2.12 might allow particle A to rotate right past E and hit F instead. It is this elastic compression which also ensures that almost all of the movement will be reversed as soon as the load is removed; frictional slip will not reverse itself –

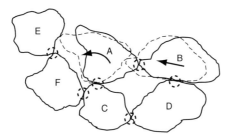

Fig. 2.12 Inter-particle motion due to strain in an unbound material

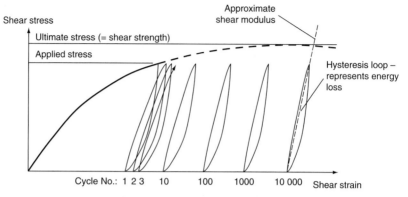

Fig. 2.13 *Idealised stress–strain behaviour of an unbound material*

but it can be reversed so long as there is enough stored compressive strain energy to achieve this.

2.1.2.2 The resulting stress–strain behaviour

Unsurprisingly, this complex interaction of compression at particle contacts, rotation and inter-particle slip cannot be expressed simply – at least not with any great accuracy. Figure 2.13 is an idealisation of the typical form of behaviour.

There is always a large difference in behaviour between the first load application, represented by the heavy line in Fig. 2.13, and all subsequent load cycles. During that first application, the particles rearrange themselves in a major way; during subsequent cycles there are only minor and ever-decreasing differences from one load cycle to the next.

Since pavements are structures which are subjected to large numbers of repeated loads, the first load application is of limited interest; it is the shape of the almost repeatable stress–strain characteristic (representing what is known as *resilient* behaviour) which determines the stiffness of the material. In fact, the shape of the stress–strain characteristic does change slightly with increasing number of cycles as the exact way that the particles interact becomes ever more efficient, but to a first approximation it may be taken to be constant.

Notice from Fig. 2.13 the shape of the resilient stress–strain characteristic. The area enclosed represents energy loss, an unavoidable consequence of inter-particle slip. However, for pavement design (and material characterisation) purposes, it is usual to ignore the detailed shape and to assume that the behaviour is equivalent to a straight line between the end points of the characteristic. The slope of this line (stress/strain) is therefore the *shear modulus* applying under these particular conditions. Refer to Part 1 (Section 1.4.2.4) for conversion from shear modulus to the more commonly quoted *elastic modulus* (more correctly known as *resilient modulus*).

2.1.2.3 *The effect of differing stress conditions*

Because strain within an unbound material includes frictional slip of one particle against another, it is unsurprising that the stress conditions are of critical importance. The most important influence is the magnitude of the *confining stress* (or bulk stress), since this is directly related to the magnitude of the contact forces between particles – and the resistance to frictional slip is directly proportional to normal contact force (see Section 2.1.1.1). In a pavement, this means that material at depth, beneath a considerable overburden, will generally appear stiffer than material near the surface, even though it may in reality be exactly the same soil or pavement material.

The second and less influential factor is the effect of *stress change*. It appears that it is the first few slips between particles which are the hardest to generate and that, once inter-particle slips begin to occur, there is a 'knock-on' effect, which means they become progressively easier. The result is that, all other things being equal, the strain when applying a stress change of 20 kPa is usually more than twice the strain when applying 10 kPa.

There are plenty of other complications, notably the tendency for a material to dilate as it shears, caused by particles 'riding up' over their neighbours, and the upshot is that any detailed material model has to be extremely complex, much more complex than is generally required for pavement engineering purposes. Table 2.1 summarises some possible options.

For many purposes it is sufficient to assume a constant modulus. For example, in analysing a thick asphalt pavement under traffic load it is generally found that the system behaves as if the granular sub-base layer had a stiffness modulus of 100–150 MPa, depending on material quality and moisture state. The layer is not a particularly significant one in its effect on the way that stresses distribute in the pavement and it is simply not necessary to use anything more sophisticated. The fact that the same layer may appear to have a quite different and much lower stiffness if it is trafficked (or tested) directly, without any intervening asphalt or concrete, is worth being aware of – but it does not invalidate the use of a single value in full pavement analysis.

Table 2.1 Models of unbound material stress-dependency

	Action	Possible model
1	Assume fully linear	$E = $ constant
2	Model confining effect[19]	$E = k_1\theta^{k_2}$
3	Model confining effect and stress change[20]	$\varepsilon_s = A\delta[\ln(\sigma_1/\sigma_3)]^B \delta\sigma^C$
4	Model as fully as possible[21]	$G = G_1 p^{1-n}$
		$K = (K_1/n)p^{1-n}/[1 + 2\beta(2-n)q^2/(np^2)]$

where: $E = $ resilient modulus or stiffness modulus; $G = $ shear modulus; $K = $ bulk modulus; $\theta = $ sum of any three orthogonal stresses; $\sigma_1, \sigma_3 = $ stresses in two orthogonal directions; $p = $ mean normal stress $(= \theta/3)$; $q = $ deviator stress $(= \sigma_1 - \sigma_3)$; $\varepsilon_s = $ shear strain at $45°$ to the directions of σ_1 and σ_3; δ means 'change in'; $k_1, k_2, A, B, C, G_1, K_1, n$ and β are all constants.

The so-called k–θ model (Option 2 in Table 2.1) is quite widely used by researchers, particularly in the US, but it immediately makes pavement analysis much more difficult, either requiring the use of finite-element techniques or else demanding that a much simplified pavement structure is assumed. The reader should also be aware that the k–θ model is not particularly correct for locations other than directly beneath an applied load.

The third option is not even expressed as a modulus but as a direct prediction of shear strain as a function of applied stresses, and so is certainly not easy to use. However, it is much closer to a correct representation of real behaviour and is simple enough for use in certain analysis situations.

The final option, for which several variant versions exist, is used by some European researchers. It has the merit that it gives a reasonably close match to real behaviour but it also allows input into finite-element or finite-difference quasi-elastic computations.[22] Several researchers have used it to model unsurfaced or thinly surfaced pavements.

Table 2.1 has done no more than give a flavour for the number and variety of stress–strain models that have been developed to represent unbound material behaviour. However, the key is to make a choice which is appropriate to the problem being tackled – and in most instances that choice will be Option 1. Nevertheless, so as to get a flavour for the true nature of the non-linearity of an unbound material, Table 2.2 is included. It presents data obtained from repeated load tests on crushed limestone sub-base aggregate using the triaxial equipment.

Table 2.2 Data illustrating the non-linearity of a crushed limestone[23]

Confining stress: kPa	Deviator stress: kPa	Axial strain: $\times 10^{-6}$	Modulus: MPa	Poisson's ratio
25	0–50	302	165	0.23
	0–150	585	256	0.47
50	0–50	115	436	0.23
	0–150	348	431	0.49
100	0–50	73	685	0.22
	0–150	209	717	0.41
250	0–50	32	1563	0.19
	0–150	111	1351	0.31

2.1.2.4 The effect of particle and mixture properties

Non-linearity is an important factor, but equally important is the fact that different unbound materials have significantly different stiffnesses, when tested under the same stress conditions. The key factors are:

- angle of friction at particle-to-particle contacts
- stiffness modulus of the parent material, from which the particles are derived
- particle size
- particle size distribution
- particle packing
- water content.

Notice that these factors differ somewhat from those discussed earlier in relation to strength. The first two did not significantly influence shear strength since their effect is seen primarily when dealing with the very small strains generated under resilient conditions. On the other hand, particle angularity, which was so important in relation to shear strength, is found to have very little effect in the small strain region. The following paragraphs discuss each of the relevant factors in turn.

Friction at particle-to-particle contacts

This is illustrated in Fig. 2.14, taken from triaxial test data. Despite the scatter, there is a clear trend that materials with higher friction, notably steel slag and certain limestones in this case, display a higher stiffness modulus (expressed as an 'indicator' in Fig. 2.14 since the data relate to tests under several different stress conditions). These findings have been supported by 'discrete element modelling' (DEM), a technique

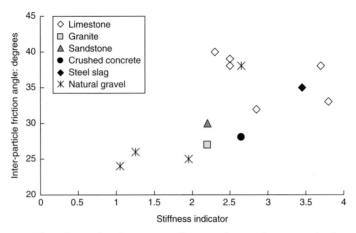

*Fig. 2.14 The relationship between stiffness and particle-to-particle friction –
triaxial data*[24]

in which individual particles and the interactions between them are
directly modelled.[25] Recent DEM work at Nottingham University
showed that a change in surface friction angle from 39° to 22° should
theoretically result in a 29% drop in overall stiffness modulus.

Parent material stiffness modulus

No laboratory test data has been found in support of the effect of this
variable, although it is essential to the explanation of granular material
strain presented earlier. However, the same set of DEM results as
quoted above showed that a 50% drop in particle stiffness modulus
caused a 37% drop in the modulus of the system as a whole.

Particle size

Figure 2.15 shows sets of data on single-sized aggregates – but of
different single sizes. The effect is clear, namely that stiffness modulus
decreases with decreasing particle size. The reasons are probably similar
to those identified in relation to strength – see Section 2.1.1.6.

Particle size distribution

This is an interesting subject. It seems intuitively reasonable that a
broadly graded material should have a higher stiffness than a single-
sized material, particularly since it has already been noted that it has

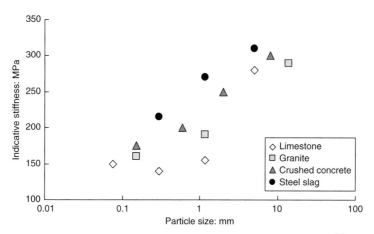

Fig. 2.15 The effect of particle size on stiffness modulus – triaxial data[26]

a higher shear strength. But, at least for dry materials, this is not actually the case. Figure 2.16 presents data obtained on a range of particle gradations (i.e. size distributions) from near single-sized to very broadly graded, all with a maximum particle size of 10 mm. The degree of 'broadness' of the gradation is expressed as a 'uniformity coefficient', the ratio of the sieve size though which 60% of the material would pass to that through which just 10% would pass. Interestingly, the trend is for the more single-sized materials to be stiffer.

This unexpected outcome is readily explicable however. The previous section has just made the point that smaller particle size leads to lower stiffness, and a broad particle gradation means an

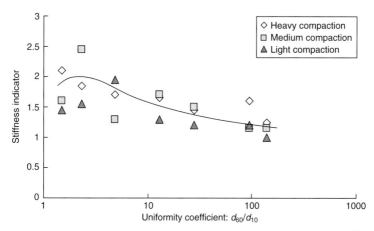

Fig. 2.16 The effect of particle size distribution on stiffness – triaxial data[27]

increased proportion of small particles. There is therefore no advantage in terms of stiffness, despite the closer packing arrangement and higher density which this allows.

Of course, use of a broadly-graded aggregate is generally dictated by the increased shear strength obtained – but one should not expect a corresponding increase in stiffness.

Particle packing

The efficiency of particle packing is affected not only by particle size distribution but also by the degree of compaction given to a material, and most engineers would certainly expect that compaction affects stiffness. However, for a dry unbound aggregate they would be mistaken – as Fig. 2.16 demonstrates. The packing efficiency has negligible effect on the stiffness of the overall aggregate matrix, presumably since the proportion of contacts which are readily able to slip when stress is applied remains almost unchanged. The potential magnitude of slip movement would logically be reduced by greater packing efficiency, but this does not seem to have any significant impact in the small strain region relevant to stiffness. The consequence is, therefore, that the stiffness of a dry aggregate is almost unaffected by compaction. Naturally, compaction is still desirable because of its effect on shear strength, but there will not necessarily be any stiffness increase.

Water content

It is common to speak in terms of water 'lubricating' an unbound material. This is not really a helpful description. In fact, the effect of water on stiffness is broadly the same as that on strength, described already in Section 2.1.1.6. At low water contents, suction can be present, giving an effective cohesion. This increases the stiffness of the matrix as a whole, just as it increases the strength, and the effect will be greatest in materials with a significant silt or clay size fraction. For this reason, despite having shown in the previous section that a broadly graded aggregate will, if anything, be less stiff than a single-sized material, this is only true when it is dry; if water is present (in suitably small quantities) then the broadly-graded aggregate will tend to be stiffer because of its enhanced suction. However, at high water contents any suction effect will disappear and be replaced by positive pore pressures as voids become filled with water, decreasing normal forces between particles and so allowing easier inter-particle slip. Just

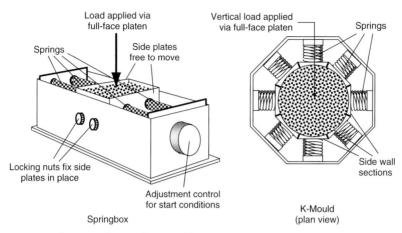

Fig. 2.17 The Springbox and K-Mould concepts

as this decreased the shear strength, so it will also decrease the stiffness – and in that sense the water could be said to have a 'lubricating' action.

2.1.2.5 Stiffness tests

The *triaxial* test, introduced above in Section 2.1.1.7 as a shear strength test, can also be used to measure stiffness so long as the equipment allows repeated load to be applied. As shown in Fig. 2.13, the stiffness on initial loading is not representative of that applying in subsequent load applications, and in fact the stiffness tends to increase slightly as increasing numbers of loads are applied. This has led to specifications in which a large number (many thousands) of loading cycles have to be applied before the stiffness is measured.

However, the problem with the triaxial test is that it is a complex piece of equipment and stiffness measurement demands the use of sensitive displacement measuring transducers, leading to a high overall cost per test.[28] Two relatively recently developed alternatives are the so-called *K-Mould*[29] and the *Springbox*,[30] illustrated in Fig. 2.17. Both have been developed as tests suited to the establishment of stiffness for pavement design purposes and they share certain common features:

- The stress conditions are less well controlled than those in the triaxial test but they allow a form of loading which is fairly closely simulative of a passing wheel load.
- Both tests are easier to set up and carry out than the triaxial.

These two tests therefore represent a practical compromise. The specimen sizes (150 mm diameter, 125 mm height for the K-Mould; 170 mm cube for the Springbox[31]) are intended to be suitable for most unbound base and sub-base materials. Calculation Sheet 2.3 illustrates the difference expected between stiffness moduli deduced from triaxial testing and those deduced from the Springbox, using a stress-dependent stiffness model for a crushed limestone sub-base aggregate. This difference is important. Triaxial tests are rarely performed with a cell pressure less than the 20 kPa assumed in Calculation Sheet 2.3, and a higher cell pressure would lead to an even higher measured stiffness. In contrast, the relatively low horizontal stress generated by the springs in either the Springbox or the K-Mould, together with the fact that the horizontal stress increases as horizontal strain takes place, leads to a much lower measured stiffness, and a stiffness which is much more compatible with those measured in situ beneath a finished pavement (using the Falling Weight Deflectometer – see Part 4).

Calculation Sheet 2.3 Differences between stiffness tests

Using the following stress–strain model:[32]

Shear strain		$\varepsilon_s = A\delta[\ln(\sigma_1/\sigma_3)]^B \, \delta\sigma^C$
Volumetric strain		$\varepsilon_v = D(\delta \ln p)^E \, \delta p^F - G\{\delta[\ln(\sigma_1/\sigma_3)]^2\}^H$

where: $\varepsilon_s, \varepsilon_v$ = shear and volumetric strains (microstrain)
σ_1, σ_3 = principal stresses (kPa)
p = mean normal stress (kPa)
A, B, C, D, E, F, G, H are 75, 0.9, 0.33, 104, 0.85, 0.29, 117, 1.0 respectively
(parameters derived from tests on crushed limestone sub-base)

Triaxial test: say cell pressure 20 kPa; deviator stress 0–100 kPa
→ ε_s = 507 µɛ; ε_v = –93 µɛ; ε_{axial} = 307 µɛ; E = <u>326 MPa</u>

Springbox test: say vertical stress 0–100 kPa; horizontal stress 2–20 kPa
→ ε_s = 521 µɛ; ε_v = 520 µɛ; ε_{axial} = 521 µɛ; E = <u>191 MPa</u>

Unbound material stiffness can also be measured in situ directly. The principal equipment used for this is the dynamic plate test (DPT), several versions of which are available. Figure 2.18 illustrates. Interpretation generally ignores the dynamic nature of the test (i.e. the inertia effect due to acceleration and deceleration of the ground mass) and also has to assume that the material beneath the point tested is uniform, infinite and linear elastic in nature, all of which are far from the truth. Nevertheless, the test is a quick, practical method of obtaining a measure of the in situ condition of a pavement foundation.

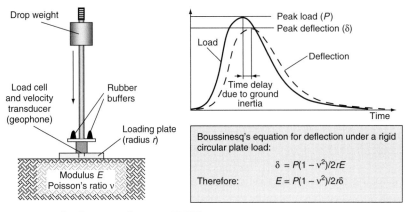

Fig. 2.18 The dynamic plate test (DPT)

Boussinesq's equations for stress, strain and displacement within a uniform half-space[33] are enormously useful in a wide range of applications. The equation quoted in Fig. 2.18 is for the specific case of deflection measured immediately under the centre of the loaded area, achieved in the DPT by means of a velocity transducer sprung lightly against the ground through a hole in the plate. Some DPT devices measure plate deflection rather than ground deflection, and the resulting measurement is commonly significantly different because of the inevitably uneven contact between the plate and the surface, resulting in large local compressions. Plate movement is therefore generally greater than average ground movement, and reliance on measuring plate movement will underestimate the true ground stiffness.

When evaluating DPT data, it is important to realise the following:

- The test is of the whole foundation *not* just the uppermost layer. The influence will decrease with depth but, in theory, all materials to a depth of about 1.5 m (the penetration of the pressure wave by the time the peak deflection is measured – typically after 10–15 ms) will influence the result to some extent.
- The calculated stiffness modulus will be lower than that pertaining once upper pavement construction has been added, because of the lack of confinement during the test. For example, a test result of about 80 MPa may typically indicate an in-service modulus of around 150 MPa.[34]
- Scatter is expected due to the difficulty in ensuring a perfect and repeatable contact between the plate and the ground. Decisions

should therefore only be made on the basis of statistical treatment of the data.

- The equations in Fig. 2.18 assume a rigid loading plate and therefore a non-uniform pressure distribution. The alternative assumption is that of uniform stress beneath the plate, in which case Boussinesq's solution requires the calculated modulus to be increased by a factor of $4/\pi$.

2.1.2.6 Typical stiffness modulus values

As in the case of shear strength, this section is included purely in order to set in context any data obtained. In reality, materials vary greatly and, of course, are enormously affected by their moisture state. Nevertheless, the figures in Table 2.3 are believed to represent typical values.

The principal reason for the discrepancies shown in the table is the differing degree of confinement. However, confinement is much less influential for clay materials whereas the magnitude of applied stress is much more so. The advice here is that both the triaxial and the DPT should be interpreted with caution.

Mention should also be made of the widespread practice of converting CBR to stiffness, a practice which should fill the reader with horror, bearing in mind that CBR is essentially a strength test and that stiffness and strength depend on such entirely different material features. Nevertheless, one should be aware of the following equations:

$$E \text{ (in MPa)} = 10 \times \text{CBR}$$

$$E = 17.6 \, \text{CBR}^{0.64}$$

Table 2.3 Typical stiffness modulus data

Material	Stiffness modulus: MPa		
	Triaxial (confining stress 20 kPa; deviator stress 0–100 kPa)	DPT (100 kPa contact pressure)	In the pavement (K-Mould and Springbox generally give similar results)
Very soft clay soil	10	5	15
Firm clay soil	50	30	80
Sandy soil	75	30	50
Gravel capping	125	50	80
Sub-base	250	75	150
Granular base	500	100	250

The first is internationally applied;[35] the second is used particularly in the UK, having been proposed by the Transport Research Laboratory.[36] Thus, for example, if the 'very soft soil' in Table 2.3 had a CBR of 1.5%, the two equations would give stiffness moduli of 15 and 22 MPa respectively, while a 'firm clay soil' with a CBR of 5% would have predicted stiffness moduli of 50 and 48 MPa. Clearly the order of magnitude is right – and so it should be since the equations are based on experience. Nevertheless, this approach cannot be recommended unless all else fails. The level of uncertainty is much too great.[37]

Finally, in any linear elastic analysis a value of Poisson's ratio will also have to be selected, and it is common to adopt 0.4–0.45 for clay soils and 0.3–0.35 for sands and granular pavement materials.

2.1.3 Deformation under repeated load

It is an unfortunate fact that all unbound materials deform progressively as more and more loads are applied, which means that there is a significant danger of a rut forming under repeated wheel loading. This form of behaviour was illustrated in Fig. 2.13.

2.1.3.1 The mechanism of plastic deformation

The point has been made that normal straining of a granular matrix involves frictional slip between particles as well as compression at particle contacts. The energy stored as contacts compress is released once the load has moved on and the material returns approximately to its original arrangement. It was also noted that the efficiency with which the material strains increases from one load application to the next (reducing the energy dissipated due to friction), and this implies a difference in the arrangement of particles after unloading compared with that applying before the load arrived. This in turn implies *non-recovered deformation* and, if possible, this important phenomenon is even more complex than that of stiffness. This type of deformation is often termed 'irrecoverable' or 'permanent', although these are not accurate descriptors since it is always possible to reverse such strains if appropriate stress is applied. However, these strains are most certainly *plastic* rather than *resilient*.

2.1.3.2 Modelling plastic deformation

This is another subject upon which numerous doctoral theses have been produced. Here, the different types of behaviour that can occur will be

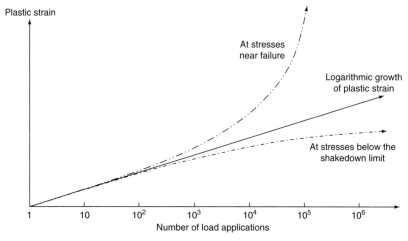

Fig. 2.19 Different forms of plastic strain accumulation behaviour

illustrated and one possible model presented. As seen already in Fig. 2.13, the tendency is for plastic strain to occur at an ever-decreasing rate as more cycles of load are applied. The effect is approximately logarithmic and is illustrated in Fig. 2.19. However, many researchers have noted that, under appropriately low stress conditions, plastic strain can actually cease altogether. This is the phenomenon known as 'shakedown' and the stress below which this occurs is known as the 'shakedown limit'. On the other hand, it has also been observed that, under stress conditions close to the failure stress, plastic strain can actually begin to accelerate to complete failure. The range of possibilities is shown in Fig. 2.19.

The following is one of many models describing such behaviour.[38] It is included here because the author has found it extremely useful when developing predictive techniques for rutting in unsurfaced roads (see Part 3).

$$\text{Plastic shear strain } \varepsilon_{sp} = -(1/L)\ln[1 - \sigma/\sigma_f - (\sigma/M)\ln(N)]$$

where σ = applied stress; σ_f = stress at failure; L and M = constants; and N = number of load applications.

This equation cannot model the stabilising effect seen at stresses less than the shakedown limit; however, it is reasonably successful at describing the acceleration of plastic strain at higher stress. The following are suggested as typical values for constants L and M for different materials.

Crushed rock:	$L = 165$	$M = 12\,\text{MPa}$
Sandy soil:	$L = 165$	$M = 3\,\text{MPa}$
Clay:	$L = 165$	$M = 450\,\text{kPa}$

In general, it is strongly advised that use of this or any other equation for prediction of plastic strain should only be made where suitable calibration against experience is possible.

2.1.3.3 The effect of material variables

Resistance to plastic strain under repeated load is largely a function of shear strength. Clearly a strong material (with a large σ_f value in the above equation) will develop relatively low plastic strain, which means that large particle size, angular particles and broad particle size distribution all contribute. Water content will also influence behaviour, since it significantly influences shear strength.

2.1.3.4 Tests for plastic strain under repeated load

The appropriate tests here are the same as those already described for stiffness measurement, namely the triaxial, Springbox and K-Mould. However, only the triaxial test (and other complex research equipment such as the hollow cylinder apparatus[39]) has sufficiently well-controlled stress conditions to enable derivation of model parameters. The K-Mould and Springbox can give a relative idea of performance under reasonably realistic stress conditions, but this then needs to be calibrated against performance in the field in order to be interpreted.

2.1.4 Permeability, suction, plasticity and frost

Water content has been identified several times as a key parameter influencing material performance. Previous sections have brought out the fact that a moderate water content generates suction within a material and is therefore beneficial to shear strength, stiffness and resistance to plastic strain under repeated load. Conversely a high water content leads to positive pore pressures and a loss of performance in all three departments. Yet water is commonly added to unbound pavement materials in order to facilitate compaction (as explained in Part 1), leaving the layer in a near-saturated state – highly undesirable in the longer term.

Permeability is therefore a key property. A highly permeable material will never be adversely affected by water so long as a drainage outlet is available. On the other hand, it won't derive any significant benefit from suction. A fine-grained low-permeability material may develop an impressive suction – but this can only be maintained if further water is prevented from entering the layer. The first option is a low-risk low-profit scenario; the second involves high risk but offers the promise of high reward. Permeability must therefore be understood.

2.1.4.1 The fluid mechanics of permeability

The coefficient of permeability, i.e. the ratio of head loss per metre to flow velocity, depends on the size of the gaps joining void spaces within a granular matrix, and this in turn is clearly a function of particle size – but which particle size? In a single-sized material, the problem is possible to analyse geometrically, at least approximately, but in a graded aggregate the difficulty is considerable.

In general, fluid flow may be either laminar (i.e. smooth and steady) or turbulent, and for most purposes flow through paving materials and soils may be considered *laminar*. This means that the so-called 'Reynolds number',[40] the dimensionless quantity used to describe the state of fluid flow, will be relatively low. The following applies to laminar flow in pipes:

Reynolds number $(Re) = DV/\nu < $ about 2000

where $D = $ pipe diameter; $V = $ flow velocity; $\nu = $ kinematic viscosity $(1.14\,\text{mm}^2/\text{s}$ for water at $20°C)$.

Laminar flow also means that the quantity known as the friction factor (λ) can be directly (although approximately) related to Reynolds number.[41]

$$\lambda \approx 64/Re$$

$$= 64\nu/DV$$

If flow through an unbound material is assumed to resemble flow through a circular pipe of diameter D, then the head loss H over a length L can be expressed theoretically as follows:[42]

$$H = 16\lambda LQ^2/(2g\pi^2 D^5)$$

where $Q = $ volume flow rate $(= V \times \pi D^2/4)$; $g = $ acceleration due to gravity $(9.81\,\text{m/s}^2)$.

Substituting for λ and Q:

$$H = 64\nu LV/(2gD^2)$$

Inserting values for ν and g and re-expressing:

$$V = 269\,000 D^2 (H/L) \text{ m/s}$$

The trick now is to know what value of D is applicable within the matrix of an unbound material and also to make an appropriate conversion from a regular cylindrical pipe to a tortuous path between particles. Any estimate is therefore likely to be highly approximate.

2.1.4.2 Predicting permeability

Permeability is expressed as a coefficient k (in m/s) and the key equation is Darcy's law:[43]

$$Q = kA(H/L)$$

where A = cross-sectional area; other quantities are as defined earlier. H/L is known as the *hydraulic gradient*.

Clearly the form of Darcy's law is similar to that derived above for pipe flow and it is therefore potentially possible to derive a coefficient of permeability purely from a consideration of geometry. A simple procedure is to assume that the water has to flow through tubes shaped as shown in Calculation Sheet 2.4. This ignores the fact that the void available for water flow opens up between the constrictions illustrated in the figure, giving a greater average cross-section, but it also ignores flow path tortuosity. The two simplifications are therefore opposite in effect.

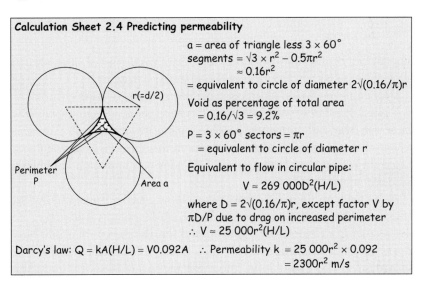

Calculation Sheet 2.4 Predicting permeability

a = area of triangle less 3 × 60° segments = $\sqrt{3} \times r^2 - 0.5\pi r^2$
 ≈ $0.16 r^2$
= equivalent to circle of diameter $2\sqrt{(0.16/\pi)}r$

Void as percentage of total area
 = $0.16/\sqrt{3}$ = 9.2%

P = 3 × 60° sectors = πr
= equivalent to circle of diameter r

Equivalent to flow in circular pipe:

$$V \approx 269\,000 D^2 (H/L)$$

where $D = 2\sqrt{(0.16/\pi)}r$, except factor V by $\pi D/P$ due to drag on increased perimeter
∴ $V \approx 25\,000 r^2 (H/L)$

Darcy's law: $Q = kA(H/L) = V0.092A$ ∴ Permeability k = $25\,000 r^2 \times 0.092$
= $2300 r^2$ m/s

(Labels in figure: $r(=d/2)$, Perimeter P, Area a)

2.1.4.3 Flow through a graded aggregate

The prediction shown in Calculation Sheet 2.4 is probably about right for a single-sized material – but unfortunately such materials are few and far between in real civil engineering. The question, therefore, is just how to choose a representative particle size within a graded aggregate – the particle size which dictates resistance to water flow.

One fundamental approach would be to compare the actual particle size distribution with that of a so-called Fuller curve. Fuller curves have already been introduced (Fig. 2.8) and obey the following formula:

% passing sieve size $d = 100(d/d_{\mathrm{max}})^n$

The concept is that at any given particle size the relative proportions of different smaller-sized particles remain the same and, as reported above, experience is that when n is around 0.4–0.5 a maximum density is achieved. At this gradation, there are just the right number of particles of each size to fill the available void spaces in the most efficient fashion, taking into account the realities of particle shape and compaction method. In theory, if the Fuller gradation was followed to an infinitely small particle size, the permeability would be zero. However, infinitely small is impossible to achieve, so deviation from the Fuller curve is inevitable, and it is logical to link the point of deviation to the *critical particle size* affecting permeability. This concept is outlined in Calculation Sheet 2.5 and a reasonably practical methodology suggested.

A relatively widely used and much simpler alternative is Hazen's formula:[44]

$$k = cd_{10}^2 \, \mathrm{m/s}$$

where c is a coefficient, usually taken to be 0.01; d_{10} is the sieve size (in mm) through which just 10% of the material passes.

Variations on Hazen's formula have been proposed using either d_5 or d_{15}, but it has to be acknowledged that such methods cannot possibly cater for the full range of possible aggregate gradations. For this reason many engineers simply fall back on assumptions of permeability based on material description and Table 2.4 contains such commonly used assumptions.

As a check on these different approaches, consider the four different materials with gradations shown in Fig. 2.20. The first is a silty clay soil; the second is a clean sand; the third and fourth are typical of sub-base layers in road construction. In each case, the critical particle size according to the Calculation Sheet 2.5 procedure is shown, as is the

Calculation Sheet 2.5 Critical particle size

The series of Fuller curves shown on the figure represent idealised gradations giving maximum packing density.
If a real grading curve is steeper, particles will be loose; if it is less steep, larger particles will 'float' among a matrix of smaller-sized particles.

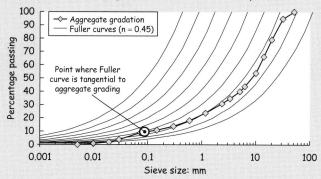

The tangential point shown is the critical size, representing the matrix through which water must flow.

Proposed equation: $k(\text{whole}) \approx k(d_{crit}) \times \%_{crit}/100 \times (1 - \text{area ratio})$

where d_{crit} = critical particle size; $\%_{crit}$ = percentage passing d_{crit}; area ratio = (area under aggregate gradation; $<d_{crit}$)/(area under Fuller curve; $<d_{crit}$).

(Particles larger than d_{crit} form impermeable barriers; the Fuller curve at sizes $<d_{crit}$ also represents very low permeability material.)

Table 2.4 Typical coefficients of permeability[45]

Material description	Typical permeability range: m/s
Well-graded gravels	10^{-5} to 10^{-3}
Poorly graded gravels	5×10^{-5} to 10^{-3}
Silty gravels	10^{-8} to 10^{-4}
Clayey gravels	10^{-8} to 10^{-6}
Well-graded sands	5×10^{-6} to 5×10^{-4}
Poorly graded sands	5×10^{-7} to 5×10^{-6}
Silty sands	10^{-9} to 10^{-6}
Clayey sands	10^{-9} to 10^{-6}
Low-plasticity silts	10^{-9} to 10^{-7}
Low-plasticity clays	10^{-9} to 10^{-8}
High-plasticity silts	10^{-10} to 10^{-9}
High-plasticity clays	10^{-11} to 10^{-9}

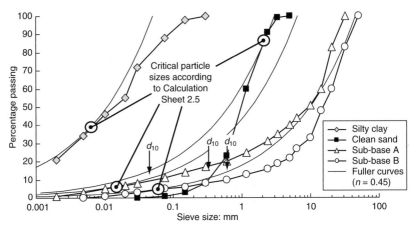

Fig. 2.20 Example materials for estimation of permeability

d_{10} value. Permeability estimates using the three techniques are given in Table 2.5.

The chief discrepancies are in the sub-base – and they are very big discrepancies indeed. And this illustrates the point that it is extremely difficult to predict the permeability of a graded aggregate. Such materials are highly sensitive to small variations in gradation, particularly in the fraction smaller than 75 µm, the details of which are not generally known. This is reflected by the large range given for silty gravel (taken to represent sub-base) in Table 2.4, and inexplicable scatter in test data is common. Notice also the fact that the Fuller curve nearly touches the grading curve for sub-base B a second time – at 30–40 mm. A slightly greater percentage of large particles, meaning insufficient fine material to fill the space available, would have resulted in a very different prediction indeed.

Table 2.5 Comparison of permeability predictions

Material	d_{10}: mm	Calc. Sheet 2.5			Predicted permeability: m/s		
		d_{crit}: mm	%$_{crit}$	Area ratio	According to description	Hazen	Calculation Sheet 2.5
Silty clay	0.0005	0.006	39	0.9	10^{-9} to 10^{-8}	2.5×10^{-9}	3.4×10^{-9}
Clean sand	0.32	2.05	87	0.4	5×10^{-6} to 5×10^{-4}	1.0×10^{-3}	1.3×10^{-3}
Sub-base A	0.044	0.014	6	0.6	10^{-8} to 10^{-4}	1.9×10^{-5}	1.1×10^{-8}
Sub-base B	0.60	0.06	4.5	0.7	10^{-8} to 10^{-4}	3.6×10^{-3}	1.1×10^{-7}

Note: d_{10} value for silty clay extrapolated from data in Fig. 2.20.

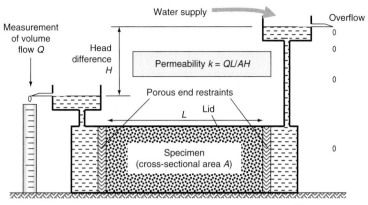

Fig. 2.21 The principle of permeability testing in the laboratory[46]

However, a key practical point is that all such materials are to some extent segregated, which means that relatively permeable paths will exist alongside almost impermeable zones. In practice, therefore, the average permeability of a graded aggregate may be one or two orders of magnitude greater than theoretically expected. It should also be noted that vertical permeability is often lower than horizontal permeability because of the dense closed surface formed under roller compaction.[47]

2.1.4.4 Measuring permeability

This is a fairly straightforward procedure when carried out in a laboratory and there are numerous test specifications to choose from. The key point is that a specimen of material of uniform cross-section has to be enclosed by walls which do not allow preferential drainage paths to develop, and it is then subjected to a small difference in water pressure between the two ends of the specimen. Figure 2.21 illustrates the concept.

The arrangement in Fig. 2.21 is particularly appropriate for unbound pavement layers since it is the horizontal permeability which is of most significance to the performance of a pavement. However, it is extremely important that the lid of the test box is pressed down into the material, generally via a layer of rubber, otherwise water will pass easily over the surface and lead to a false result. The other common arrangement, particularly for soils, is a vertical cylinder of material.[48]

2.1.4.5 Partial saturation and suction

This subject is highly relevant to pavement foundations. They are constructed wet, usually at 90–95% saturation, in order to aid compaction, but it is expected that their long-term condition will be much drier than this. However, that depends on the propensity of the material to retain water, which in turn depends on particle size, very much as permeability does. The point is that the surface tension effect at an air–water interface generates a pressure difference between the water collected near to a particle contact and the surrounding air, and this acts to resist water drainage. Calculation Sheet 2.6 presents a technique for approximate prediction of the suction applying in a wet material; Fig. 2.22 shows the consequent development of negative pore pressure.

Calculation Sheet 2.6 Predicting suction

Surface tension T (N/m) acts along the edge of the air–water interface, at an angle ϕ to the face of the particle (0° if wet; up to 30° if dry). The water pressure is p below the air pressure.

Geometric relationships: $\alpha = (\pi/2) - \theta - \phi$
$r = R\,(1 - \cos\theta)/\sin\alpha$

Horizontal surface tension force $= 2 \times T \times 2\pi R \sin\theta \times \sin\alpha$

Horizontal force due to $p = 2p \int 2\pi(R \sin\theta + r \cos\alpha - r \cos\beta) \times r \cos\beta\, d\beta$
from 0 to α
$= 4\pi pr[(R \sin\theta + r \cos\alpha) \sin\alpha - \tfrac{1}{2}r \sin\alpha \cos\alpha - \tfrac{1}{2}r\alpha]$

Balance forces:

$p = TR \sin\theta \sin\alpha / \{r[(R \sin\theta + r \cos\alpha) \sin\alpha - \tfrac{1}{2}r \sin\alpha \cos\alpha - \tfrac{1}{2}r\alpha]\}$

Vertical inter-particle force due to $p = \int p \times 2\pi R \sin\gamma \times R d\gamma \times \cos\gamma$
$= \pi pR^2 \sin^2\theta$ from 0 to θ

$\therefore$ Effective pressure due to suction given by: $\pi pR^2 \sin^2\theta / \pi R^2 = p \sin^2\theta$

The negative pore pressures shown in Fig. 2.22 are highly beneficial to the performance of an unbound layer, and these benefits will only accrue if the material contains a significant fine particle fraction. However, there is a price to pay. If the particle sizes are too small, then the permeability will be correspondingly small, and the equilibrium degree of saturation will be large, which means: (1) that a small increase in water content can drastically affect material properties; and (2) that, once the water content has increased, it will take a long time to drain. For sensible design, therefore, it is usual to compromise, allowing enough fines for some suction to be generated, but not so much as to prevent drainage.

The computation in Calculation Sheet 2.6 and Fig. 2.22 relates to a highly idealised material. For a graded aggregate, it is suggested that the concept of *critical particle size* (Calculation Sheet 2.5) should be applied,

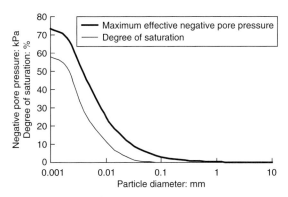

- Surface tension of 73 mN/m assumed
- Single-sized aggregate, 40% void space
- Drained condition (i.e. equilibrium)

Fig. 2.22 The effect of surface tension in an idealised single-sized aggregate

which would give effective suctions of about 18 and 6 kPa respectively for sub-bases A and B in Fig. 2.20 and Table 2.5 under drained conditions. Calculation of equilibrium degree of saturation for a graded aggregate is more difficult, and a rough estimate is probably all that can sensibly be achieved.

2.1.4.6 Plasticity
Many of the issues of suction, degree of saturation and the corresponding influence on mechanical performance can be tied into the concept of 'plasticity'. Plasticity is a property associated with clays, but it also occurs in any unbound material with a proportion of its particles in the clay size range – which means 2 µm, or less. It is, of course, the presence of such small particles that leads to low permeability, high suction and a high equilibrium degree of saturation; however, measurement of plasticity introduces a relatively easy method of reducing a highly complex problem to convenient numbers. The numbers concerned are as follows:

- *Plastic limit (PL)*: the water content at which a soil (or other unbound material) makes the transition from a dry, crumbly state to a plastic, malleable state.
- *Liquid limit (LL)*: the water content representing the transition from a plastic, malleable state to a liquid, flowing state.
- *Plasticity index (PI)*: $PI = LL - PL$.

Plastic limit and liquid limit are conceptually like the freezing and boiling points of a liquid – but rather less well defined. In fact, measurement is decidedly non-scientific. The standard PL test involves rolling

105

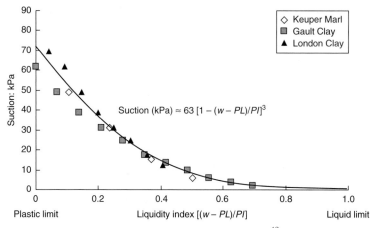

Fig. 2.23 *Relationship between suction and water content*[49]

out a 'sausage' of material; if it crumbles the water content is less than the PL value, if not it is higher. The traditional LL test involves tapping a small container of soil in order to close a groove cut in the surface, although nowadays it is usual to measure penetration of a weighted needle instead. In terms of the particulate nature of a soil, the PL marks the point where there is just enough water to saturate the material with the particles in a densely packed state. The LL on the other hand describes the water content when the particles are in their loosest possible arrangement while maintaining particle-to-particle contacts. The actual water contents will depend on particle shape and gradation, although 15–25% is a common range for the PL and 40–60% for the LL.

The key point is that these two measures represent actual physical behavioural properties with clear meaning to engineers. If the water content is kept at or below the PL value, the material will have high suction, high strength, high stiffness etc.; if it exceeds the LL value, it will be soft, weak, deformable etc. In general, soils are 'uncomfortable' at a water content lower than the PL; the resulting non-saturated state induces suction, which means that any water that is available will be absorbed until the PL is reached. Even at the PL the particle packing arrangement will still be uncomfortably tight and zero suction will only be achieved once sufficient water has been absorbed for the particle structure to be 'at rest'. Experimentally it is possible to show that the 'at rest' state is a little less than the LL. Figure 2.23 gives measured suctions for three quite different clay soils, plotted against a parameter known as the 'liquidity index', indicating relative position on the PL to LL scale – and the data are impressively consistent.

In reality, subgrade soils will vary in water content (and therefore in suction) throughout the year, and this is critically dependent on drainage design.

The concept of plasticity is widely used by geotechnical engineers in characterising soils. In particular it is useful to distinguish between soils that are sensitive to water content changes and those that are not. If the PI is high, then a moderate change in water content will have relatively little effect on material properties. On the other hand, low PI (say 15% or less) means a small difference between PL and LL, such that a modest change in water content will drastically alter the soil's behaviour. This is as important in the context of pavement subgrades as anywhere else and should certainly be taken into consideration when pavement design decisions are being made.

Plasticity also applies to layers other than the subgrade. The tests themselves can only be carried out on the finest fractions of a mixture (material passing the 425 μm sieve in most standards), so if this fraction only represents a minor part of the whole mixture the relevance of a plasticity value becomes questionable. Once more the concept of a *critical particle size* is relevant. If this is larger than 425 μm, then plasticity is fairly meaningless. In practice, it is common to insist that base layers are 'non-plastic', which means that it is impossible to achieve a plastic state at any water content (indicating an almost total lack of clay-size fines). For sub-bases and cappings, a small plasticity may usually be permitted without significant reduction in performance so long as the fines fraction is not too large (i.e. small critical particle size).

2.1.4.7 Frost heave and frost damage

A particular problem of fine-grained materials is frost heave. It is not a subject which will be discussed at any length here, but the reader should be aware that any pavement layer (including the subgrade) which becomes frozen will tend to undergo a volume change due to the growth of ice crystals and that this volume change can be much greater than that expected simply as a result of water volume being replaced by ice volume. This is because, as ice crystals grow, they push soil or fine aggregate particles apart, creating void space. This void space, lying on the water–ice boundary, invites further water ingress if there is surplus water available; this then freezes and the result can be a large volume increase, leading to a raised and uneven road surface. Worse, when the ice melts the water content remains much higher than it was before freezing – which leaves a very weak subgrade (or aggregate).

Qualitatively the solutions are: (1) do not use frost-susceptible materials within the frost zone; (2) do not allow water to accumulate. If the second point can be confidently adhered to then the first becomes irrelevant; however, if there is a danger of high water content within the frost zone, then it is sensible to ensure that none of the materials within this zone are frost-susceptible. A *frost heave* test[50] has been used in the UK for many years in order to exclude undesirable materials. However, the simplest method of overcoming any danger of frost heave is to use a relatively open-graded (and therefore free-draining) material. Of course, there are climatic zones where frost penetration is so deep that frost heave cannot be prevented, and in such cases the overlying pavement has to be designed such that it can accommodate large heave (and subsequent settlement) without excessive damage; see Part 3.

On a related note, there are certain aggregates which can be severely damaged by frost. These are weak, porous aggregates such as chalk and other soft limestones. Specifications guard against such materials in upper pavement layers by insisting on a level of particle hardness, determined indirectly from tests such as the Los Angeles Abrasion (LAA) or Micro-Deval, or by insisting on soundness against chemical attack.[51] However, it must be remembered that damage can occur during construction; for example, if a capping layer consisting of a soft aggregate material is exposed during the winter season it can suffer catastrophic damage – damage which is not always recognised at the time.

2.1.5 Summary

The foregoing sections have given the (correct) impression that unbound materials are extremely complex, both in terms of their mechanical properties and also with regard to the effect of water. However, for practical engineering purposes, it is important to remember a few key points.

- All unbound materials are stress-dependent. This means that the strength or stiffness measured under one set of conditions will differ from measurements under a different set of conditions. Care is therefore needed when assessing properties for pavement design.
- Aggregates with large particle size tend to be stronger, stiffer and more resistant to deformation.

- Nevertheless, it is beneficial to increase the fines content (reducing the characteristic particle size) up to a point, because of the increased potential for suction to develop.
- However, permeability should not be allowed to reduce to the point where water ingress exceeds drainage capacity.

Water is almost always the principal cause of problems in unbound materials, and pavement foundation design therefore has to recognise this and take measures (e.g. drainage; pavement sealing) which limit water content to within suitable limits.

2.2

Hydraulically-bound material

Hydraulic binders such as Portland cement rely on a chemical reaction with water, resulting in the generation of a hard, strongly adhesive mortar. It is not the purpose of this book to delve into the science of these binders, a science which is rapidly changing, leading to ever-stronger concretes, increasingly effective shrinkage control etc. However, it is important to understand the physical characteristics of such materials, the factors which affect their properties and the potential for them to become damaged during their lives as components within a pavement.

It is also worth noting that similar physical properties, test methods etc. also apply to sulphur-bound or polystyrene-bound materials, although these are not commonly used in pavement applications and they will not be discussed separately in this book.

2.2.1 Strength

Strength, the level of stress which can be withstood prior to fracture, is thought by most to be the key characteristic of a hydraulically-bound material. Up until fracture, a hydraulically-bound material is a virtually non-deformable solid. After fracture, it is nothing more than a collection of pieces – basically an unbound material, albeit one with rather large particles.

The cause of fracture is generally considered to be *tensile stress* – although a good case could be made for *tensile strain* actually being the key quantity determining the point of failure. This may seem a fairly irrelevant detail since stress and strain are directly linked via the *elastic modulus* of the material which, in contrast to the case of unbound materials, is an approximately constant property, independent

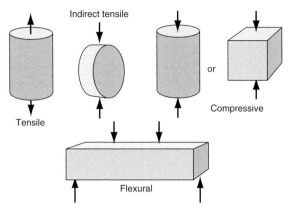

Fig. 2.24 Modes of test configuration for hydraulically-bound materials

of stress conditions. However, this irrelevant detail does indeed become relevant when stress is applied in more than one direction at a time, as is the case under certain test conditions – and also in a pavement. For convenience, however, this section will follow convention and work in terms of stress.

The common modes of strength measurement are shown in Fig. 2.24. In each case, the test is interpreted on the assumption that the material under test is a homogeneous linear elastic solid.

2.2.1.1 Tensile strength
Tension is the fundamental failure mode. However, the problem with tensile strength is that it is not easy to measure. Tests have been devised

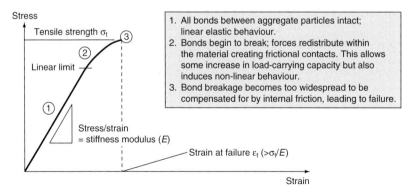

Fig. 2.25 Typical tensile stress–strain relationship for a hydraulically-bound material

– for example an EU norm[52] based on an earlier French standard – but they are not easy to carry out as a standard procedure, which means that alternative measures of strength are sought. Nevertheless, if tension really is the fundamental mode, it is important to take a look at the typical stress–strain relationship which a tensile test generates, and this is shown in Fig. 2.25.

The explanation offered in the inset in Fig. 2.25 acknowledges the fact that a hydraulically-bound material is not really a homogeneous solid but is actually a collection of aggregate particles bonded together and, as these bonds begin to break, the material adopts some of the frictional characteristics of an unbound aggregate.

2.2.1.2 Flexural strength

This is a much more convenient mode in which to test. It is also reasonably representative of the way that stress is felt in a pavement layer under applied wheel load. Two different arrangements are possible, namely four-point (as shown in Fig. 2.24) or three-point, in which the inner two loads are replaced by a single load. The advantage of four-point is that it induces a zone of uniform bending moment in the central part of the beam, allowing the material to fail at a natural point of weakness (which will be dependent on the exact arrangement of aggregate within the mixture). A three-point arrangement has a single plane of maximum bending moment and therefore allows little freedom regarding the location of failure.

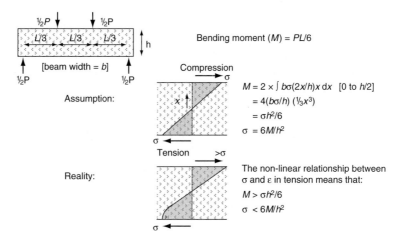

Fig. 2.26 Stress distribution in concrete under bending

The failure load in either test arrangement allows the maximum bending moment to be calculated. This then has to be interpreted in terms of a maximum tensile stress, assuming that the material is linear elastic. Figure 2.26 illustrates the assumptions and the consequent error. A given moment at failure M will be interpreted in terms of a *flexural failure stress* σ_f $(= 6M/h^2)$. However, the equivalent *tensile failure stress* σ_t will actually be smaller because of the non-linear (and consequently more efficient) stress distribution which is present in reality. The difference between the two strength measures is typically 10–15%. Calculation Sheet 2.7 presents predictions for this difference based on the shape of the tensile stress–strain relationship.

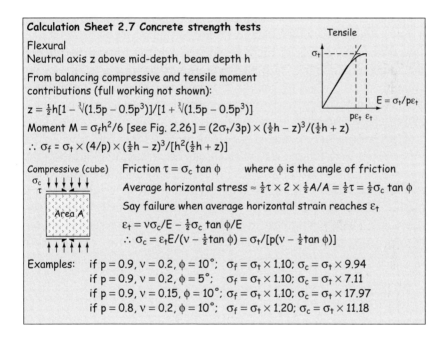

Calculation Sheet 2.7 Concrete strength tests

Flexural
Neutral axis z above mid-depth, beam depth h

From balancing compressive and tensile moment contributions (full working not shown):

$z = \frac{1}{2}h[1 - \sqrt[3]{(1.5p - 0.5p^3)}]/[1 + \sqrt[3]{(1.5p - 0.5p^3)}]$

Moment $M = \sigma_f h^2/6$ [see Fig. 2.26] $= (2\sigma_t/3p) \times (\frac{1}{2}h - z)^3/(\frac{1}{2}h + z)$

$\therefore \sigma_f = \sigma_t \times (4/p) \times (\frac{1}{2}h - z)^3/[h^2(\frac{1}{2}h + z)]$

Compressive (cube)   Friction $\tau = \sigma_c \tan \phi$ where ϕ is the angle of friction

Average horizontal stress $\approx \frac{1}{2}\tau \times 2 \times \frac{1}{2}A/A = \frac{1}{2}\tau = \frac{1}{2}\sigma_c \tan \phi$

Say failure when average horizontal strain reaches ε_t

$\varepsilon_t = v\sigma_c/E - \frac{1}{2}\sigma_c \tan \phi/E$

$\therefore \sigma_c = \varepsilon_t E/(v - \frac{1}{2}\tan \phi) = \sigma_t/[p(v - \frac{1}{2}\tan \phi)]$

Examples: if $p = 0.9$, $v = 0.2$, $\phi = 10°$; $\sigma_f = \sigma_t \times 1.10$; $\sigma_c = \sigma_t \times 9.94$
if $p = 0.9$, $v = 0.2$, $\phi = 5°$; $\sigma_f = \sigma_t \times 1.10$; $\sigma_c = \sigma_t \times 7.11$
if $p = 0.9$, $v = 0.15$, $\phi = 10°$; $\sigma_f = \sigma_t \times 1.10$; $\sigma_c = \sigma_t \times 17.97$
if $p = 0.8$, $v = 0.2$, $\phi = 10°$; $\sigma_f = \sigma_t \times 1.20$; $\sigma_c = \sigma_t \times 11.18$

2.2.1.3 *Indirect tensile strength*

The reason for carrying out indirect tensile (or 'Brazillian splitting') strength determination is that it can be conducted on cored specimens. It is therefore ideal for proving the in situ condition of a pavement layer. Detailed analysis of the stresses induced has led to use of the following equation for the horizontal stress applying over most of the central zone of the specimen:

$$\sigma_{it} = 2P/\pi Dt$$

where P = load, D = horizontal displacement, and t = specimen thickness.

However, this equation suffers from the same assumption of material linearity as that for flexural strength. The actual stress distribution as failure is approached will be slightly more efficient than the linear elastic assumption implies, just as was the case for the flexural test, and the result is also similar. Indirect tensile strength, interpreted using the above equation, also tends to be 10–15% higher than the real tensile strength.

2.2.1.4 Compressive strength

Although much the *least meaningful* strength test, compressive strength is nevertheless the most common strength measure used in practice. The reason lies purely in the ease with which the test can be carried out. Test set-up takes only seconds and there is no need for any complex grips or loading platens. For purposes of quality control it is therefore an ideal test, but it has serious limitations as a design measure. Figure 2.27 illustrates.

The problem here is that there are three different influences on the relationship between tensile and compressive strength. The first is the non-linear characteristic in tension, the effect which has already led to differences between tensile, flexural and indirect tensile strengths; the second is the variation in Poisson's ratio (typically 0.15–0.20); the third is the uncertainty regarding the frictional restraint offered by the end platens. This unfortunately means that the ratio of

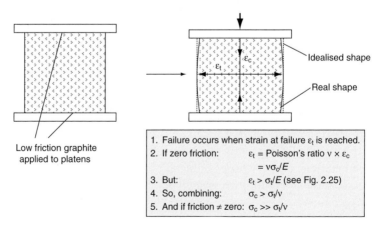

Low friction graphite applied to platens

Idealised shape

Real shape

1. Failure occurs when strain at failure ε_t is reached.
2. If zero friction: ε_t = Poisson's ratio $v \times \varepsilon_c$
   = $v\sigma_c/E$
3. But: $\varepsilon_t > \sigma_t/E$ (see Fig. 2.25)
4. So, combining: $\sigma_c > \sigma_t/v$
5. And if friction ≠ zero: $\sigma_c \gg \sigma_t/v$

Fig. 2.27 Stress distribution in concrete under compression

compressive to tensile strength can be anything from around 5 (almost linear tension characteristic; Poisson's ratio of 0.2) to 15. The Poisson's ratio and degree of non-linearity in the tension characteristic are affected by aggregate type and also strength of mixture. Calculation Sheet 2.7 presents the numerical relationship between compressive strength and other strength measures and the examples given demonstrate the wide range possible.

Compressive strength, whether measured on a cube or a cylinder, is therefore *not a fundamental measure*. It should *never* be relied upon in pavement design. Although experience allows certain 'rules of thumb' to be applied, compressive strength is an inherently *unreliable* measure of actual quality.

Rules of thumb
1. Strong mixes have low Poisson's ratio.
2. Limestone aggregate results in low compressive:tensile strength ratio (e.g. 7).
3. Granite aggregate results in moderate compressive:tensile strength ratio (e.g. 10).
4. Gravel aggregate results in high compressive:tensile strength ratio (e.g. 12).

2.2.1.5 Strength gain with time

A useful property of all hydraulically-bound materials is that they become stronger with time. The initial chemical reactions may take place over a period of a few hours, but other slower reactions are set in motion which take much longer – many years in fact. The ratio of rapid reaction to long-term strength gain is a function of the chemical details of the binder and is not the subject of this book. Suffice it to say that the full spectrum of possible materials ranges from rapid-hardening mixtures – designed for use in repairs to concrete pavements, and which can be trafficable within an hour or two – to ash- or slag-bound mixtures, which may take six months or a year to achieve their design strengths. Figure 2.28 shows compressive strength data for a concrete with ordinary Portland cement (OPC) binder.

For practical reasons it is common to design based on a 28-day strength since it is usual to have at least 28 days between pavement construction and opening to traffic and it is administratively convenient to work in whole numbers of weeks. However, for quality control

115

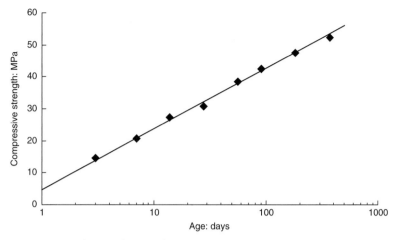

Fig. 2.28 Typical strength gain of OPC concrete

purposes it is common to test at seven days or sometimes three days in order to give early warning of potential problems. The appropriate ratio of seven-day to 28-day strength depends on the binder, but 0.7 is commonly assumed for OPC concrete.

In the case of slow-setting materials, the design properties are typically those at 365 days, in which case 'early' warning of problems would commonly come from the ratio of 90-day to 365-day strength; it is impractical to specify tests more than 90 days after construction. Inevitably, use of such materials will result in less certainty of long-term performance during the construction phase – which should logically be compensated for by use of a larger safety margin.

2.2.2 Fatigue

As is the case with all pavement materials, hydraulically-bound layers rarely fail under a single load application. However, they can most certainly fail under multiple applications of a stress considerably less than the ultimate strength of the material. This is illustrated in Fig. 2.29.

The data in Fig. 2.29 have been expressed in what has become the usual way for hydraulically-bound materials, namely as a plot of numbers of load applications to failure against the ratio of applied stress to ultimate stress at failure. Notice that the best-fit line suggests that a stress greater than the ultimate failure strength would be required to induce failure in a single load application – which cannot be correct. This is actually further evidence that the fundamental measure is *strain*

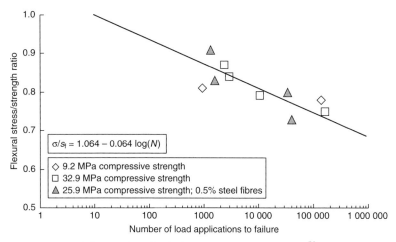

Fig. 2.29 Typical fatigue data for hydraulically-bound material[53]

ratio rather than *stress ratio*, and the non-linearity in the tensile failure characteristic is reflected in a non-linearity in the fatigue characteristic at stress levels close to failure. The data in Fig. 2.29 are compatible with a '*p* value' (see Calculation Sheet 2.7) of around 0.9.

In truth, this is a very complex area and there are various subtle factors which affect fatigue life. However, experience is that a line approximately as shown in Fig. 2.29 can be applied to all but the weakest materials. This leads to the rule of thumb that so long as the stress is less than 50% of the failure stress, the life will be long. The form of the relationship, a straight line on a log-linear plot, isn't really compatible with a power law, but the part which most usually concerns designers (stress ratios of 0.3–0.4) has an approximate exponent of 12 (or −0.083 depending on the way the equation is formulated). As presented later, this contrasts strongly with the exponent found to apply to asphalt – around 4 or 5.

It is useful to consider for a moment just what this process of fatigue actually is. It is quite different in a hydraulically-bound material from the case of a metal, where fatigue consists in the propagation of flaws within the molecular structure. In a hydraulically-bound material, fatigue principally represents the progressive breakage of bonds between individual pieces of aggregate. As a tensile stress is applied, it will not be uniformly distributed within the mixture, and there will inevitably be certain points, certain key bonds between aggregate particles, which approach their fracture strength even at relatively low overall stress

117

levels. This is a function of the complex geometry of the aggregate matrix. As the first bonds break, this results in a redistribution of the loads within the matrix. Furthermore, it means that the detailed pattern of straining within the material will be slightly different following a bond breakage. This will result in other bonds, probably near to the broken ones, coming under excessive load and breaking in their turn – and so the process continues. Since bonds may be between particles of any size down to silt-sized fractions, the process may be a slow one, taking a very large number of load repetitions.

2.2.3 Durability

One of the advantages of a well-designed hydraulically-bound material in a sensibly designed and constructed pavement is that it should have a long life. In fact, the strength of such materials should actually continue to increase throughout their lives, as chemical bonds continue to develop. However, this will only be true if appropriate precautions are taken.

The key to durability is a low *permeability* – which means small non-interconnecting voids. The principal agent of damage to the structure of a hydraulically-bound material is *water* and, so, if water is unable to penetrate then damage will not occur. Permeability of hydraulically-bound materials can be measured directly using a high-pressure permeameter, although this is rarely carried out in practice. Of more likely importance, however, is the permeability local to an interface between pavement layers, in particular at the bottom of a layer where compaction may not have been as effective as higher up.

2.2.3.1 Water damage

Pavements are rarely in a fully dry condition. Even dense asphalt materials are not 100% impermeable and there is always a tendency for voids within all types of pavement material to become partially filled with water. At the base of an imperfectly compacted layer, water is therefore likely to be able to penetrate relatively easily. The danger comes when voids become filled with water and there is no clear escape path. Figure 2.30 illustrates the potential problem conceptually.

Testing for susceptibility to water damage is not a usual part of hydraulically-bound material design since it is normally assumed that water will never be allowed to accumulate within the material to the

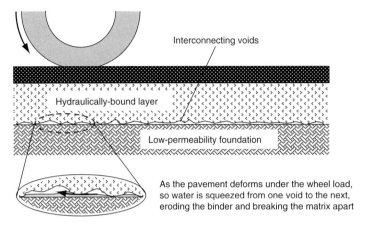

Fig. 2.30 A mechanism of water damage in a hydraulically-bound layer

extent that damage is caused. However, where it is carried out, the usual approach is to measure a so-called *retained strength ratio*.

$$\text{Retained strength ratio} = \frac{\text{strength after soaking in water}}{\text{strength unsoaked}}$$

Various soaking procedures with varying temperatures and durations have been tried and specified, a seven-day soaking period being a typical compromise between realism and practical duration. It is usual to specify that the retained strength should be no less than 80% of the unsoaked strength. However, it is important not to be lulled into a false sense of security since the test specimen is likely still to be undergoing 'curing', i.e. it would naturally gain in strength during the soaking period. Thus, when evaluating a result from such a test, it should be appreciated that a zero change in strength may in reality imply that sufficient 'damage' has occurred to approximately offset the strength gain due to curing.

Note also that a high retained strength does *not* necessarily guard against moisture damage under traffic action, since the test does not include any simulation of dynamic loading. To protect a material against such damage, there is no substitute for proper pavement design – see Part 3.

2.2.3.2 Frost damage
In many climates this is a potentially serious problem. Water expands when it turns to ice, which means that if the water is inside a

nearly-closed void at the time it freezes then the expansive pressure is likely to fracture the surrounding material. In concrete, this can be seen as areas of surface flaking, giving a very rough ride quality to vehicles.

Measures to combat frost damage include the following:

- *Air entrainment*; this technique deliberately introduces tiny air bubbles (typically around 5% by volume) into a concrete by using a chemical additive in the mix.[54] Air voids allow local distortion of the concrete to take place without any damage occurring.
- *Maintain high strength*; experience is that if the strength is high enough (perhaps around 5 MPa flexural strength) then the expansive pressure from frozen trapped water is resisted. In part, this is due to the inevitably very low void content in a strong mixture, reducing the possibility of water ingress.

2.2.4 Thermal properties

A problem with all hydraulically-bound materials is that they are rigid solids, which means they are susceptible to thermal expansion and contraction. In many forms of construction this can be ignored – but not in most pavements (other than indoor pavements such as those for warehouse floors). The problem is that when a kilometre of continuous concrete road cools by 10°C it wants to contract by about 10 cm and, since the ends will be firmly restrained by the continuous nature of road construction, the result will be a tensile failure. This is the reason for the use of joints, mentioned already in Part 1.

However, the question then arises as to how far apart such joints should be, and this depends on the property known as the *coefficient of thermal expansion*, given the symbol α. The value of α depends on the ingredients comprising the material, of which the large aggregate fraction is usually dominant. Thus, α depends on the rock (or other aggregate) used. Table 2.6 gives typical values.

Other thermal properties, not normally used in design, but which do in reality affect the performance of a pavement, are the 'thermal

Table 2.6 Typical values of coefficient of thermal expansion α

Aggregate	Coefficient of thermal expansion α (per °C)
River gravel	13×10^{-6}
Igneous rock	10×10^{-6}
Limestone	7×10^{-6}

conductivity' (the measure of how quickly heat can flow through) and 'specific heat capacity' (the energy required to heat the material by 1 K, i.e. 1°C). These two, together with the density, determine the relationship between pavement surface temperature and temperature at depth, and this in turn influences the far-from-negligible thermally-induced stresses in a hydraulically-bound pavement layer. Typical values are as follows:

- thermal conductivity: 2 W/mK
- specific heat capacity: 880 J/kgK.

2.2.5 Stiffness

Unlike unbound materials, hydraulically-bound materials can reasonably be considered as *linear elastic*, although Fig. 2.25 has illustrated the limitations of this assumption, namely that its validity reduces as the fracture strength is approached.

2.2.5.1 Stiffness measurement

There are two principal methods of measuring stiffness in the laboratory. The first is to use the same test types that have already been introduced for strength measurement, namely tensile, flexural, indirect tensile and compressive. The usual test procedure is simply to control the load and to record the load at failure, but the addition of a sensitive measurement transducer for strain allows elastic modulus (E) to be calculated. Calculation Sheet 2.8 gives details of stiffness derivation from flexural beam testing.[55]

One reason why such tests are uncommon is the difficulty (and time cost) in obtaining an accurate deflection reading. There are standards, notably the EU standard for obtaining stiffness from uniaxial (compression/tension) tests on hydraulically-bound base layers,[56] but such procedures are rare. A simpler technique from the operator's point of view is *ultrasonic* testing, in which pulses of stress are applied to the end of a beam and the time taken for the pulse to travel down the beam, reflect from the end and return is measured. Pulse wave velocity, which is the direct measure obtained, is a function of material density and stiffness modulus and so, if the density is known, the stiffness modulus can be obtained.

This is quick and convenient; unfortunately it is not necessarily correct. Experience suggests that the ultrasonic test produces significantly

121

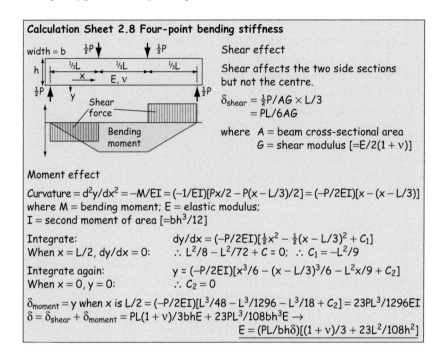

Calculation Sheet 2.8 Four-point bending stiffness

Shear effect

Shear affects the two side sections but not the centre.

$\delta_{shear} = \frac{1}{2}P/AG \times L/3$
$= PL/6AG$

where A = beam cross-sectional area
G = shear modulus $[= E/2(1 + v)]$

Moment effect

Curvature $= d^2y/dx^2 = -M/EI = (-1/EI)[Px/2 - P(x - L/3)/2] = (-P/2EI)[x - (x - L/3)]$
where M = bending moment; E = elastic modulus;
I = second moment of area $[= bh^3/12]$

Integrate:
When $x = L/2$, $dy/dx = 0$:

$dy/dx = (-P/2EI)[\frac{1}{2}x^2 - \frac{1}{2}(x - L/3)^2 + C_1]$
$\therefore L^2/8 - L^2/72 + C = 0; \ \therefore C_1 = -L^2/9$

Integrate again:
When $x = 0$, $y = 0$:

$y = (-P/2EI)[x^3/6 - (x - L/3)^3/6 - L^2x/9 + C_2]$
$\therefore C_2 = 0$

$\delta_{moment} = y$ when x is $L/2 = (-P/2EI)[L^3/48 - L^3/1296 - L^3/18 + C_2] = 23PL^3/1296EI$
$\delta = \delta_{shear} + \delta_{moment} = PL(1 + v)/3bhE + 23PL^3/108bh^3E \rightarrow$
$$E = (PL/bh\delta)[(1 + v)/3 + 23L^2/108h^2]$$

higher stiffnesses than those measured by direct mechanical means, perhaps by 30–50% (based on the author's experience).[57] Part of the problem may be that the level of stress applied in the ultrasonic test is just too small and that the first (normally invisible) part of the stress–strain relationship is actually steeper than the remainder, possibly a function of the non-homogeneous nature of the material (stiff particles in contact, less stiff paste surrounding).

General advice, therefore, would be to use ultrasonic measurement for comparative purposes but not to base any design on such measurements.

2.2.5.2 Influences on material stiffness

Although it is quite acceptable to consider a hydraulically-bound material as linear elastic and homogeneous for most purposes, this isn't really the case and it does not promote real understanding of the way such a mixture works. The reality is that a hydraulically-bound material consists of an aggregate, the particles of which are bonded together. In a sense, it is an unbound material without the possibility of slip between particles (so long as the bonds don't break). If inter-particle slip is denied, the only deformation mechanism which remains is compression at particle contacts – and this is therefore the fundamental mode of strain within a hydraulically-bound material. Calculation Sheet 2.9 presents a methodology for modelling mixture stiffness on this basis.

Calculation Sheet 2.9 Stiffness modelling approach

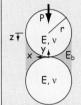

Granular matrix

Bulk stress $= \sigma$; coordination number (average number of contacts per particle) $= n$

$\therefore$ Total average force/particle $= \sigma \times 4\pi r^2$ [assume spherical]

$\rightarrow$ Force per particle contact, $P = 4\pi\sigma r^2/n$

Hertz contact equation: $z = [9P^2(1 - v^2)^2/(2rE^2)]^{0.333}$

$\therefore$ Matrix bulk modulus $K_{mat} \approx \sigma/(z/2r) = \sigma/\{[144\pi^2\sigma^2 r^4(1 - v^2)^2/(16r^4 E^2 n^2)]^{0.333}\}$
$$= [(\sigma E^2 n^2)/(9\pi^2(1 - v^2)^2]^{0.333}$$

and elastic modulus $E_{mat} = 3K_{mat}(1 - 2v_{mat})$ where $v_{mat} = v$ of aggregate matrix ≈ 0.3

Including binder

(a) Work out approximate radius of contact area, $r_c = \sqrt{(rz)}$ [intersecting chords]
(b) With binder of modulus E_b, integrate binder compression force P_b between r_c and r, replacing the circular particle shape by a parabola of equation $y = x^2/2r$

$\rightarrow P_b = \int (z/2y) E_b\, 2\pi x\, dx = \int (zr/x)\, 2\pi E_b\, dx = 2\pi zr E_b[\ln(r) - \ln(r_c)]$

(c) Calculate bound material stiffness as $E_{mat} \times (P + P_b)/P$

Notice that the matrix stiffness in Calculation Sheet 2.9 is independent of particle size. It does however depend on the coordination number n (the average number of contacts each particle makes with its neighbours), which will vary according to particle size distribution and, of course, compaction. In a single-sized aggregate, n might be around 7–9; in a graded aggregate it will be significantly more, typically around 12.

The key additional parameter affecting the stiffness of a bound material is the stiffness modulus of the mortar, another highly variable quantity. In the case of dense continuous cement paste it is suggested that the value should be around 1000 MPa, but the figures for other binders or if significant air voids are present may be considerably different. Table 2.7 gives illustrative predictions, all for an aggregate particle modulus of 200 GPa (typical of hard rock) and Poisson's ratio (of particles; not of mixture) of 0.45.

In no way should this predictive approach be taken as accurate, particularly in special cases such as porous concrete, but it is presented in order to make the reader aware of the factors which determine the stiffness of a particular hydraulically-bound mixture. It should also be

Table 2.7 Stiffness predictions based on aggregate gradation

Coordination number	Stress: kPa	Modulus of mortar: MPa	Predicted modulus: MPa	
			Matrix alone	Full mixture
8 (single-sized)	200	1000	2500	19 000
	200	2000	2500	35 000
	600	1000	3600	18 000
12 (graded)	200	1000	3300	27 000
	200	2000	3300	52 000
	600	1000	4700	27 000

appreciated that these values represent the maximum stiffness possible; the value will reduce as soon as inter-particle bonds begin to break.

2.2.5.3 Typical material stiffness values

If the foregoing section represents a reasonable picture of what is actually occurring within a hydraulically-bound material, then the clear conclusion is that stiffness is sensitive to mixture details, aggregate type etc. Nevertheless, it is possible to draw out typical values for different types of material, since each type tends to make use of a restricted range of ingredients. Table 2.8 represents the author's accumulated experience, based largely on field testing. For the weaker materials, the values quoted will certainly be affected by the presence of microcracking.

A key point to appreciate is that a material of lower stiffness than those in the table is *not* necessarily inferior. Indeed, high stiffness in a concrete pavement attracts high stress – inviting failure unless the strength is correspondingly high, which is not always the case.

Table 2.8 Typical stiffnesses of hydraulically-bound materials

Mixture type	Typical stiffness: MPa
Pavement quality concrete (PQC)	30 000–40 000
Strong cement-bound base	15 000–25 000
Weak cement-bound base	5000–15 000
Slag etc. bound base	3000–10 000
Hydraulically-bound sub-base	2000–5000
Stabilised soil	100–300

Table 2.9 Stiffness predictions based on material strength

Predictive equation[58]		Predicted elastic modulus: MPa			
	Compressive strength: 5 MPa	10 MPa	20 MPa	40 MPa	
$E = 21\,500\,C(\sigma_{c,failure}/10^{-7})^{0.333}$ [MPa]					
C = 1.2 – basalt, dense limestone	20 500	25 800	32 500	40 100	
C = 1.0 – quartzite	17 100	21 500	27 100	34 100	
C = 0.9 – most limestones	15 400	19 400	24 400	30 700	
C = 0.7 – sandstone	11 900	15 100	19 000	23 900	

Numerous concrete pavements with PQC stiffnesses well below 30 000 MPa are performing satisfactorily throughout the world.

2.2.5.4 Relationship between stiffness and strength

Numerous claimed relationships between strength and stiffness have been published. However, it should always be appreciated that, like the stiffnesses in Table 2.8, such relationships can only be approximate for the excellent reason that strength and stiffness are not directly related. Strength depends on bond strength between particles, which is a function of binder quality and quantity; stiffness also depends on aggregate gradation and the stiffness of individual particles. It is of course usual for strong mixes to make use of high strength aggregate, and such aggregate will usually also have high stiffness – but the relationship can never be other than an indirect one. Table 2.9 presents predictions based on one of the more commonly quoted relationships.

2.2.5.5 The effective stiffness of a discontinuous layer

A knowledge of material modulus can be useful, but in many cases a hydraulically-bound material is designed to end up in a cracked state – which means that its apparent stiffness in situ will inevitably be less than that of the intact material. Experience suggests that a cement-bound base layer with an initial stiffness of 10 000–20 000 MPa can easily end up with an apparent in situ stiffness of no more than 5000 MPa. And it is this apparent stiffness which affects the way the layer spreads load to underlying materials and supports overlying layers.

Figure 2.31 illustrates a rational approach to estimation of that stiffness. Basically, the approach is to acknowledge that there are three elements to the 'compliance' (the inverse of stiffness) of a cracked

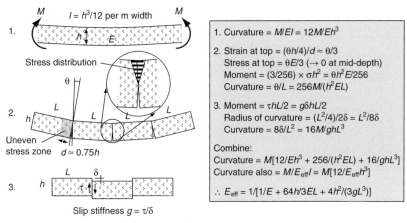

Fig. 2.31 Bending of a cracked layer[59]

layer. First, there is the bending of the intact material; second there is angular rotation at crack locations; and third there is relative vertical movement across cracks. In each case, a relationship between bending moment and curvature can be estimated.

Full calculation details have been omitted from Fig. 2.31, partly due to lack of space, but also because such details are not in any way fundamental; it would be possible to derive alternative, slightly different, but no less valid approximations for E_{eff}.

However, the formula in Fig. 2.31 at least allows an estimate to be made. Take the common case of a lean concrete layer of material modulus $E = 15\,000\,\text{MPa}$. Such a layer commonly breaks naturally into blocks of 5 m length or less or, nowadays, is deliberately pre-cracked into 3 m long blocks (see Part 3). This pre-cracking minimises crack width, maximises interlock and therefore also maximises 'slip stiffness' g. Admittedly, slip stiffness is not a commonly used quantity, but experience (e.g. from falling weight deflectometer testing – see Part 4) suggests that it may have a value of around $5000\,\text{MN/m}^3$ for a new pavement layer, reducing with time and traffic. If the layer is 150 mm thick, then Fig. 2.31 suggests an effective layer modulus E_{eff} when new of 7250 MPa. In fact, the third element of the equation, namely that due to vertical slip at cracks, is almost negligible with 3 m crack spacing, so effective stiffness is only likely to decrease significantly if additional cracks appear. Many lean concrete base design methods assume around 5000 MPa as a long-term effective stiffness.[60]

Use of this formula is believed to be appropriate for most hydraulically-bound layers, but *not* in the case of stabilised soils. In general, it

126

is advised that a stabilised soil should be assigned a stiffness no more than about three times that of the non-stabilised material beneath.[61] In effect, it should be assumed to act as an unbound material, whatever laboratory data may suggest.

2.2.6 Mixture design

Practical mixture design is primarily concerned with strength. Material specification may also include a durability requirement but fatigue life, stiffness and thermal properties will not normally be either specified or measured. They all affect pavement performance but to a far less significant degree than strength. The key, therefore, is to achieve the design strength, ideally a *flexural strength*.

2.2.6.1 Wet-formed mixtures

Traditional concrete is mixed to a consistency at which it can be poured and readily compacted by means of vibration. The water content should be adequate for the chemical reaction needed to convert the cementitious binder into hard-setting compounds (typically 0.22–0.25 g of water per gram of cement); if not, then some of the binder will remain unused, reducing the strength. However, if the water content is too great (greater than around 0.45 g per gram of cement), then the excess water will inhibit the formation of the most effective compounds, also reducing the strength. Thus, there is an *optimum water content* – or in practice there is a range of water contents which give acceptably high mixture strength. Once a certain strength is selected, requiring a certain cement content, this therefore places limits on the range of possible water contents.

Nevertheless, the concrete must also be sufficiently workable, a property most commonly specified by means of a 'slump' test, a highly practical site measure of the amount by which a truncated cone of concrete slumps once the conical mould is removed. If the desired combination of aggregate type and gradation plus cement type/content cannot achieve this slump with a water content in the permissible range, then the mixture has to be redesigned, which may involve adjustment to the fines content or even a change of aggregate type. However, the fact is that wet-formed mixtures are only suited to binder contents above a certain figure, and in practice this means either PQC or high-strength base concrete (often known as 'wet lean concrete'), with a typical flexural strength of 3 MPa or over. Figure 2.32 illustrates the constraints applying.

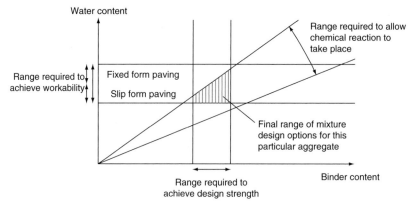

Fig. 2.32 Constraints on design – wet-formed mixtures

To some extent the design also depends on the paving equipment being used. Slip-form pavers have become the machines of choice for large areas of concrete pavement because of the high productivity achievable, but they can only be successful if the concrete is able to retain its paved shape right from the moment it emerges from the paver. This demands lower workability and therefore lower slump and lower water content, and places an upper limit on the appropriate binder content since anything beyond this will not have sufficient water to activate it. Admittedly binder chemistry can be adjusted to help overcome this, and specialist cements (and chemical additives) allow very high strength to be achieved at remarkably low water contents – but at a price.

2.2.6.2 Roller-compacted mixtures

Compaction by roller is quite different from wet-forming. When first laid, all hydraulically-bound materials are effectively *unbound* and they will therefore compact like unbound materials. When wet-formed, either using side forms or the side panels of a slip-form paver, water content must be relatively high, even approaching saturation, to allow relatively easy compaction under moderate compactive effort. Roller-compaction, on the other hand, introduces a much higher compactive effort and therefore a significantly *lower optimum water content* to achieve maximum compacted density. Since the ratio of water to cement (or other hydraulic binder) is still of critical importance to the eventual strength of the mixture, this means that roller compaction is generally suited to weaker materials than those suited to wet-forming. However, this is a generalisation and it is still possible for roller-compacted concrete to achieve

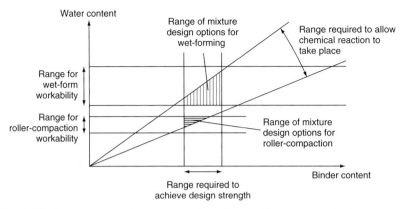

Fig. 2.33 Constraints on design – wet-formed and roller-compacted mixtures

strengths suited to PQC (e.g. 6 MPa flexural; typically >40 MPa compressive) with certain mixtures, particularly those making use of limestone aggregate. Figure 2.33 illustrates such designs.

Roller compaction is an attractive option for many hydraulically-bound mixtures simply because it removes the need for a specialist concrete paving machine, saving on costs and, probably, time. Placement can either be by means of a standard asphalt-type paver or, where level tolerances are less critical, by tipping and grading as for a granular pavement layer.

2.2.6.3 Typical concrete mixtures

Because of the enormous range of possible hydraulic binders and combinations of binders, this section is confined to those using Portland cement, i.e. concretes. The proportions given in Table 2.10 should, of

Table 2.10 Typical mixture proportions

Mixture type	Design strength at 28 days: MPa		Cement content: kg/m^3	Water content: l/m^3
	Flexural	Compressive		
Strong PQC	6	(45)	460	200
Standard PQC	4.5	40	420	180
Strong lean concrete	(3)	20	320	150
Medium lean concrete	–	10	220	150
Weak lean concrete	–	5	150	150

Note: flexural strength is particularly appropriate to strong layers which fail primarily in bending. Values shown in brackets would not normally be used in material specification.

129

course, be seen as indicative only, highly dependent on the aggregate and gradation used. The descriptions given are generic terms and may not relate to the names used in particular specifications.

2.2.6.4 Fibre-reinforced concrete

Fibres are introduced into concrete for two basic reasons: first to control shrinkage cracking; and second to reinforce. Shrinkage crack control is not normally achieved using fibres in pavement layers since it is more economic and more effective to use curing compounds on the pavement surface but, if fibres were to be used, they would be of low-strength polymeric materials. Reinforcement on the other hand demands that the fibre takes considerable stress – and this generally implies the use of *steel*.

The introduction of fibres into a mixture does not usually lead to any significant change in aggregate proportions or water or cement content. In effect, the fibres act as long, thin pieces of aggregate. They come in numerous shapes (as illustrated in Fig. 2.34) and sizes, representing a compromise between mechanical efficiency, which is optimised by a long, thin shape, and 'mixability'. Economics dictate that steel fibres are rarely used at over 0.5% by volume.

The effect of fibre reinforcement is most clearly seen in a tensile (or flexural) stress–strain plot, as illustrated in Fig. 2.34. While the concrete is fully intact, the fibres do nothing other than acting as stiff pieces of aggregate; however, as soon as local fractures between aggregate particles start to occur, the fibres begin to take control. Figure 2.25

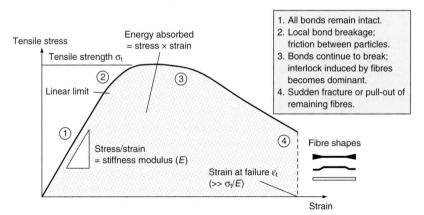

Fig. 2.34 Stress–strain behaviour of steel-fibre-reinforced concrete

has already introduced the concept that frictional interaction between aggregate particles begins to play a part in behaviour as soon as the first fractures occur. With fibres present, this frictional phase is enormously extended because of the highly efficient shape of a fibre. Each fibre interlocks with numerous pieces of aggregate, requiring large energy input into the system in order to overcome it, hence the greatly increased failure strain shown in Fig. 2.34. Despite the lack of any increase in failure stress, the high failure strain means that the concrete requires a lot more energy to fail it, important in impact situations such as safety barriers, and potentially useful in pavements also.

2.2.6.5 Relationship between laboratory and site

This is a very delicate area. Nevertheless, it is not one which can be dismissed. There are many reasons to expect a laboratory mixture to display a higher strength than material actually in a pavement. Control of mixture proportions may be better; curing may be better controlled. But the principal reason is that compaction will generally be better in a confined mould. Whatever the cause or combination of causes, many studies have shown that strengths of paving material compacted into moulds on site, and cured outside adjacent to the pavement, consistently outperform those measured on cores taken directly from the pavement layer, and this is found in both wet-formed and roller-compacted materials. The difference is often as much as 30%.[62]

Where pavement designs are based purely on experience, this finding is of little importance. The difference is taken into account by the calibration process from which the design method was developed. However, in analytical design the difference cannot be ignored.

2.2.6.6 Slow-curing materials

Mixture designs for Portland cement concrete are not too difficult to validate since a good idea of long-term properties can be obtained at seven days. However, for materials which take many months to reach their design strength, it is unrealistic to wait the many weeks necessary before carrying out representative tests, and to overcome this difficulty it is common practice to use an *accelerated curing* technique. Strength gain is highly temperature dependent, and a typical accelerated curing regime therefore consists of placing specimens in a 40°C oven (for 28 days in current UK standards[63]). Though much criticised by purists, this practice is the only sensible way of obtaining early data

131

on which to base mixture design. It does, of course, make the assumption that the actual material in situ will be sufficiently protected from the weather (notably rain and frost) and traffic (construction traffic in particular can cause irreparable damage) to achieve a similar level of performance to that of accelerated-cured specimens.

Note that, while accelerated curing is undeniably useful in mixture design, it is not advised as a specification requirement. That should preferably be based on materials cured under site conditions and tested at an appropriate age, typically 90 days.

2.2.6.7 In situ stabilised materials

In situ mixing presents its own unique problems. For a start, the 'aggregate' is usually a natural soil, which inevitably varies in properties from place to place. Second, the difference between laboratory and site is likely to be much more pronounced for in situ stabilised than plant-mixed material, since the mixing process is clearly less well controlled on site. Third, most in situ stabilised materials are slow-curing, compounding the uncertainty. And fourth, many soils include chemicals which are potentially detrimental to the long-term health of some binders.

However, despite these very real difficulties, in situ stabilisation is often the obvious and most economic way to improve a subgrade to a state suitable for pavement construction – so it has to be taken seriously. That being the case, it is important to understand the processes involved. These are:

- modification
- binding action (i.e. stabilisation proper).

Modification simply means a changing of a soil's plasticity characteristics. It is achieved by the action of lime (or other products that include free lime) and the result is a modification to the particulate structure of the material. Its effect is that the plastic limit value increases and, if the water content remains unchanged, the behaviour at that water content will become more 'plastic' and less 'liquid'. In engineering terms, the suction will increase and with it the strength, stiffness and resistance to deformation. Since the hydration of the lime also results in a (probably temporary) reduction in water content, the effect is made even more impressive. In the field, modification is optimised by allowing the mixed material to lie in a loose state for about 24 h, a phase known as 'mellowing'. Once the material properties have been modified, compaction can take place or, in some cases, stabilisation by the addition of further binder. For example it is not uncommon to apply 2–3% lime to modify a soil, followed a day later by Portland cement as a stabiliser.

Binding action (i.e. *stabilisation*) occurs following modification if there is surplus binder, which means if more than about 3% lime has been added or if a second binder has been used following modification. Here, the chemical reaction which takes place produces similar cementitious products to those produced in conventional hydraulically-bound materials, and the result is that soil particles are actually bonded together. The effect is chemically irreversible – although this does not of course prevent bond breakage under physical stress.

So, in situ stabilisation is conceptually not hard to grasp. Unfortunately, confident design is much less easy, which means that a reasonably generous safety margin should be maintained. The following steps should ensure a satisfactory product.

- Check the chemical composition of the soil, particularly for sulphates and sulphides. These cause expansion and consequent disruption to the structure of the material.[64]
- Mix and compact test specimens in the laboratory (usually cylinders or cubes).
- Apply an accelerated curing regime (e.g. 28 days at 40°C), except where Portland cement is the main binder.
- Carry out mechanical tests (compressive strength for stronger materials; CBR for weaker materials).
- Soak specimens to assess durability (many different procedures exist). The same soaking regime may also be used to evaluate whether excessive volumetric expansion is likely – see below.
- Retest to evaluate potential strength loss under water action.

With the exception of the question of volumetric expansion, the procedure is relatively straightforward. Specifications vary regarding mixing procedure, compaction technique, specimen shape and size, soaking procedure and testing regime, but conceptually they are all aiming to prove the physical properties of the material under controlled conditions, including evaluation of the effect of water. *However*, the combination of unknowns present on site (soil properties, water content, mixing efficiency, curing conditions, stressing during early life) means that the properties measured in the laboratory certainly *cannot* be assumed on site. A strength (or CBR) 50–75% of that measured in the laboratory is advised as realistic.

This leaves the tricky problem of *volumetric expansion*. It certainly happens; there have been several high-profile failures during construction due to this mechanism. However, it is still not properly understood. Behaviour appears to be sensitive to the exact combination of chemistry, water content and temperature, not to mention the type of test regime applied. The well-recognised development of ettringite crystals, for instance, occurs when the temperature drops to 15°C or below, immediately invalidating those many soaking regimes where 20°C is specified. Expansion is also highly sensitive to water availability. In tests where the specimen is encased in a steel mould and water is only given access through a porous plate at the base, there may be insufficient supply to generate significant expansion in the laboratory, whereas on site there may be plenty. The steel walls of a mould also have the effect of resisting expansion by friction. A further important question in laboratory evaluation is just how soon after specimen preparation the water should be applied. In short, this is an area where research is still very much in progress and the engineer should certainly be ready to question test data rather than automatically accept results. As in many fields, the fact that a test is carried out to some national or international standard unfortunately does not prove material suitability.[65]

2.2.7 Summary

In a sense, hydraulically-bound materials are not as complex as unbound. However, what they lack in complexity in material characterisation, they more than make up for in terms of the sheer range of different materials possible, from weak soil-cement to heavy-duty concrete for airfields, which means that it is not easy to generalise. Nevertheless, the following are some of the key points pertaining.

- There is always a strength gain process, which may be one of hours in the case of rapid-set concretes, weeks in the case of conventional concretes or months in the case of slow-setting hydraulically-bound mixtures. The environmental and loading conditions during this 'curing' process are critical to the eventual performance of the material.
- Appropriate water content is essential to achieving design strength and is also constrained by the needs of material compaction.
- Since hydraulically-bound mixtures are, for practical purposes, elastic solids, they are susceptible to stress generated by restrained thermal expansion or contraction.

- The general mode of failure for all hydraulically-bound materials is tensile, occurring when the tensile strain limit is exceeded.
- However, failure can occur under multi-cyclic loading at strains much lower than the tensile limit due to the phenomenon known as fatigue.
- Slow-setting mixtures, particularly those mixed in situ, present additional problems in assuring a product of suitable quality.

2.3

Asphalt

An asphalt is basically a granular material with an extra ingredient, bitumen, and a proper understanding of granular material is therefore of considerable assistance when trying to make sense of asphalt. However bitumen, the added ingredient, undeniably has a very important influence on behaviour and so the first task is get to grips with bitumen and the properties which make it such a useful binder in a pavement. This book will not go into the production of bitumen, which is basically a residue from the distillation of heavy crude oil, nor will it delve too deeply into the chemistry of bitumen, which is complex and still the subject of differing opinions regarding molecular interaction. However, the physical properties of bitumen are extremely important to a full understanding of asphalt.

2.3.1 Bitumen

Bitumen is a very different binder from cement – and the resulting mixture, asphalt, is quite different in its behaviour from concrete. Although not discussed separately in this book, the same principles apply to so-called 'bio-binders', alternatives to conventional bitumen, derived from plant oils. Both bitumens and bio-binders remain *liquid*, even in service. This means that the primary mechanical property is viscosity and, as for any liquid, this is a function of temperature.

2.3.1.1 Viscosity

Viscosity can be measured directly in various ways.[66] Figure 2.35 shows typical results for different so-called grades of bitumen (see Section 2.3.1.2) and the dramatic effect of temperature is clear. In general, about 0.2 Pa.s is required for mixing, giving a temperature range of

136

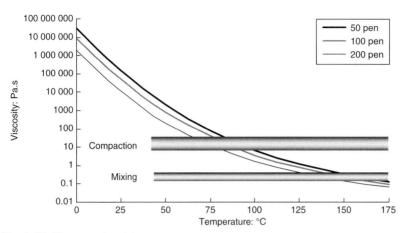

Fig. 2.35 Bitumen viscosities

140–180°C; 30 Pa.s is a maximum value for compaction, giving a minimum compaction temperature of between 70 and 80°C. The tremendous variation in in-service viscosity can also be seen, between a hot summer's day, when the pavement temperature may be well over 40°C, and that expected in the winter. It is therefore immediately obvious that asphalt performance will be quite different in summer compared to winter.

2.3.1.2 Penetration and softening point

Just as liquid and plastic limits and California bearing ratio are still commonly used to characterise soils, and compressive strength is commonly used to characterise hydraulically-bound materials, so bitumen has its own index tests – equally non-fundamental, equally practical. The 'penetration' is inversely related to viscosity since the test measures the viscous resistance to the penetration of a needle into a container of bitumen. The 'ring and ball softening point', on the other hand, is a temperature at which the bitumen has a certain viscosity (about 800 Pa.s), the viscosity being that at which a steel ball drops through a prepared disk of bitumen. Figure 2.36 shows both tests and also defines a quantity known as Penetration Index, related to the temperature susceptibility of the binder.

The most common way to describe a bitumen is still with reference to the penetration test. For example, a 40–60 penetration grade bitumen (colloquially known as 50 pen) would have a penetration of between 4 and 6 mm in the penetration test. The softening point, in combination with the penetration, is designed to give a practical measure of the

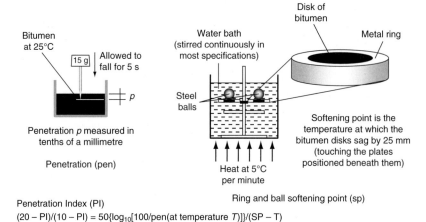

Penetration Index (PI)

$$(20 - PI)/(10 - PI) = 50\{\log_{10}[100/pen(\text{at temperature } T)]\}/(SP - T)$$

Fig. 2.36 The penetration and softening point tests[67]

temperature susceptibility, important in the context of performance at high summer temperatures (which can easily reach 50°C on the pavement surface even in temperate climates).

2.3.1.3 Visco-elasticity

Although viscosity is the primary mechanical property, bitumen is actually a very unusual liquid because its viscosity is so high. This means that the elastic (i.e. recoverable) component of deformation becomes significant at in-service temperatures. Not only that, but there is actually a truly visco-elastic element, i.e. a deformation which, though eventually recoverable, is time dependent. Figure 2.37 illustrates the full visco-elastic behaviour expected.

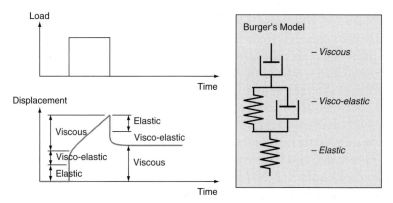

Fig. 2.37 The visco-elastic nature of bitumen

This is undeniably complex and of keen interest to bitumen specialists. Many will fit parameters to a model such as the Burger's Model shown in Fig. 2.37. However, for the general pavement engineer it is sufficient simply to appreciate the different components without getting bogged down in the modelling details, particularly since the practical use of such modelling is slightly questionable.

Data on visco-elastic properties can be generated quite simply nowadays using a *dynamic shear rheometer* (DSR – see Calculation Sheet 2.10), a device that applies repeated torsion to a small cylindrical sample of bitumen and, since the test is straightforward, it is often carried out. However, interpretation is less straightforward. Figure 2.38 shows data for four quite different bitumens and, while the differences are obvious, the meaning – i.e. which will form the best binder – is not. In fact, it is still common for engineers to ignore the detailed data in favour of the derivation of an 'equivalent penetration' value.

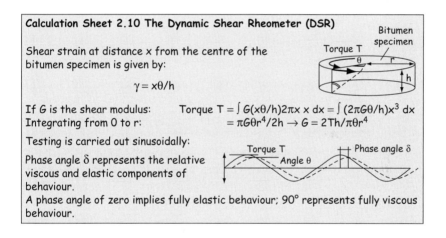

Calculation Sheet 2.10 The Dynamic Shear Rheometer (DSR)

Shear strain at distance x from the centre of the bitumen specimen is given by:

$$\gamma = x\theta/h$$

If G is the shear modulus: Torque $T = \int G(x\theta/h)2\pi x \, dx = \int (2\pi G\theta/h)x^3 \, dx$
Integrating from 0 to r: $= \pi G\theta r^4/2h \rightarrow G = 2Th/\pi\theta r^4$

Testing is carried out sinusoidally:

Phase angle δ represents the relative viscous and elastic components of behaviour.

A phase angle of zero implies fully elastic behaviour; 90° represents fully viscous behaviour.

The quantity which is most usually quoted is known as the *complex modulus* (G^*) – complex because it includes both an elastic (G') and a viscous (G'') component. G' is known as the *storage modulus* and G'' as the *loss modulus*. Basically, G^* is the absolute magnitude of shear stress divided by the absolute magnitude of shear strain, ignoring any time lag between them due to viscous effects.

Complex modulus G^* gives an idea of the stiffness of a bitumen at a given temperature and loading rate. The other useful parameter is the phase angle difference δ between stress and strain. In a perfectly elastic material, stress and strain will be perfectly in phase – which means that

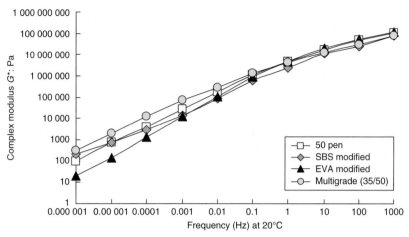

Fig. 2.38 DSR data for different bitumens[68]

the phase angle is zero; in a perfectly viscous material, they will be 90° out of phase.

$$G' = G^* \cos \delta$$

$$G'' = G^* \sin \delta$$

$$[G^*]^2 = [G']^2 + [G'']^2$$

At 20°C and 10 Hz (a frequency typical of pavement loading), G^* is typically 10–30 MPa.

The US 'Superpave' specification[69] is in terms of direct visco-elastic measurements carried out in the DSR and may therefore be considered much more scientifically based than those that use penetration and softening point. Lower limits are placed on $G^* \sin \delta$ (to protect against rutting) and $G^* / \sin \delta$ (to protect against fatigue cracking). It also incorporates measurement of low-temperature visco-elastic properties using a *bending beam rheometer*, a device which induces flexure in a bitumen specimen, 6.35 mm × 2.7 mm in section.[70]

2.3.1.4 Fracture and fatigue
This is an absolutely key area of bitumen performance. If stress is applied slowly enough, bitumen will simply deform viscously (with negligible elastic and visco-elastic components). However, if load is applied rapidly – or if the temperature is low – it can fracture. This behaviour is fundamental to a proper understanding of asphalt. The

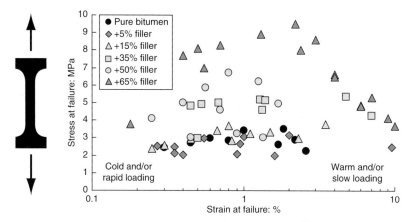

Fig. 2.39 Direct Tension Test data – 50 pen grade bitumen[73]

principal equipment for investigating fracture is the Direct Tension Test (DTT),[71] illustrated in Fig. 2.39, and it is usual to conduct tests at low temperature, recognising the tendency for cracks to appear at night in cold climates (thermal cracking – see Part 3). The best-known alternative low-temperature fracture test is the 'Fraass breaking point test'.[72] Both the DTT and the Fraass test are intended to measure the susceptibility of a binder to fracture in cold weather.

However, the DTT equipment can be used over a wide range of temperatures and loading rates and Fig. 2.39 shows such data for a particular 50 pen grade bitumen, including specimens with various filler contents (by mass) – see next section.

This is another highly complex aspect of behaviour, although to a first approximation bitumen can be seen to have a constant *fracture strength* (i.e. tensile stress at failure) but a highly variable fracture strain. In Fig. 2.39, the fracture strength value is around 3 MPa, becoming slightly less at very low temperatures or high loading rates – a reason why low-temperature tests are appropriate. At the other end of the range, when the strain rate is slow enough or the temperature is high enough, fracture does not occur at all; it is replaced by steady-state creep.

Bitumen can also suffer *fatigue*, i.e. failure under repeated load at a stress less than the fracture strength – although such testing demands specialist equipment and so would not normally be carried out. Figure 2.40 shows a fatigue characteristic, in this case derived from repeated load axial testing of a small disc of bitumen, and it is noticeable that the DTT fracture strength is close to the projected single load

141

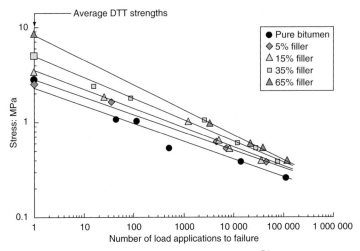

Fig. 2.40 *Bitumen and bitumen-filler mortar fatigue data*[74]

application failure stress. In fact, just as bitumen can be considered to have a single fracture strength so, to a first approximation, it has a single fatigue characteristic when plotted against stress, independent of loading rate and temperature – over a certain range.

2.3.1.5 The bitumen-filler mortar system

'Filler' is the term used for silt-size particles which are added to a bituminous mixture as a means of extending and enhancing the performance of the bitumen, and it is common to consider the filler as a bitumen additive rather than as a component of the aggregate. It has the effect of stiffening and strengthening the bitumen. Figure 2.39 illustrated the increased strength. Figure 2.40 shows that a bitumen-filler mortar also has an improved fatigue characteristic in the sense that the life to failure is extended for a given level of applied stress. It can also be demonstrated that the stiffness of a bitumen-filler mortar is similarly increased. Calculation Sheet 2.11 outlines the theoretical effect of spherical filler particles. The actual effect is greater and typically amounts to an increase in both strength and stiffness by a factor of 2–3.

Experience (and theory) indicates that it is beneficial to a mixture to include a certain proportion of filler, typically a slightly higher percentage by mass than that of bitumen, which equates to about a 2:1 bitumen to filler ratio by volume. If larger quantities are used, the

---

Calculation Sheet 2.11 Bitumen-filler mastic

Stiffness

First approximation: assume filler particles are infinitely stiff and do not interact;
→ $E_{mastic} = E_{bit}/(1 - V_f)$ where V_f = filler volume fraction

In reality, particles interact, particularly at V_f of 0.5 or more → increased stiffness

Strength   Assume fracture plane deviates around each particle

Integrate from ϕ to $\pi/2$: $F = \int \sigma_{fb} r \, d\theta \, 2\pi r \cos\theta/\sin\theta$
$$= 2\pi r^2 \sigma_{fb} \ln(r/z)$$

z has equal probability between 0 and r

∴ Integrate: Average $F = \int 2\pi r^2 \sigma_{fb} \ln(r/z) \, dz/r$
$$= 2\pi r^2 \sigma_{fb}$$

Acting over average area of $\int \pi(r^2 - z^2) \, dz/r = 2\pi r^2/3$

→ Average stress normal to fracture plane at particles
of $2\pi r^2 \sigma_{fb}/2\pi r^2/3 = 3\sigma_{fb}$

→ Overall average stress normal to fracture plane of
$$3\sigma_{fb} V_f + \sigma_{fb}(1 - V_f) = \sigma_{fb}(1 + 2V_f)$$

In reality, particles are non-spherical → increased strength

---

filler begins to form part of the aggregate skeleton rather than acting as a bitumen enhancer. The principle governing the role of the filler is similar to that illustrated for an unbound mixture in Calculation Sheet 2.5. When the aggregate (including filler) gradation is compared to the appropriate Fuller gradation, a point of contact between the two can be found, defining a *critical particle size*. Larger sizes form the aggregate skeleton; smaller sizes are 'lost' in the void spaces and would have no structural role at all were it not for the bitumen. Thus, there is an optimum filler content above which increased quantities no longer give improvement; in fact, excessive filler will result in poorer performance since such small particles do not form an effective component in the aggregate skeleton. Figure 2.41 illustrates for a typical asphalt base mixture.

The result of all this is that an appropriate volume of added filler will raise the tensile strength of the binder from around 2–3 MPa for pure bitumen to 5–8 MPa for a bitumen-filler mortar, with a similar increase in fatigue strength and stiffness.

2.3.1.6 Bitumen chemistry

The foregoing sections have treated bitumen as an inert fluid of indeterminate chemistry and, since this is not a book on chemistry,

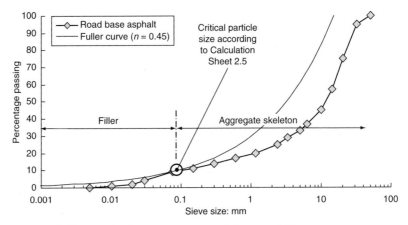

Fig. 2.41 Differentiating between aggregate skeleton and filler

this is good enough for most pavement engineering applications. However, it is useful to have a broad appreciation of what actually goes into a bitumen. It is a byproduct of oil refining and, since oils are complex and varied organic compounds, it is unsurprising that bitumens are similarly complex. The individual molecules in a bitumen are large and non-uniform, varying tremendously in molecular weight and therefore in resulting physical attributes. While bitumen chemists may criticise the following simplification, for engineers it is useful to discern the following four broad classes of molecule:

1. asphaltenes
2. resins
3. aromatics
4. saturates.

Asphaltenes are 'polar', which means the molecules carry positive and negative charge at different points and that bonds between the molecules can therefore form easily. Basically, the more asphaltenes there are in a bitumen, the harder and more viscous that bitumen is likely to be. At the other end of the scale, saturates are a lighter non-polar fraction and they form a 'soup' surrounding the other types of molecule, giving fluidity to the overall compound. A bitumen with plenty of saturates will be softer and have a lower viscosity and may also be more readily able to 'heal', i.e. to self-repair and re-form broken bonds.

The other molecule types, resins and aromatics, are intermediate components in the soup. Resins, like asphaltenes, are highly polar

144

and they strongly affect the degree to which asphaltenes are dispersed within the bitumen. Aromatics make up the largest volume fraction; they are non-polar and act as a solvent to both asphaltenes and resins.[75]

2.3.1.7 Bitumen ageing

It is an unfortunate fact that the chemistry of bitumen tends to change with time and that this can result in a loss of performance. This effect is termed 'ageing'. There are two main forms which ageing takes.

1. *Oxidation.* Many of the polar molecules within a bitumen are readily able to combine with any free oxygen they find. The result is additional cross-linking between molecules and a general stiffening and increase in viscosity. A less beneficial consequence is a reduction in fracture strain.
2. *Absorption by aggregate.* The lighter saturate fraction of a bitumen, with smaller molecular size, has significant affinity for aggregate with the right absorptive quality. This is helpful in making sure that the bitumen adheres to the aggregate, but the long-term effect is that the molecular balance in the remaining bitumen is altered in favour of the harder and more brittle asphaltene fraction.

As well as there being two mechanisms, it is also usual to distinguish between two time frames. Short-term ageing occurs during mixing, transporting, placing and compacting, while the bitumen is at an elevated temperature, and is responsible for a significant change in properties, amounting to a viscosity increase of over 50% (about 25% loss of initial binder penetration). Long-term ageing occurs gradually such that bitumen becomes ever harder during its service life. Figure 2.42 presents data from three roads in the US to illustrate the point. In hot climates it is not uncommon to recover bitumen with a penetration of well under 10 (tenths of a millimetre), when the initial value would typically have been between 50 and 100.

Susceptibility to ageing by oxidation is most commonly measured by means of the 'rolling thin-film oven test' (Fig. 2.42),[76] in which samples of bitumen are rotated and allowed to flow continuously around the inside of glass containers at a temperature of 163°C, while air is regularly blown into the containers. The properties of the bitumen are measured both before and after ageing. There is no current test to look specifically at ageing due to binder absorption by aggregate.[77]

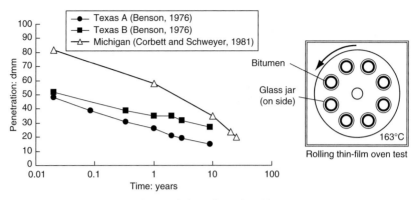

Fig. 2.42 Bitumen ageing data and the rolling thin-film oven test

Because of the complexity of ageing and the large variation according to mixture type and climate, there is no reliable substitute for experience in predicting likely long-term binder properties.

2.3.1.8 Bitumen modification

This is a specialist area and one which is changing all the time as bitumen chemists continue to develop new additives. However, it is important that pavement engineers have a broad understanding of the issues, possibilities and pitfalls. An unmodified bitumen has certain weaknesses: it can 'flow' at high temperature, leading to pavement rutting; it can fracture at low temperature, leading to pavement cracking; the adhesion between bitumen and aggregate can break down under a combination of ageing and water attack. There are numerous products on the market which are claimed to improve performance in one or more of these areas. They can be crudely categorised as follows:

- *Polymers.* Bitumen is already a complex group of varied polymers, but it is possible to design additives which emphasise beneficial properties while retarding others. Styrene–butadiene–styrene (SBS), styrene–butadiene rubber (SBR) and ethyl vinyl acetate (EVA) are three of the more commonly used and, to varying degrees, these products will increase the viscosity (and visco-elastic stiffness) of the bitumen at high temperatures but not at low temperatures. They may also give benefit in fatigue life, particularly in the case of SBS. However, polymer usage is a specialist field and not all bitumens are suited to blending with all modifiers. It is quite possible to blend an otherwise excellent additive with a given bitumen and to achieve no benefit at all.

- *Natural rubbers.* Various forms of rubber can be added to bitumen in an attempt to enhance the 'resilience' of a binder, i.e. the resistance to damage. In recent years, much of the pressure for this has come from the need to find ways of recycling used vehicle tyres. The benefits (or otherwise) are still subject to debate.

- *Simple chemicals.* Sulphur and manganese have both been used in significant quantities. Manganese addition is really just a means of increasing the cross-linkage of bitumen molecules and thereby increasing viscosity and stiffness. However, the disadvantage is that the bitumen becomes more brittle. Sulphur, which is a liquid at >115°C, enhances workability at high temperature; as a solid at in-service temperatures it then acts as aggregate.

One of the inevitable problems with bitumen modification is its complexity and this means that it is difficult for engineers to specify with confidence. However, the performance grade approach taken in the US Superpave specification, in which upper and lower in-service pavement temperature limits are stated (e.g. PG 64–22; suitable from −22°C to +64°C),[78] represents a sensible way forward.

2.3.1.9 Bitumen emulsion

Excellent though bitumen is as a binder of aggregate particles, one of its drawbacks is that it will only adhere to aggregate properly if that aggregate is heated sufficiently to drive off all moisture, and this is a costly and energy-intensive procedure. Thus, there are strong economic and environmental drivers towards so-called *cold-mix* technology, utilising a form of bitumen that is workable at ambient temperatures and which can mix with cold, wet aggregate. Bitumen emulsion would therefore seem to be the fulfilment of everyone's dreams.

An emulsion is a suspension of one liquid in another, in this case of bitumen in water. It is manufactured by putting hot bitumen through a high shear colloid mill, which reduces it to tiny droplets, no more than a few tens of microns across, at the same time as feeding in an emulsifying agent and water – see Fig. 2.43. The emulsifying agent is a chemical with charge at one end, either positive or negative, and a long polymer tail with strong affinity to bitumen. As these emulsifier ions attach themselves to the bitumen droplets these are converted into charged particles, each repelling its neighbour; the droplets therefore float in

147

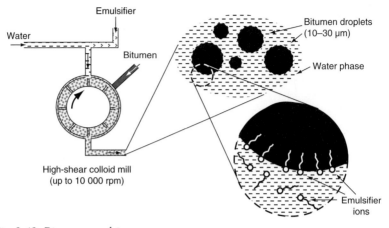

Fig. 2.43 Bitumen emulsion

the water, prevented from coalescing. The specific gravities of bitumen and water are very similar (1.02–1.03 for bitumen) so there is little tendency for the droplets to sink under gravity and the result is a very stable product. Occasional light stirring is sufficient to ensure a long 'shelf life'.

Since the water phase is continuous, the fluidity of bitumen emulsion is not much reduced from that of water, despite the bitumen comprising between 40 and 70% of the total volume. This means it can readily be piped, sprayed and mixed with aggregate. The difficulty of course is to achieve the transformation from an unbound material with water containing individual bitumen droplets to a genuine bitumen-bound mixture, and this is discussed further in Section 2.3.7.5.

2.3.2.10 Foamed bitumen

An alternative form of cold-mix asphalt utilises bitumen in the form of a foam. Figure 2.44 illustrates the method of production.

The foam is produced by the very rapid transformation of water into steam as it comes into contact with hot (typically 160–180°C) bitumen, aided by the addition of air. The water content within the foam is generally between 2 and 5% of the bitumen volume but, once transformed into steam, the foam expands to many times the volume of the bitumen itself, and in this state it can readily be mixed into an aggregate. The ratio of peak foam volume to original bitumen volume is known as the 'expansion ratio', while the time until this peak volume is halved

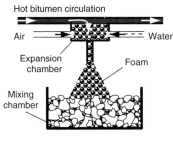

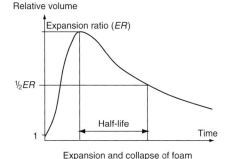

Foamed bitumen production   Expansion and collapse of foam

Fig. 2.44 Foamed bitumen

is known as the 'half-life'. The expansion ratio is typically between 5 and 20; the half-life is typically between 10 and 40 s.

Foamed bitumen therefore contrasts with emulsion. Emulsions can be stored for months before use, whereas foamed bitumen has to be used within a few tens of seconds of production. However, the advantage is that foamed bitumen requires less water and, as will be explained in Section 2.3.7.5, water presents the principal challenge to the successful use of both forms of cold mix.

2.3.2 The mechanics of asphalt behaviour

If a true understanding of asphalt is to be achieved then it is necessary to think about the interaction between individual aggregate particles. An asphalt consists of an aggregate skeleton – as in the case of an unbound material – and a binder, which includes filler-size particles within it. There will also be a certain percentage of air voids. If strain is to take place, then this means that the aggregate skeleton has to deform and, as in the case of an unbound material, there are two basic mechanisms:

1. compression at particle contacts
2. inter-particle slip (combined with rotation and separation).

If no slip were to take place between particles, then the approximate stiffness of the material could be predicted from the stiffness modulus of the rock from which the aggregate is formed (say 200 GPa), a contact law and a means of calculating the additional effect of the binder – in fact exactly the approach given in Calculation Sheet 2.9 for hydraulically-bound materials. In the case of an asphalt, the bitumen stiffness at 20°C and traffic loading frequency is typically between 20 and 50 GPa, with bitumen-filler mortar stiffness around 2.5 times this. This gives a predicted mixture stiffness of 5300–7000 MPa, which is only slightly greater than the expected range for undamaged materials. The implication is that the bitumen initially allows very little inter-particle slip or separation to occur; it is only as damage occurs that this situation changes.

2.3.2.1 The micromechanics of asphalt damage

In a typical dense asphalt mixture the aggregate occupies some 85% of the total volume (of which about 5% is filler), with about 10% bitumen and 5% air voids. Thus, if the filler is considered as a binder additive, then the skeleton represents about 80% of the volume and three-quarters of the remaining space is filled with bitumen-filler mortar. Figure 2.45 illustrates the situation at a particle contact. If slip (or particle separation) is to take place, then this must impose a strain in the mortar, a strain which becomes ever larger the closer to the point of contact one looks. In fact, mathematically the strain right at the contact point becomes *infinite* – and there is only one mechanism capable of producing infinite strain and that is *fracture*. Damage to an asphalt, visible as a reduction in stiffness under repeated loading (e.g. comparing materials from trafficked and untrafficked areas in a highway), therefore takes the form of localised fractures at particle contacts, allowing slip and separation to occur, and experience is that such damage commences from the very first load application – see for example the data presented in Section 2.3.4.5.

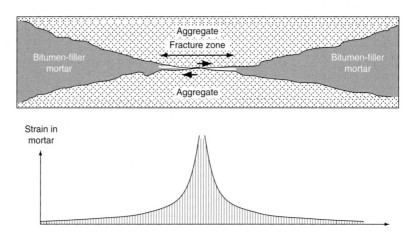

Fig. 2.45 Slip at particle contacts

Logically, where slip (± rotation or separation) takes place, a fracture zone will extend out from the contact point until it reaches a region where the strain is low enough not to cause fracture. This then gives a measure of freedom to the two particles involved. They can slip (or separate) by a small amount.

This is an area which is very imperfectly understood. Logically, these localised fracture zones cannot be static. Low temperature will lead to stiff binder and restricted inter-particle movement, which means additional stress taken through the binder and therefore an increased chance of fractures occurring – and of existing fracture zones expanding. However, high temperature represents much more than the mere absence of high binder stress; it also allows the phenomenon known as *healing* to occur. Bitumen is a liquid, fractured or not, and this means that the molecules either side of a fracture can, over time, recombine to create continuous binder phase once more. This will happen most easily when binder viscosity is at its lowest, which means at high temperatures. Thus, there is a state of dynamic flux present. Winter leads to high stiffness but increased damage; summer leads to low stiffness but also healing. In theory, a state of dynamic equilibrium can be reached – but this of course depends just how much damage the traffic is doing and how quickly.

2.3.2.2 Linear or non-linear?

Since unbound aggregate has been shown to be highly non-linear and bitumen is visco-elastic rather than elastic, one might expect the stiffness behaviour of an asphalt to be very far from linear – but not so. Why not? The point here is that the magnitude of strain taking place within the aggregate skeleton is small compared to that common in an unbound material, and in the small-strain region the stiffness of an unbound material is approximately constant. Furthermore, the loading rate is usually high enough to ensure that the bitumen is kept near the elastic end of its visco-elastic behaviour spectrum. The combination is sufficient to give an approximately linear stress–strain response. However, the actual value of stiffness modulus will vary significantly with bitumen properties – which in turn depend on temperature and loading rate.

2.3.2.3 Bitumen adhesion

The micromechanical explanation given above makes one crucial assumption, namely perfect bond between bitumen and aggregate, i.e.

perfect adhesion. If this is the case then there is no preferential fracture plane within the binder and the resistance to fracture at a particle contact will simply be the cohesive strength of the binder itself. However, if there is any lack of adhesion then fracture will clearly take place preferentially along one of the interfaces between an aggregate particle and the adjacent bituminous mortar, and the development of such a fracture will occur more easily than it otherwise might have. Thus, adhesion is a very important property.

Unfortunately, it is not a property which is readily measurable.[79] However, the effects of lack of adhesion can certainly be observed indirectly from mixture tests and, more dramatically, in failed asphalt pavements. Mixture tests would indicate low stiffness, low fatigue resistance and high permanent deformation under multi-cyclic load, since all three properties are strongly related to the ease with which internal fracture occurs.

So the question arises: what causes poor adhesion?

One important part of the answer appears to be the *acidity* or *alkalinity* of the aggregate. Limestone aggregate generally makes for high-quality asphalt whereas many igneous rocks have proved to be less trouble-free,[80] as have many natural gravels (although a rounded particle shape would cause poor performance even with good adhesion). A particular issue is that most aggregates would attract water if it were available in preference to bitumen – hence the need to ensure that particles are absolutely dry before mixing with bitumen.

However, all is not lost. If acidity is the problem, then a logical move is to include an additive in the mixture, often *hydrated lime* although other chemical additives are marketed and have also proved effective.[81] This can have a dramatic effect and, while there are some who doubt that the influence of such an additive is permanent, it certainly seems to be long-lasting enough for practical and economic usage.

2.3.3 Asphalt stiffness

The most basic property of an asphalt for pavement design is its stiffness modulus. However, from the foregoing discussion, it is clear that an asphalt does not have a single stiffness value; it is both temperature and loading rate dependent because it depends on the efficiency with which the binder restricts inter-particle movement in the aggregate, and this in its turn depends on binder stiffness. It is also, unsurprisingly, dependent on the mixture proportions used.

2.3.3.1 Predicting asphalt stiffness

The first requirement is to predict binder stiffness, itself a complex visco-elastic quantity. For this, many equations and procedures have been devised but the most widely adopted is undoubtedly that known as 'van der Poel's nomograph',[82] a chart from which binder stiffness (E_{binder}) is derived from temperature (T) relative to softening point (SP), the penetration index (PI) of the binder (refer to Section 2.3.1.2 for details) and load pulse duration (t). The following approximate formula[83] matches the predictions from the nomograph over a restricted range of input parameters.

$$E_{binder} = 1.157 \times 10^{-7} \times t^{-0.368} \times 2.718^{-PI} \times (SP - T)^5 \, \text{MPa}$$

The parameter which investigators have found to be the most useful in describing mixture proportions is *voids in mixed aggregate* (VMA), basically the percentage of a mixture which is not aggregate or, to put it another way, the binder volume plus the air void volume. Here too, many different equations have been proposed, of which the following is one.[84]

$$E_{mixture} = E_{binder} \times \{1 + (257.5 - 2.5VMA)/[n \times (VMA - 3)]\}^n$$

where $n = 0.83 \times \log_{10}(4 \times 10^4 / E_{binder})$ and VMA is in percentage.

Notice that binder content is not taken into account except as a component of VMA. This is logical since it will only be the relatively small amount of binder which sits in the immediate vicinity of a particle contact which significantly influences mixture stiffness. VMA itself acts as a broad measure of the efficiency with which the aggregate particles are packed together.

In reality, such predictions can be no more than approximate. VMA is a very crude measure of packing when the infinite number of possible aggregate gradations is considered. Furthermore, since inter-particle slip is an element in asphalt strain, this means that the frictional properties at contacts should also be relevant. In fact, it may well be that the commonly observed difference in stiffness between limestone and granite mixtures[85] is at least partly due to a difference in frictional properties, something which often leads to a similar proportional difference in unbound mixtures.

2.3.3.2 Measuring asphalt stiffness

The basic range of possible laboratory tests for asphalt stiffness is similar to that for strength and stiffness of hydraulically-bound materials,

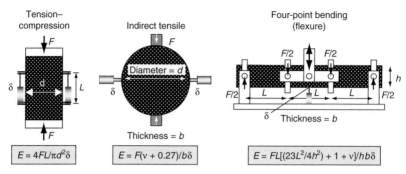

Fig. 2.46 *Asphalt stiffness tests*

namely tension–compression, indirect tension and flexure. Figure 2.46 illustrates.

Of these, the tension–compression test has the least complex stress conditions and is therefore favoured by many researchers; however, it is the least practical to carry out.[86] The indirect tensile test is very quick and easy to conduct and is therefore favoured by industry, but suffers from having highly complex stress conditions, particularly near to the loading points, and the interpretation is therefore less certain.[87] The four-point bending test would not usually be carried out except when testing for fatigue, but it also gives a very satisfactory stiffness measurement. One of the key drivers is to be able to test a specimen which can be prepared from a core taken from the pavement – which means that the indirect tensile test scores highly.

It is worth making the point here that stiffness measured in any of these test modes cannot be used directly in pavement analysis and design without correction. Test temperature is, of course, important, and testing should preferably be carried out in a temperature-controlled environment, the specimen having also been stored at test temperature for several hours prior to test. However, loading rate used is also critical. A pulse of load from a vehicle on a road may typically take about 10–15 ms to reach peak stress, whereas most of these tests are generally carried out at a considerably slower rate. Thus, for example, in the commonly-used pneumatically-powered 'Nottingham Asphalt Tester',[88] with about 125 ms to peak, the stiffness measured would typically be only around 70% of that applying under fast-moving traffic.

2.3.3.3 Typical stiffness values

As with similar sections in this book, the information given here is intended to give the reader a general idea of what to expect from

Table 2.11 Typical stiffness modulus data – new asphalt

Material	Stiffness modulus (MPa) at 20°C	
	In the laboratory (125 ms to peak load)	In the pavement (10 ms to peak load)
Dense asphalt base (50 pen binder)	5000	7000
Dense asphalt base (100 pen binder)	3500	5000
Surfacing	2000	3000
Cold-mix asphalt base	2000	2500

various generic material types, but should definitely not be taken as applying in every case. Table 2.11 compares typical stiffness moduli at 20°C, while Fig. 2.47 presents data on different asphalt types, together with a possible stiffness conversion equation.

Notice that the values in Table 2.11 are for new asphalt, which means asphalt which is only a matter of weeks old. As reported already, bitumen 'ages', which means that the stiffness of a mixture will tend to increase throughout its life as the viscosity of the binder increases. For example, if a new dense asphalt base with 50 pen binder has a stiffness in the road of about 7000 MPa at 20°C at the start of its life (by which time the penetration of the bitumen has already decreased to around 35 purely as a result of mixing and laying), then this will probably have increased to 9000 MPa after ten years in a climate such as the UK, with much more rapid stiffness increase in hotter climates.

Notice also the cold-mix asphalt examples in Fig. 2.47. They are lower – and one of them is less temperature sensitive. The reason is that bitumen

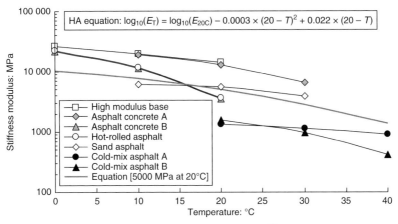

HA equation: $\log_{10}(E_T) = \log_{10}(E_{20C}) - 0.0003 \times (20 - T)^2 + 0.022 \times (20 - T)$

Legend:
—□— High modulus base
—◇— Asphalt concrete A
—△— Asphalt concrete B
—○— Hot-rolled asphalt
—◇— Sand asphalt
—●— Cold-mix asphalt A
—▲— Cold-mix asphalt B
······ Equation [5000 MPa at 20°C]

Stiffness modulus: MPa — Temperature: °C

Fig. 2.47 The effect of temperature on asphalt stiffness[89]

coating of the aggregate is generally less good, giving situations in which two pieces of aggregate interact without the restraint of bitumen. This immediately increases the freedom of movement, thus decreasing stiffness; all such dry contacts will also obviously be independent of bitumen viscosity, thus decreasing temperature and loading rate sensitivity. The same effect can be seen in a partially fatigued conventional asphalt.

Finally, it should be noted that a value of 0.3 or 0.35 is commonly adopted for Poisson's ratio of asphalt.

2.3.4 Fracture and fatigue of asphalt

One of the key design issues for an asphalt pavement is cracking. Cracks may arise for a number of reasons – as described in Part 3 – but they are always a problem, leading to loss of ride quality and also allowing water to enter the pavement foundation. They should therefore be properly understood.

2.3.4.1 Low-temperature fracture

This is a significant problem in continental climates, including desert climates such as North Africa. In fact, the label 'low-temperature' is slightly misleading since the primary driving force is that of a large day–night temperature difference. The point is that asphalt, like any other material, expands and contracts with temperature changes. Bitumen itself is particularly susceptible, giving asphalt a typical thermal expansion coefficient α of around 1.8×10^{-5} per $°C$, significantly higher than that of hydraulically-bound materials. This means that night-time cooling imposes a significant volumetric strain. If the bitumen is soft, the asphalt can readily accommodate this by adjusting itself such that all the strain occurs either vertically or laterally rather than longitudinally (i.e. along the road). However, if the bitumen is hard then such self-adjustment induces high internal stress and, in the limit, the stress level will be high enough to cause fracture. Parts 3 and 4 cover the typical form of damage which results.

In climates such as North America, Northern Europe and Central Asia, the critical point occurs when the night-time temperature drops well below zero; in climates such as the deserts of Arabia and the Sahara, it is still the night-time minimum which is the problem; although the temperature might seem to be high enough for safety (often still above freezing), the problem is the rapid ageing of bitumens in desert climates, making them brittle enough to fracture.

Tests for susceptibility to low-temperature fracture are empirical. The primary tests are those already mentioned for the bitumen itself (Section 2.3.1.4), but it is also not uncommon to carry out fracture strength tests on the mixture. For example, the Indirect Tensile Strength Test (as described for hydraulically-bound materials in Section 2.2.1.3) is sometimes carried out on asphalt using a suitably low temperature. Interpretation is based on experience.

2.3.4.2 Fatigue damage

There is much misunderstanding of this subject among pavement engineers. Part of the problem is that engineers are often taught about fatigue in the context of metals, in which a crack first has to 'initiate' at some defect within the material and then 'propagate'. This is an excellent representation of what happens in a relatively uniform material such as a metal and expressions such as the well-known Paris law[90] have been derived to describe this behaviour. However, this is not the situation in an asphalt. It is not really the situation in a hydraulically-bound material either (see Section 2.2.2), but in the case of an asphalt the difference becomes highly significant.

Asphalt consists of an aggregate skeleton surrounded by binder, with air voids scattered around. The key stress concentration points are at particle-to-particle contacts and, as described above, local fracture has to occur if damage is to take place. Fatigue therefore consists of the enlargement of these fracture zones at contacts and the development of new fractures.[91] The effect is primarily controlled by movement within the aggregate skeleton, i.e. strain within the mixture; large movement will rapidly expand fracture zones and initiate new ones. Thus, it is not surprising to find that fatigue life is primarily a function of the 'elastic' strain under load within the mixture.

2.3.4.3 Tests for fatigue of asphalt

Many of the same test configurations that have been introduced already are also suited to fatigue testing. Tension–compression, indirect tensile and flexural tests have all been successfully employed, as well as more complex configurations such as torsion. Tension–compression induces the simplest stress conditions and is used extensively by researchers, but it is not as convenient as other configurations. The most popular are undoubtedly indirect tensile and flexural, with four-point bending and trapezoidal providing alternative flexural testing options. The

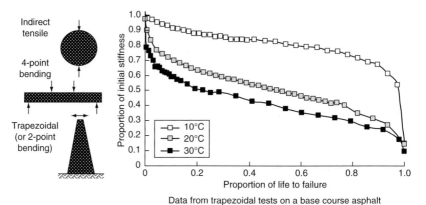

Data from trapezoidal tests on a base course asphalt

Fig. 2.48 Asphalt fatigue tests[92]

trapezoidal shape may seem awkward, but it has the advantage that it produces a maximum tensile stress well away from any stressed boundary (typically at about one third of the specimen height). Figure 2.48 illustrates the test modes and also presents typical test data, expressed as loss of stiffness as a function of number of load cycles (relative to the number of cycles to specimen failure).

A very important distinction exists between tests which are load controlled, in which strain increases during the test, accelerating towards failure at the end of the test, and those which are displacement controlled, in which stress reduces during the test as damage occurs and stiffness reduces. These two types of test give quite different fatigue lives, even with identical stress and strain at the first load cycle. In the case of displacement control, there is often no actual failure of the specimen and no visible damage at all until the stiffness has reduced to a small fraction of its original value.

Specialists argue as to which type of test is the more appropriate for pavements, generally coming to the conclusion that displacement control is appropriate for thin asphalt layers, where strains are principally influenced by other layers, whereas load control is more appropriate for thicker layers, where the asphalt is the dominant material. The truth is that neither is realistic of course. Furthermore, laboratory loading can never be realistic since it can never duplicate the sequences of multiple loads followed by at least a second or two of 'rest' induced by real vehicle loading. The result is that those who wish to apply laboratory fatigue data in practice commonly have to treat the test as an indicator and then apply a considerable adjustment factor to the data in order to arrive at a usable result.

Key practical test requirements are as follows:

- The specimen size should not be so small in any of its dimensions that the result can be greatly influenced by local aggregate orientation.
- The test should be simple enough for practical application.

It is also desirable to avoid excessive permanent deformation during a test, a significant criticism of the indirect tensile test if carried out under compressive load only.[93]

2.3.4.4 Development of a fatigue characteristic

Whichever test is used, it is necessary to express the data in a meaningful way. The first task is to select a failure criterion. If the test is load controlled, as in the example in Fig. 2.48, this is no problem; the specimen falls apart at the end of the test. However, if displacement control is used, then it is usual to work to 50% stiffness loss in place of total failure. This is an arbitrary value, but is justified as commonly representing the point where damage begins to accelerate after a relatively stable phase. Note that the data in Fig. 2.48 suggest that, for any given material, this assumption is only valid over a certain temperature range.

Next a series of tests has to be carried out at different levels of load (and therefore stress) or displacement (or therefore strain), generally at least six and preferably ten. The results can then be plotted as shown in Fig. 2.49. It is usual to plot against strain (strain at the first load cycle in the case of a load-controlled test) rather than stress since experience is that the resulting 'characteristic' is approximately independent of temperature and loading rate, at least within a broad range, whereas this is not the case in a plot against stress. This is not unexpected since Section 2.3.4.2 has argued that damage is primarily related to inter-particle movement, i.e. strain.

Here, a warning must be given against assuming that test temperature will never affect fatigue life so long as it is expressed against strain – something which should be obvious from a glance at the different forms of behaviour shown in the example in Fig. 2.48. Experience is that life will be longer, i.e. the fatigue characteristic in Fig. 2.49 will be further to the right, if the temperature exceeds a certain value. This value will generally be over 30°C but not in all cases. This means that it is *not* automatically acceptable to adjust test temperature upwards in order to allow a target strain to be reached at a lower load level.

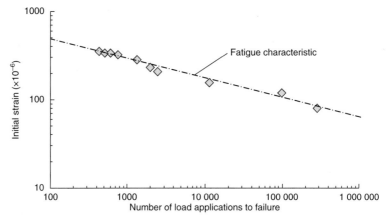

Fig. 2.49 *An asphalt fatigue characteristic*

Part 3 will explain the use of a fatigue characteristic in pavement analysis and design.

2.3.4.5 Healing

This phenomenon has been referred to already in relation to asphalt stiffness, the point having been made that bitumen fracture at particle contacts tends to occur in cold weather, but that binder continuity can be restored in warm weather due to viscous flow and molecular remixing. The healing effect is responsible for the improved fatigue lives found in tests at high temperature; it also means that there will be differences between tests depending on the details of load pulse frequency and any 'rest periods' allowed between load pulses. This is illustrated in Fig. 2.50.

However, it has to be admitted that understanding of healing is still incomplete. It is largely because of healing that it is not possible to apply a laboratory fatigue characteristic directly in pavement performance prediction, since the degree of healing in the pavement will be quite different from that in the laboratory test; a 'shift factor' will be required. See Part 3 for details.

2.3.5 Permanent deformation

As in the case of stiffness and fatigue, it is necessary to remember the fundamental structure of asphalt when considering permanent deformation. Asphalt can only deform if the aggregate skeleton

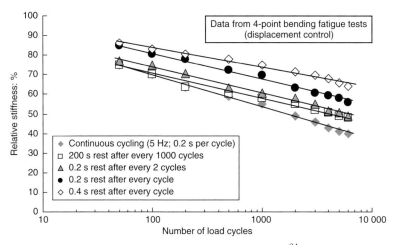

Fig. 2.50 The influence of rest periods on fatigue behaviour[94]

deforms; thus, the resistance of an asphalt to deformation is intimately tied in with the stability of that aggregate skeleton. This means that the same properties which lead to low plastic strain in an unbound material (angular particles, broad gradation, large particle size) also give stability to an asphalt. Thus, though binder technology may help, it is impossible to produce a deformation-resistant mixture without an appropriate aggregate skeleton.

2.3.5.1 The influence of binder

Despite the secondary nature of the role of the binder, it is still extremely important. Plastic strain of the aggregate skeleton is of course greatly inhibited by the binder. In fact, throughout most of the year in a temperate climate, when pavement temperature is cool or moderate, plastic strain will be negligible. This is because the binder takes much of the stress away from particle contacts. However, as the temperature increases, the stress taken across particle contacts increases, leading to increased danger of inter-particle slip – and some inter-particle slips will be irreversible. The binder may self-heal, but the aggregate skeleton will be permanently deformed.

So, a hard binder means that the temperature of the pavement has to climb higher before the onset of significant plastic deformation. In practical terms, experience is that it is dangerous to let the pavement temperature reach the ring and ball softening point of the bitumen.

However, despite its beneficial binding action, bitumen also carries with it a latent danger. Surprising though it may sound, bitumen can actually exhibit the same sort of *pore pressure* effect as exhibited by water in an unbound material. As the aggregate skeleton strains elastically under load, some of the intervening voids will naturally decrease in size and some will increase, purely as a result of the aggregate geometry. If there is plenty of air in the system this is no problem since air will readily expand and contract. However, a void that is full of binder cannot change its volume, which means that the binder may have to carry more load than is good for it. Extra compressive stress in the binder means less normal stress at aggregate contacts, which means easier slip and therefore more plastic strain. This is important. Many pavements develop rutting simply because there is not enough air in the system to prevent this pore pressure effect. Most specifications guard against this by insisting that a minimum of 3% air voids is built into the mixture, but the engineer should be aware that further compaction under traffic is quite possible and that an air void content under 2% will almost certainly lead to deformation, i.e. rutting.

2.3.5.2 Measurement of permanent deformation

There is no single property defining resistance to permanent deformation, which means that testing can only be indicative. The most usual forms of test are:

- a repeated load *axial* test (RLAT), whereby a cylinder of material is loaded repeatedly in compression and the resulting axial deformation measured;
- a repeated load *triaxial* test – simply an axial test with the addition of confining stress; confinement can be applied by means of an external pressure within a surrounding cell, or by means of a (partial) vacuum applied to the specimen when sealed by a flexible membrane;[95]
- a *wheel-tracking* test.

The axial test is the most convenient since the test arrangement is simple and the specimen can be obtained from a core through a pavement. The test is often criticised as overly severe on base materials, where a considerable degree of confinement would in reality be present; however, since it is not intended to be more than an index test, this is probably not a fair criticism. In fact, the severe nature of the test means that intrinsically poor materials show up very clearly indeed, giving the designer useful information when considering whether and at what

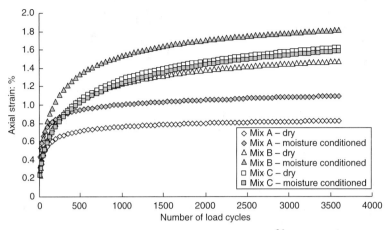

Fig. 2.51 Repeated load axial test data – 100 kPa, 40°C[96]

level in the pavement such materials may be used. Figure 2.51 presents data sets for materials of differing quality. As a rule of thumb, under the test conditions of Fig. 2.51, 1% strain represents a safe limit, 2% spells danger and 3% means that deformation is practically certain if the material is placed within about 100 mm of the surface. Note that in this case tests were carried out both dry and following 'moisture conditioning' – see Section 2.3.6.2 – since many materials are found to perform worse when water is present.

The triaxial test undoubtedly allows a more accurate representation of the real stress regime applying in a pavement, and also in theory allows the depth at which the material is to be used to be simulated by setting the level of confinement appropriately. However, the test is more complex than the axial set-up and the 'appropriate' level of confinement is open to debate. Since it is still only an index test, it is not clear that the triaxial test has sufficient advantages to warrant its general use, although it is undeniable that it gives a much better indication of the performance of low-stability materials such as porous asphalt (see Section 2.3.7).

Many specifications, however, insist on a wheel-tracking test, at least for surface course materials. All are relatively small-scale tests such that the device can be contained within a temperature-controlled cabinet. Details of the load used and test temperature vary from specification to specification, but it is usual to use a high temperature (40–60°C) in order to give a relatively rapid result.[97] The close simulation of reality which wheel-tracking gives means that the results, though still index numbers, can be treated as directly related to deformation susceptibility in the pavement.

2.3.6 Durability

Durability is a catch-all word, and it actually includes several different phenomena, the common theme being that they all take time to develop. Unfortunately, the differences between the different aspects of durability are not always recognised, which means that it is all too easy to allow substandard materials to 'slip through the net'. This section will consider each aspect of durability in turn.

2.3.6.1 Ageing

This subject has been identified already (Section 2.3.1.7) as affecting all bitumens. Chemical changes with time mean that bitumen becomes stiffer – a good thing – and more brittle – not so good. Thus, a fatigue characteristic, plotted against applied strain as in Fig. 2.49, should tend to shift slightly to the left as ageing takes hold. Experience, however, suggests that this shift is rarely significant in standard tests carried out at standard (often 20°C) temperature, which unfortunately suggests to some that ageing isn't a problem at all. The trouble is that standard tests are always rapid, producing failure in a matter of hours rather than years, and this means that the vital component of asphalt behaviour described in Section 2.3.4.5, namely *healing*, is not properly taken into account; and an aged bitumen will heal much less readily than an unaged bitumen. To put it another way, the temperature threshold above which healing is able to occur will be higher for an aged binder. Either way, the result is that, in the pavement, asphalt is often observed to reach a state of ageing where distress accelerates.

It is important to understand the factors that affect ageing. These are: *temperature, aggregate absorption* (of binder) and the presence of *oxygen*. Ageing will therefore occur most severely in hot climates, near the road surface, in voided mixtures and where high-absorption aggregates are used. In a dense base, in a temperate climate, using a standard aggregate, ageing should be extremely slow, giving many decades of trouble-free life. Here, then, is another excellent reason to achieve good compaction at construction.

2.3.6.2 Water damage

The point has been made that it is essential to dry aggregate thoroughly during asphalt production in order to ensure good bitumen adhesion, and even then it is sometimes necessary to add lime or some other adhesion agent in order to facilitate its development. The implication

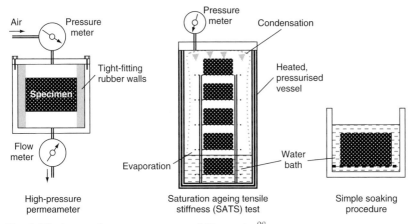

Fig. 2.52 *Approaches to water-susceptibility testing*[98]

is that the bitumen–aggregate interface is potentially vulnerable to water. Once again, the key is high density and low permeability. If no water ever reaches these vulnerable interfaces, there will never be any water damage.

There is no agreement as yet on the most appropriate tests to determine susceptibility to water damage. Permeability can be measured directly in a high-pressure permeameter, although this is not a standard tool. Void content can, of course, also be determined,[99] and experience suggests that a void content of about 5% or less almost certainly means a sufficiently low permeability for water damage to be ignored. Direct testing can also be conducted by soaking specimens in water, usually at an elevated temperature, and then measuring the 'retained' stiffness (or strength), i.e. a percentage value compared to the unsoaked condition.[100] As in the case of hydraulically-bound materials, a value of 80% or more is usually taken to represent non-water-susceptible material. Figure 2.52 illustrates some of the 'tools of the trade'.

Even with these different tools and methods, the issue being addressed by no means covers the whole subject of water damage. The key element which is missing is the dynamic movement of water within and between void spaces under the action of traffic. For this issue, no test exists other than for purely research purposes.[101] The effect is most likely at the base of a layer, where voids tend to be highest, and where water may become trapped due to high density at the top of the layer beneath. It is also likely where pavements suffer flooding. However, the subject is so complex that it is hard to envisage any direct test which could help. It must therefore simply be remembered that if water is allowed to penetrate and accumulate within an asphalt then there will be trouble.

2.3.6.3 Frost damage

This is yet another subject which cannot be readily quantified. It is commonly observed that pavements suffer significant damage immediately following severe frosts, and it is not difficult to imagine some of the mechanisms at work. Water expands to form ice so, as in concrete, this immediately causes pressures within the matrix of an asphalt, causing local fracture at aggregate particle contacts. The interaction between water-filled and ice-filled voids during freezing and melting may also give rise to unusually high dynamic pressures under traffic loading. The fact that the bitumen is most brittle (very small strains required to cause fracture) when it is cold does not help matters of course – but the effect cannot possibly be quantified.

The secret of protection against frost is more or less the same as that of protection against water. If the asphalt is dense ($\leq$5% voids) then water will not find it easy to penetrate and ice formation will therefore not be a problem. If water is allowed to penetrate, expect problems.

2.3.6.4 Biodegradation

This is a topic which very few pavement engineers take seriously. Yet, it is a fact that certain bacteria can digest bitumen.[102] This may help with eco-friendly credentials, but it is no help at all in ensuring a long-life road. On many occasions pavement cores have revealed an almost totally disintegrated asphalt base and, while it is difficult to prove the cause, the apparent lack of visible binder strongly suggests a biological agent.

Unfortunately, this is not an area which is even being seriously researched yet, so it is certainly not possible to comment on which brands of asphalt are the tastiest!

2.3.7 Mixture design

There are a lot of potential pitfalls in designing a bituminous mixture, as the foregoing sections have explained, and a lot of variables to be 'juggled' in coming up with an optimised solution. The only sensible route forward therefore is to tackle the problem one step at a time.

2.3.7.1 Aggregate particle size distribution

Here the choice will be based primarily on the role of the material in the pavement. Base layers will usually tend to contain larger-sized particles because they are placed in reasonably thick layers, and this also allows the content of (relatively expensive) bitumen to be minimised. Surface courses will have a smaller maximum particle size, partly to give optimum ride quality but also because such layers are usually thin; they also typically require a relatively high binder content to ensure low voids and high durability – the exception being *porous asphalt*, which is deliberately designed with a high void content (around 20%) in order to act as a drainage material.

Having selected a maximum particle size, the next issue is the gradation. Here, the approach taken by the US 'Superpave' specification,[103] in which a comparison has to be made to an idealised Fuller curve, is believed to be fundamentally sound. Fuller curves, as introduced previously, represent particle size distributions which obey the following formula:

$$\% \text{ passing} = (d/d_{\max})^n$$

The advice given in Superpave is that $n = 0.45$ represents a 'perfect' gradation, in which there is just enough room between particles at every size to accommodate all the smaller-size fractions in the mix. This implies that a mix which follows the $n = 0.45$ Fuller curve will develop excellent interlock between particles and will require minimum binder content to 'glue' the particles together because the void space has been minimised. It will not be possible to pick out a single critical particle size; all size fractions will be 'pulling their weight' equally. Around the world, this sort of gradation is known as *asphalt concrete* or, in the UK, *dense bitumen macadam*. Figure 2.53 illustrates.

Now consider what happens if the gradation deviates from the perfect Fuller curve. A less steep gradation curve means that there are always more fine particles at every stage than are needed to perfectly fill the spaces between larger particles. The consequence is that the larger particles will be pushed apart and will 'float' in a sea of smaller material. The dominant particle size will be small (but not infinitely small because the curve cannot in reality follow such a path for ever at the small-size end of the spectrum) and the binder demand will increase. The result will tend to be a less 'stable' mix because of the dependence on small-size particles in the aggregate skeleton, and therefore a greater susceptibility to permanent deformation; however, it will be a relatively easy mix to work with and compact and the final void content should be

167

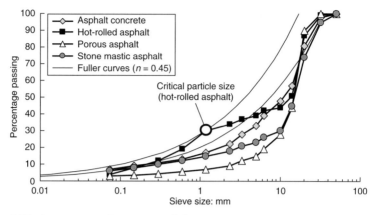

Fig. 2.53 Aggregate gradations in asphalt mixtures

very low indeed. Stiffness will be slightly lower than for the 'perfect' gradation, but fatigue resistance will be high because of the higher binder content. The traditional UK material known as *hot-rolled asphalt* has this sort of gradation.[104] If Fig. 2.53 is a fair description, the *critical particle size* (where the grading touches the Fuller curve) will be 1–2 mm.

However, what happens if the gradation is steeper than the $n = 0.45$ Fuller curve? In this case, there are never enough smaller particles to fill the voids between larger stones. The result will be an aggregate skeleton comprising the larger stones and the remainder of the material loosely packed into the spaces between. This is a recipe for high stability; it is also a recipe for high voids, low stiffness, high susceptibility to water damage and low fatigue life. In short, it is not desirable unless there is an overwhelming reason to adopt such a mix, and the only reason likely to be powerful enough is the desirability of *porous asphalt* surfacing for drainage of surface water and low tyre noise. If this sort of mix is to be used, then it is necessary to take special precautions, notably maintaining a respectably high binder content by the addition of cellulose fibres to prevent the binder from draining out of the mixture.[105]

Of course, most practical mixtures are compromises. *Stone mastic asphalt* follows a steep gradation initially, leading to a skeleton of large stones, but then flattens such that there are nearly enough fine particles to fill the voids, overcoming the problems inherent in porous asphalt. However, this means that it is an inherently 'dangerous' mixture choice, i.e. a mixture which is very sensitive to small changes in gradation. A little too many fines and the stability provided by the large aggregate skeleton will be lost; a little too few and the problems of porosity, permeability, water damage etc. may reappear. The key for the engineer is to be aware of the particular characteristics likely from each generic mixture type. One should never take the view that all asphalt mixtures are equivalent.

2.3.7.2 Binder content

Having established the gradation to be used, the next question is how much binder to add. At this stage it is worth stating the obvious point that binder content as a percentage by mass is quite different from its percentage by volume – because the specific gravity of bitumen is so much less than that of rock. The volume percentage determines mixture properties and is typically in the range 8–12%; however, it is the mass percentage (typically 4–6%) that is most easily measured and it is therefore the figure specified and 'understood' by practical engineers.

The following subsections present the two best known methods of mixture design in use today.

The Marshall mix design method[106]

This practical technique was developed in the 1950s and its longevity speaks volumes for its user-friendliness and general reliability, despite the severe criticisms of purists. The designs steps are as follows:

- Select a gradation.
- Make up a series of mixes at different binder contents.
- Prepare specimens using a Marshall hammer for compaction (see Fig. 2.54).
- Measure achieved densities.
- Carry out Marshall tests (Fig. 2.54) at 60°C and derive 'stability' and 'flow' values.
- Determine optimum binder content based on stability, flow and density.

There are numerous modifications to the procedure in different specifications around the world, for example making use of a quantity known as the Marshall quotient (stability divided by flow) or replacing overall density by aggregate packing density, but in essence the procedure is as outlined in Fig. 2.54.

The Marshall method gives optima for stability – logically linked to permanent deformation resistance, and density – linked to stiffness

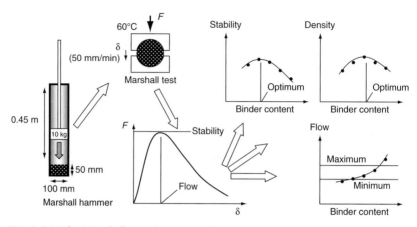

Fig. 2.54 The Marshall mix design procedure

and durability. The limits placed on flow also guard against both poor workability (low flow) and excessive deformability (high flow). The exact choice of binder content will be a compromise. The user should, however, be aware of the following limitations of this method:

- While density may be linked to stiffness, it certainly isn't a stiffness measure, and so gives no guarantee of a suitable value.
- There is no measure of fatigue resistance.
- It is unlikely that an adhesion problem would show up at 60°C.

In short, the Marshall method is a practical way of choosing a binder content, but on its own it does not ensure adequate performance in the pavement. It should always be used in conjunction with other checks.

The Superpave mix design method

This design approach grew out of research in the US in the 1990s and is principally concerned with optimising mixture volumetrics.[107] The key steps are as follows:

- Select a gradation (only broadly graded mixtures covered; filler–binder ratio by mass between 0.6 and 1.2).
- Make up a series of mixes at different binder contents.
- Prepare specimens using a gyratory compactor (see Fig. 2.55).
- Measure achieved densities.
- The optimum binder content is the one that gives a void content of 4%.
- Prepare further specimens at the optimum binder content.
- Check voids at light and heavy compaction.

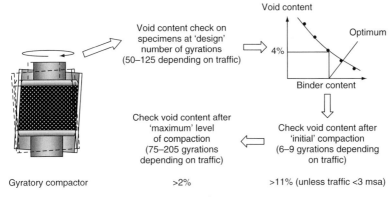

Fig. 2.55 The Superpave mix design procedure

The additional checks at the end are to ensure that compaction does not occur too easily, an indicator of poor aggregate interlock, and that void content will never fall below 2%, even under heavy trafficking. Both checks are intended to avoid the danger of rutting.

Some of the same criticisms often levelled at the Marshall method could also be applied to the Superpave approach. It is another reasonably practical method for optimising volumetrics, but it does not in itself guarantee performance since there are no performance-related tests involved.

2.3.7.3 Binder grade
This depends largely on climate, explicitly so in the Superpave design approach, implicitly so elsewhere. The key point is that the binder should be able to perform satisfactorily over the full range of temperatures experienced in the pavement. Typically, these might be as shown in Table 2.12.

Low temperature presents the danger of fracture and fatigue whereas high temperature can lead to rutting, and this means that there is a desirable working range of binder viscosity, approximately 5×10^3 to 10^7 Pa.s. Thus if, for example, the long-term binder penetration (of an unmodified bitumen) was expected to be about 50, this desirable viscosity range would equate to a temperature range of around -10 to $+45°C$. In this example, therefore, the binder would be expected to perform well in a temperate climate, but not in other climates.

In many climates it is just not possible to find a conventional binder which covers the expected temperature range satisfactorily; either the

171

Table 2.12 Temperature ranges typical of different climates

Climate	Pavement surface temperature: °C			
	Winter		Summer	
	Low	Mean	Mean	High
Temperate (e.g. UK)	−10	+5	+20	+45
Cold Continental (e.g. Canada)	−40	−15	+30	+50
Hot Continental (e.g. India)	0	+15	+35	+60
Desert	−5	+15	+35	+65

viscosity will be too low at high temperature or it will be too high at low temperature. In these cases there are two options:

1. Accept that damage will occur and plan accordingly.
2. Pay extra and use a modified binder, extending the working temperature range.[108]

2.3.7.4 Filler

Filler, the proportion of aggregate passing the 75 μm sieve, is an extremely important component of the mixture. Since any practical aggregate gradation will give a critical particle size of more than 75 μm, this means that filler will never form part of the asphalt skeleton; it simply loses itself between the larger aggregate particles, which puts it in the same ball park as the bitumen. It is therefore rightly seen as a binder additive rather than as part of the aggregate.

Referring back to Section 2.3.1.5, filler can actually make a very effective binder additive indeed, multiplying the fracture and fatigue strength by a factor of up to about 3 (depending on exact filler content and type), and the stiffness by a similar factor. In fact, it appeared in Section 2.3.1.5 that the more filler one mixes into a bitumen, the better the properties of the composite binder will become. Filler is therefore a 'good thing' – in principle, and it is critical to the properties of the resulting mixture. The successful use of a good-quality filler will:

- enhance mixture stiffness and fatigue strength
- assist chemically in promoting aggregate–bitumen adhesion
- inhibit drainage of hot binder off the aggregate during transportation
- not prevent proper mixing
- not prevent proper bitumen–aggregate contact.

The last two points effectively put a limit on the filler content. Experience suggests that filler percentage by volume should always be less than bitumen percentage by volume in order to avoid mixing problems, and to ensure that the large aggregate finds enough bitumen to coat it properly. In fact, mixtures are commonly found to work well when filler percentage by mass is approximately equal to the bitumen percentage by mass – although of course this depends on the specific gravity and shape of the filler particles.

The second point in the above list is also important. Limestone and other alkaline fillers are known to be chemically supportive of adhesion development; other filler types may perform perfectly well in most situations, but not with every aggregate type.

2.3.7.5 Cold mixes

Properly designed and constructed, conventional hot-mix asphalt is an excellent material – but in order to achieve this level of excellence it is necessary to drive every last drop of water away from the aggregate particles. This can only be achieved by heating the aggregate, which means by inputting large amounts of energy, and this is therefore costly and environmentally undesirable. It also restricts the choice of aggregate to those which are able to withstand heat without either being damaged or else giving off excessive noxious fumes. Cold-mix technology opens the door to a brave new world of possibilities.

Sections 2.3.1.9 and 2.3.1.10 have already introduced the principal forms of binder used in cold mixtures, namely *bitumen emulsion* and *foamed bitumen*. One could also add in *cut-back bitumen*, basically bitumen dissolved (or partially dissolved) in kerosene or a similar light oil fraction, although there is pressure to avoid its use nowadays because of the fumes generated. This section will therefore concentrate on emulsion and foamed bitumen. In both cases the binder is temporarily rendered fluid (by the action of water or a foaming process), in which state it is mixed with an aggregate. The result is that the bitumen is dispersed throughout the mixture in the form of very small droplets, adhering to individual aggregate particles. However, the coverage is far from continuous and the quality of adhesion is initially poor. In this state, the mixture is still workable; it can be stored loose for several weeks before use – another attractive property.

Once compacted into the pavement, however, the process of strength gain known as 'curing' commences; in fact the action of compaction pressurises some of the binder between aggregate particles,

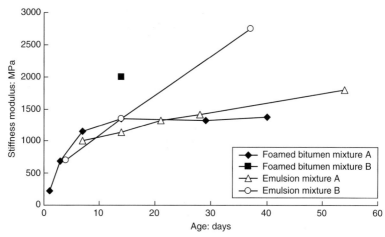

Fig. 2.56 The cold-mix curing process[109]

promoting binder adhesion. Over a period of time, commonly between one and six months, the remaining water becomes ever less able to prevent good bitumen–aggregate adhesion; the droplets of binder also work their way, under gravity, to particle contact locations, and the result is a steady increase in strength and stiffness. Figure 2.56 presents examples of early curing data.

A key difference in mixture designs for cold mixes is that an additional component has to be allowed for, namely *water*. Cold aggregate inevitably contains water, even if it has been protected from the rain for some time; furthermore, cold mixes need water in order for bitumen droplets to disperse within the mixture during mixing. In an emulsion, the water phase already carries the bitumen within it but it is the presence of water in the aggregate which allows the bitumen to move freely during mixing. In the case of a foamed bitumen mixture, the water in the aggregate is equally necessary to allow the foam to disperse properly. Furthermore, an optimum quantity of low-viscosity liquid is needed to allow good compaction. In an unbound material, this liquid is entirely water; in a hot-mix asphalt it is hot bitumen; in a cold-mix asphalt it is a blend of water and bitumen. The upshot is that water is an *absolutely essential* ingredient in the mixture.

But if there is water in the mixture then, compared with a hot mix, there has to be less of something else – and that something usually includes bitumen. Take for example an idealised dense hot-mix asphalt, with 85% of the final volume taken up by aggregate, 10% by bitumen (about 4–5% by mass) and 5% by air voids. If the same aggregate

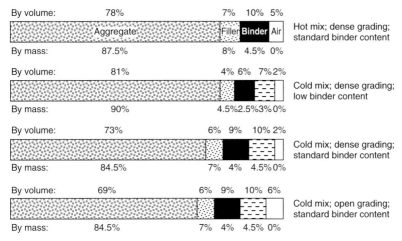

Fig. 2.57 Alternative cold-mix asphalt volumetrics

gradation is used in a cold-mix then, in order to achieve good compaction, there still needs to be about 10% fluid content by volume. Perhaps this can be pushed up to around 13%, but it is hard to squeeze the air void content down to less than about 2% during compaction. However, even 13% fluid by volume is only about 5–6% by mass, about half of which comes from the water present in the cold aggregate in order to facilitate binder mixing. This leaves no more than 3% added binder (by mass) and, in the case of an emulsion, this means no more than about 2% bitumen. Frankly, this is not enough to bind the particles together properly – and it leaves cold-mix designers with an insurmountable problem: it is *physically impossible* to replicate a well-compacted dense asphalt using cold-mix technology; there just isn't room.

These are the alternative approaches which may be considered (illustrated in Fig. 2.57):

- Accept a low bitumen content. Make sure that the filler content is also correspondingly low or contact between bitumen and large aggregate will be poor, resulting in poor mixture properties. The result will be a stiff and deformation-resistant mixture, but one with low durability and fatigue resistance.
- Increase the bitumen content to a more suitable 4% by mass. This means that the final VMA content (bitumen, water and air) will have to increase significantly, reducing stiffness and deformation resistance.
- Change to a more open gradation, with a naturally higher void content at full compaction. This allows a higher bitumen percentage to

175

be used, but also brings a reduced stiffness and deformation resistance in comparison with a dense gradation.

Unfortunately, the presence of water during compaction means there is no way to avoid a relatively high air void content once the water has evaporated. It is very tempting for cold-mix practitioners to pretend that they can produce a direct equivalent to hot mix, using identical gradation and bitumen content, but this is a very dangerous claim to make; the aggregate skeleton will be less efficient than that in a hot mix because of the lower aggregate density achieved due to the presence of water. Not only so, but the very low air voids left immediately after compaction will make it hard for the water to evaporate, and without evaporation the result will be a very poor material indeed.

The use of an open gradation is the safest option because the high air void content encourages evaporation; however, the resulting mixture will have a relatively low stiffness.

2.3.7.6 Grouted macadam mixes

A grouted macadam consists of a very open-graded asphalt (air void content typically 25–30%), which is then grouted up using a cementitious grout. The grout has to be suitably fluid such that it flows readily through the asphalt 'receiving course', leaving practically zero air voids. Figure 2.58 illustrates the resulting material.

Grouted macadam is included here because it is, in practice, a type of asphalt. If perfectly constructed, the material is a zero-air-voids mixture, the individual blocks of grout acting as aggregate particles and interlocking highly efficiently with the aggregate of the original open-graded asphalt. This near-perfect interlock effectively prevents permanent deformation, which makes grouted macadam suitable for high stress locations such as bus lanes or aircraft stands.

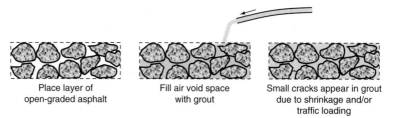

| Place layer of open-graded asphalt | Fill air void space with grout | Small cracks appear in grout due to shrinkage and/or traffic loading |

Fig. 2.58 Grouted macadam

However, this material is sufficiently different from a conventionally produced asphalt not to follow any standard mixture design rules. The following guidance can be given based on recent research.[110]

- *Aggregate particle size and gradation.* The key here is that the void content must be high enough to permit the grout to flow easily through from void to void. In practice this means that the critical particle size (as defined on Calculation Sheet 2.5) should probably be no lower than around 8 mm, which usually means a near single-sized distribution.
- *Binder content.* The principle here is to use as low a binder content as possible while ensuring that all aggregate particles are fully coated. Reducing the binder content lowers the final VMA (since there will always be zero air voids), increasing stiffness; yet tests show that there is no corresponding decrease in fatigue life – a result which is in contrast to conventional asphalt. The logical interpretation is that, with zero air voids, a crack has to follow the same path between aggregate particles and grout whatever the thickness of the intervening binder film.
- *Binder grade.* There is no unanimity on this point. A harder grade means a higher stiffness, which is generally desirable; however, there will be a corresponding reduction in fatigue life due to the loss of self-healing properties within the binder. In the opinion of this author, it is almost always wiser to opt for a softer binder (e.g. 200 pen grade) and accept a reduced stiffness; the stiffness will still be greater than in all conventional asphalts other than those using the hardest binder grades, and the crack resistance will be maximised.
- *Grout strength.* Since the blocks of grout within each 'void' area are expected to act as aggregate particles, they have to be strong enough for this role. Initially there will be no direct contact with aggregate particles due to the binder film – but this will change as the material deforms under load. Bearing in mind that successful conventional asphalts are produced from rocks such as hard lime-stones (or even harder igneous rocks), it is suggested that a grout compressive strength of around 100 MPa is required. Anything less and long-term durability may be a problem.
- *Grout fluidity.* It is almost certainly necessary to include a product such as micro-silica to ensure a sufficiently low grout viscosity for the filling of the voids. Those producing grouted macadam mixtures generally insist on a flow test (e.g. through a funnel) as a check on the grout prior to usage.

If correctly produced, a grouted macadam is a very high-quality material indeed. It will have high stiffness (typically around 10 GPa at 20°C), near-perfect resistance to permanent deformation, and a perfectly adequate fatigue resistance. It will not, however, have high skid resistance (unless special measures are taken) and so is suited to low-speed applications only if used as a surface course. With two production phases, it will also be expensive.

2.3.8 Summary
There is no doubt that asphalt, in its various forms, has become the premier pavement construction material, and it therefore needs to be well understood if correct decisions are to be made. Here are some of the more important points of which a pavement engineer should be aware.

- Bitumen is a visco-elastic liquid, even at in-service temperatures. It can 'flow' and permanent deformation of asphalt can therefore occur.
- The viscosity and elastic stiffness of bitumen are temperature and loading rate dependent, which means this is also true of an asphalt mixture.
- Asphalt 'works' by forming a skeleton of interlocking aggregate particles. Inter-particle movement is restricted by the bitumen surrounding each particle contact. Performance therefore depends on the effectiveness of the aggregate skeleton, the properties of the bitumen, and the strength of bitumen–aggregate adhesion.
- In every mixture there is a critical particle size, above which the particles form the skeleton and below which they act as binder extenders. In practice this means that filler should be seen as a binder additive, increasing both the stiffness and the fracture resistance.
- Mixture design involves firstly the selection of an appropriate aggregate gradation for the material's role in the pavement, then the choice of an appropriate binder grade and content. This should give optimum density and stiffness, as well as ensuring there is enough binder for fatigue and durability purposes and enough air voids to avoid 'pore pressure' and permanent deformation.
- Cold mixes can never compete directly with dense hot mixes because of the presence of a significant volume of water during compaction. Designs must ensure that the water is able to evaporate and escape at an early age.

2.4

Reinforcing products

Steel reinforcement of concrete is a familiar concept, and Section 2.2.6.4 has already introduced fibre-reinforced concrete as a material in its own right. However, the range of possible reinforcing products for use in pavements is much greater than this and it is important that a competent pavement engineer knows something of them.

2.4.1 Unbound material reinforcement

In the well-known case of reinforced concrete, the reinforcement addresses the principal weakness of concrete, namely a relatively low tensile strength. In a similar way, in unbound materials, reinforcement needs to address their principal weakness, which is a zero tensile strength. Even a small change here has the potential to make a large difference in overall behaviour.

2.4.1.1 Reinforcing mechanism

The key problem is how best to 'bond' a reinforcing element into an unbound material. By definition, this cannot be achieved directly since there is no binding action available. This means that it is necessary to make use of the one mode in which an unbound material performs well, namely shear – achieved by means of the interlock between particles. The reinforcement must therefore achieve excellent interlock with individual particles. The *critical particle size* should logically be an important element in the design of reinforcement. In soils this may only be a matter of microns (μm), which means that a membrane of some sort having an appropriate surface texture is likely to be effective; to reinforce a granular base layer on the other hand, the 'texture' required

179

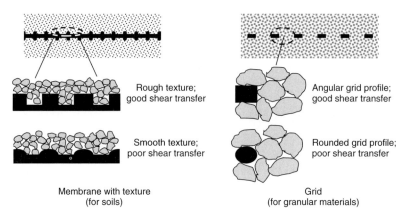

Rough texture;
good shear transfer

Smooth texture;
poor shear transfer

Angular grid profile;
good shear transfer

Rounded grid profile;
poor shear transfer

Membrane with texture
(for soils)

Grid
(for granular materials)

Fig. 2.59 Reinforcement mechanism – unbound materials

would render a membrane impractical and a grid becomes the logical
choice. Figure 2.59 indicates the key features for efficient shear transfer.

The illustrations in Fig. 2.59 imply that the particle size is very
important, and ideally a grid or membrane should be matched to the
particular material to be reinforced. The 'texture' illustrated might be
referred to as the 'macro-texture', generating interlock with individual
particles. However, there will also be a 'micro-texture' effect, giving an
angle of friction at slip between each particle and the material of the
membrane or grid, and this will also affect the efficiency of the system.

2.4.1.2 Reinforcement effect

Shear transfer is one of the two mechanisms by which stress is distributed through an unbound material, the other being compression, which
means that good shear transfer to the reinforcement allows it to form
an integral part of the system. However, unlike the surrounding
material, the reinforcement can withstand tension, and this means
that any extensile strain in the plane of the reinforcement will be
small and almost entirely recoverable. The effect will be to limit
strain, particularly irrecoverable strain, in all directions in the region
of the reinforcement. Logically, the effectiveness with which strain is
limited will decrease with increasing distance away from the plane of
the reinforcement.

This explanation can only be conceptual with the present state of
knowledge since research has not yet solved the very complex problem
of predicting the zone of influence of unbound material reinforcement.
Indeed, it probably never will since it depends on so many parameters.

However, the key point is that successful reinforcement can transform a layer of unbound material into one with much increased resistance to permanent deformation and, sometimes, increased stiffness. The potential for reducing rutting in unbound pavement layers is clear.

2.4.1.3 Membranes

The generic term 'membrane' has been used here since in principle there is no restriction on such products other than that they take the form of a continuous layer through which particles of the surrounding material cannot pass. However, most suitable products would fall under the heading *geotextiles*. These can be further subdivided into 'woven' or 'non-woven', depending on the manufacturing process, and the material used can be polyester, polypropylene or glass fibre, as well as more traditional plant-based products. The point is that they should almost always be *pervious*, permitting the passage of water but not soil. Only in special cases such as the design of so-called 'drainage pavements' (see Part 3) is it likely that an impermeable membrane would be required.

The subject of geotextiles is a specialist one and will not be covered in depth here. In many cases, the primary reason for use is not reinforcement but *separation* of soil and granular material, preventing soil from rising into a granular matrix and clogging up the pore spaces, in which case the porosity and hydraulic conductivity become the principal design considerations. Rupture strength may also be important where large particles are involved or where construction activities might cause damage. Nevertheless, reinforcement is often at least one of the hoped-for effects from a geotextile, in which case the properties of surface roughness described above become important. In-plane stiffness is obviously a key factor, although the stiffness of the individual strands of fibre which interlock with soil particles may be equally important. It is at this scale that the true effectiveness of geotextile–soil shear transfer is determined.

2.4.1.4 Grids

The term *geogrid* is commonly used here, meaning a grid reinforcement product used in the ground – or in a pavement. Grids can be manufactured from steel, glass fibre, polyester or polypropylene, as well as natural organic products such as bamboo. Figure 2.60 shows three widely used generic types.

181

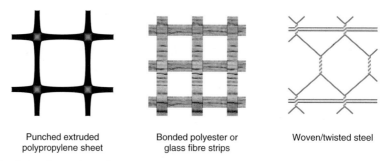

| Punched extruded polypropylene sheet | Bonded polyester or glass fibre strips | Woven/twisted steel |

Fig. 2.60 Geogrid reinforcement types

Clearly these three types are very different in appearance and also in the way in which they act – yet all are intended to perform a similar function. The truth is that they all have their strengths and weaknesses. The needle-punched polypropylene is likely to have the most advantageous (i.e. angular) strand profile and therefore the best interlock with surrounding stones; the bonded strips probably command a price advantage and may also be stiffer longitudinally, but they will have a poorer strand profile and also a poorer out-of-plane bending stiffness; steel gives the stiffest strands of all in bending, but the profile will usually be poor (i.e. rounded) and the longitudinal stiffness will be low due to the woven nature of the product. Unfortunately, these differences leave the user in a confused state. Venturing an opinion, however, the most important quality may be interlock, which demands a good strand profile and/or a stiff strand in bending. The actual influence of geogrid reinforcement on the performance of surrounding material will be discussed further in Part 3.

2.4.2 Hydraulically-bound material reinforcement

Steel reinforcement for concrete is a subject which extends way beyond pavement engineering, and although the use of reinforced concrete will be introduced in pavement designs in Part 3, the properties of steel and the manufacture of reinforcing bars are assumed here to be part of the reader's background knowledge, or at least within reach through other technical literature. With a stiffness of 210 GPa, steel is around five times as stiff as pavement quality concrete (PQC), while the tensile strength of high-yield steel (about 450 MPa) is nearly a hundred times that of PQC. Steel as a material therefore has something to offer to concrete, in pavements as in other applications.

The slightly different case of steel fibre reinforcement has been covered already in Section 2.2.6.4.

Moving to materials other than PQC, reinforcement is rare. Fibre reinforcement can be used in strong lean concrete but this is not common practice.[111] In weaker materials there is no economic case to use steel, and there would inevitably be durability problems due to the more voided structure and consequent presence of moisture. Other products such as polypropylene could in theory be used but their properties add relatively little value to most hydraulically-bound materials.

2.4.3 Asphalt reinforcement

This is an important subject in the field of pavement rehabilitation. As in the case of unbound materials, reinforcing products can be included between asphalt pavement layers, and the same types of membrane and grid can all be used. The following sections describe the rationale for their inclusion.

2.4.3.1 Sealing

The need to keep water out of the lower layers of a pavement has been referred to already and will be highlighted in several places in Parts 3 and 4. This is a role for which dense asphalt is ideally suited and many (although certainly not all) surface courses may be considered practically impermeable. However, this impermeability is fatally compromised as soon as cracks develop, and general pavement deterioration is likely to accelerate until the surface is resealed. Part 4 will discuss the various techniques for this, but one method is to use a so-called *paving fabric*, a geotextile which is placed on top of a bituminous spray coat, before applying a new surface course overlay. The geotextile soaks up the bitumen and forms an effective seal so that, even after the new surface course starts to crack, water is prevented from entering the pavement.

For this role, a paving fabric needs no particular strength or stiffness and no interlock with any other material; it simply has to have an appropriate absorbance, typically holding between 0.5 and 1 litre of bitumen per square metre.

2.4.3.2 Inhibiting cracking

This is the most common role of asphalt reinforcement. The following comments stem from the author's own experience, both in practice and in research,[112] and it is hoped that they will assist the reader; however, they do not represent universally accepted truth.

The logical approach is to return first to the general matter of asphalt cracking. Earlier sections have introduced the concept that bonds between aggregate particles will start to fracture, even under 'normal' elastic straining, and that fatigue damage, at least in its early stages, consists of the enlargement of local fracture zones and the initiation of new fracture points. If this is occurring, then it follows that a degree of aggregate particle realignment is also taking place; this is the only physical mechanism through which new fracture points can be formed. The word 'realignment' is used here rather than 'permanent deformation', because the effect is purely local and certainly cannot be seen in measurable deformation of the whole mass of the asphalt; yet, locally, permanent deformation is actually what is meant. So, at a fundamental level, fatigue damage and permanent deformation are inextricably linked.

A reinforcing product at the interface between two asphalt courses will have negligible effect on elastic behaviour – most products simply aren't stiff enough to do so – but reinforcement is particularly successful at inhibiting permanent deformation; this is the main reason for its use in unbound materials. In the case of asphalt, if local permanent deformation is prevented then local fatigue damage is also prevented since no particle rearrangement can occur. This seems likely to be the fundamental reason why, under the right conditions, reinforced asphalt works. Its effectiveness depends on the quality of interlock between the reinforcement and the aggregate skeleton of the asphalt.

However, explaining the mechanism involved is one thing; predicting the effect on fatigue is quite another. Nor can this book add anything conclusive. Experiments have suggested that the rate of fatigue damage in the zone above and below the reinforcement can be reduced by a *factor of up to 4*,[113] probably more in some cases, but the extent of this zone is not agreed; ±40 mm is likely to be a conservative estimate.

Thus, if the reinforcement is in the right place, i.e. within about 40 mm of a region susceptible to fatigue damage, and it is of good quality and well installed, then reinforced asphalt can certainly be effective. The most obvious usage would be as an inclusion in a relatively thin overlay treatment to a cracked pavement, a location which lends itself to both paving fabrics and geogrids. Another successful application is in an asphalt overlay to a jointed or cracked concrete pavement, so long as the principal mode of damage is found to be through thermally-induced (day–night; expansion–contraction) movement rather than that due to traffic; in this case, geogrids are strongly preferred to paving fabrics, which do not generally reinforce so successfully under slow rates of strain.

2.4.3.3 Reducing permanent deformation

Since the previous section has made much of the effectiveness of reinforcement in preventing permanent deformation, this would seem to be a logical application in asphalt, just as it is in unbound material. And in fact tests have revealed that grid reinforcement placed beneath the surface course can reduce rutting significantly. The problem is, however, that it usually isn't worth doing. When the cost is compared to that of tackling the problem in other ways, such as improving the mixture used, reinforcement almost always works out too expensive, as well as being slightly risky in the sense that installation problems can occur and later recycling can be more problematic. Thus, deformation reduction is generally only seen as a side-benefit in cases where the prime motivation is inhibiting cracking.

2.4.4 Summary

Despite the lack of certainty regarding the performance of reinforcing products, it is commonly observed that significant benefits can accrue – and it is therefore important not to ignore the option of using reinforcement. Part 3 will outline ways in which the performance of reinforced pavements can be predicted, while Part 4, on the subject of pavement rehabilitation, will identify occasions where reinforcement of asphalt should be seriously considered.

2.5

Conclusion to Part 2

Pavement materials are varied in nature and have to cope with a variety of roles. They also, of course, vary greatly in cost and availability, which means that sensible compromise choices have to be made all the time, balancing the advantages and disadvantages, uncertainties and risks inherent in all materials. The natural soil is always available, whether we like it or not, so it makes sense to optimise its use, stabilising it where feasible rather than replacing it with more expensive imported material; but in situ stabilisation always brings risk. This is a fact of life. The trick is to get the risk–benefit equation right. The same is true to a lesser extent of any material which takes more than a few days to reach its design strength, for example slag-bound bases or cold-mix asphalts; yet in both these cases there are sound economic and environmental reasons why these materials should be used. The pavement engineer has to be able to appreciate the dangers as well as the potential advantages, if appropriate decisions are to be taken. There will be failures of course; this has to be appreciated. However, if, statistically, the benefits accruing outweigh the cost of a few failures then the right decision has been made.

The key points relating to each material type have already been summarised at the end of the relevant sections, so there is no need to repeat them here. However, one absolutely fundamental issue is worth repeating, and that is the concept of a *critical particle size*, the size above which particles form a skeleton and below which they are simply 'lost' in the voids. This concept was helpful in understanding the mechanical behaviour of both unbound and hydraulically-bound materials and in understanding permeability, and it was also key to understanding asphalt mixture design. It is not a concept which the

186

reader will normally see presented in this way, but it is recommended here as an extremely helpful approach.

It is also to be hoped that the reader may have gained an understanding of those materials which are still relatively unfamiliar to pavement engineers — materials such as lime-stabilised soil, cold-mix asphalt, grouted macadam and the various reinforcing products available. If sensible choices are to be made, both in material and pavement design, then the full range of options needs to be both known and understood.

Notes

1. In a linear elastic material, the Mohr circle construction can be used equally for stress or strain. It represents a convenient way of visualising a complex situation.
2. Dry stone walls, walls which make no use of cementitious mortar, can stand many feet in height with vertical faces, so long as individual stones are carefully selected to fit neatly into the gaps between neighbouring stones, producing a strongly interlocking structure. Near the base of such a wall, the vertical stress may be 20–30 kPa, while the horizontal stress is effectively zero.
3. Thom (1988) records a maximum interlock of around 30 kPa for a dry, broadly graded aggregate.
4. At its most basic, cohesion represents negative pore pressure, whatever the cause of such pressure may be. See specialist geotechnical literature for detailed discussion.
5. See Thom and Brown (1989).
6. Most specifications for unbound materials include assurance of particle 'integrity', e.g. by means of the Los Angeles abrasion test (CEN, 1998a; AASHTO, 2002a; ASTM, 2003, 2006a). However, this is really to ensure that no long-term degradation takes place, resulting in serious change to the nature of the material. It is not directly related to shear strength requirements.
7. See Hertz (1895).
8. See Thom (1988).
9. See Thom and Brown (1988).
10. See Fuller and Thompson (1907).
11. See Highways Agency (2007).
12. The most common laboratory compaction tool worldwide is the Proctor hammer (CEN, 2004a), a 2.5 kg weight, 50 mm diameter

steel cylinder which is allowed to drop repeatedly through a height of 305 mm. A standard number of drops (e.g. 25) are specified for each compacted layer. Alternatives are the heavy Proctor (4.5 kg weight, 457 mm drop height – also CEN, 2004a) or vibrating hammer compaction (CEN, 2003d). The aims are always: (1) to simulate site conditions; (2) to obtain repeatable measurements; and (3) to achieve these quickly and cheaply. It seems to be generally acknowledged that both the heavy Proctor and the vibrating hammer are capable of approaching in situ compaction levels.

13. Numerous specifications describe the CBR test, with only minor variations. See for example CEN (2004c).
14. These equations are my own approximate digitisations of Terzaghi's original curves (Terzaghi and Peck, 1967).
15. See, for example, Overseas Road Note 31 (Transport Research Laboratory, 1993).
16. Specifications require particles larger than 20 mm size to be removed; however, this immediately invalidates the result.
17. See Highways Agency, 2006c.
18. The equation quoted in Highways Agency (2006c) was developed by Day (1981).
19. The $K–\theta$ model (see for example Hicks and Monismith, 1971) stemmed from suggestions put forward by various researchers in the 1960s. Additional terms have since been proposed to refine model accuracy, generally based on triaxial test evidence.
20. See Thom (1988).
21. See Boyce (1980).
22. See Hornych *et al.* (2000).
23. See Thom (1988).
24. See Thom and Brown (1989).
25. The advent of discrete element modelling (e.g. Cundall and Strack, 1979) means that the stress–strain behaviour of unbound materials can now be simulated very realistically indeed. The discontinuous nature of the material means that continuum models such as those in Table 2.1 can never hope to be more than approximate.
26. See Thom (1988).
27. See Thom and Brown (1988).
28. The most widely used specification for triaxial testing is given in AASHTO (2002b). EN 13286:7 (CEN, 2004b) is a European specification for a more sophisticated (and therefore less user-friendly) triaxial test. The AASHTO test measures platen movement only; the European test utilises on-sample instrumentation.

29. See Semmelink and de Beer (1995).
30. See Edwards *et al.* (2005).
31. The Springbox model referred to here was developed by Scott Wilson Ltd in the UK; further development is proposed.
32. See Thom (1988).
33. See Boussinesq (1883).
34. These figures match those in the UK Highways Agency's standard IAN73 (Highways Agency, 2006c) for a high-quality granular sub-base.
35. See, for example, AASHTO (1993) and AASHTO (2007b).
36. See Powell *et al.* (1984).
37. Brown *et al.* (1987) report data showing a factor of over 3 between the highest and lowest stiffnesses for different soils of the same CBR (e.g. 24–80 MPa at 5% CBR), tested under the same stress conditions.
38. Adapted from Thom (1988).
39. The hollow cylinder apparatus is a useful research tool, allowing the combinations of stress under a moving wheel to be reproduced, but it is much too time-consuming for general use. Chan (1990) describes use of the equipment and also gives a good overview of the subject of permanent strain accumulation under multi-cyclic loading.
40. Reynolds number is a very widely used and powerful descriptor of the state of fluid flow. Refer to specialist fluid mechanics texts for details.
41. This approximation is derived from the so-called 'Poiseuille equation' for laminar flow; see for example Webber (1971).
42. See Webber (1971).
43. See Darcy (1856).
44. See Hazen (1892).
45. The soil descriptions are based on the Unified Soil Classification System (USCS) given in ASTM (2001); the permeability ranges quoted are simply intended as broad estimates.
46. See Jones and Jones (1989b).
47. Jones and Jones (1989a) give an excellent overview of the subject of permeability estimation for unbound pavement materials.
48. The easiest form of test to carry out involves allowing water to permeate vertically through a cylinder of material under gravity. However, problems are: (1) that the hydraulic gradient is unrealistically large for pavement conditions; and (2) that vertical permeability is less important than horizontal permeability in most pavement situations.
49. The data are plotted from information in Brown *et al.* (1987).

50. See Croney and Jacobs (1967).
51. Specifications include: for Los Angeles Abrasion – AASHTO (2002a), ASTM (2003, 2006a), CEN (1998a); for Micro-Deval – AASHTO (2006c), ASTM (2006e), CEN (1996); for Soundness – AASHTO (1999), CEN (1998b); for Freeze–thaw – AASHTO (2007a).
52. See CEN (2003e).
53. See Thompson *et al.* (1999).
54. A range of different chemical additives have been used successfully to produce air entrainment. They include natural resins, synthetic detergents and fatty acids. The entrained air content is also affected by cement quality and the nature of any other fine material used in the mixture.
55. Note that it is common to ignore the shear contribution shown in Calculation Sheet 2.8; no clear reason is seen for this.
56. See CEN (2003f).
57. This is exemplified by comparing the range of ultrasonic stiffnesses quoted by the UK Transport Research Laboratory (Nunn, 2004) for cement-bound base materials – about 38 GPa for a 20 MPa compressive strength mix – with those commonly measured in situ – typically around 25 GPa.
58. See Comité Euro-International du Béton (1993).
59. Modelled on the approach by Thom and Cheung (1999).
60. For example, British Airports Authority (1993).
61. The assumption of a maximum factor of 3 between sub-base stiffness and that of the underlying material was used in deriving current UK design standards (Powell *et al.* 1984).
62. See for example Griffiths and Thom (2007).
63. See Highways Agency (2007).
64. All stabilisation specifications and guidelines include limits on sulphur in one form or another.
65. There are two current EU norms that can be applied to soaking of hydraulically stabilised soils. In EN 13286:47 (CEN, 2004c), a specimen enclosed in a CBR mould is wetted from below for four days, commencing three days after manufacture. In EN 13286:49 (CEN, 2004d), the unprotected specimen is submerged in water after a period of just 1.5 to 2 times the workability period, and the soaking period is seven days (at 40°C). Unsurprisingly, the effect can be quite different in the two cases.
66. Any test arrangement whereby resistance to a controlled viscous flow is recorded will result in a measure of viscosity. The most

common technique nowadays is by means of a rotational viscometer – a cylinder rotated in a vessel of bitumen (e.g. ASTM, 2006d; AASHTO, 2006a).

67. For specification of the penetration test see ASTM (2006b) or CEN (2007a). For softening point determination see ASTM (2006c) or CEN (2007b).
68. See Rahimzadeh (2002).
69. See Asphalt Institute (2003).
70. See Asphalt Institute (2003).
71. See Asphalt Institute (2003).
72. The Fraass breaking point (Fraass, 1937) is found by repeatedly flexing a thin strip of metal with 0.5 mm of bitumen applied to its surface while lowering the temperature. The temperature at which the bitumen fractures is the Fraass point and it gives an idea of the minimum serviceable temperature for that binder. Other impact-type tests for bitumen 'cohesion' are also in use, but none have achieved widespread recognition.
73. Thom *et al.* (2006).
74. Thom *et al.* (2006).
75. For a useful introduction to bitumen chemistry, see Read and Whiteoak (2003).
76. See ASTM (2004), AASHTO (2006b) or CEN (2007c).
77. Bell (1989) provides an excellent summary of asphalt ageing and the tests available to evaluate it.
78. Superpave SP-1 (Asphalt Institute, 2003), describes the testing required to prove the applicable temperature range of a bitumen. The principal tests used are the dynamic shear rheometer for high and medium temperatures, and the bending beam rheometer for low temperatures.
79. The pneumatic adhesion tensile testing instrument (PATTI) – see ASTM (2002) – has been used for measurement of bitumen adhesion, but is certainly not an industry standard.
80. Collop *et al.* (2004) are among those who report a significantly enhanced performance with limestone aggregate compared to granite, although use of an additive negated this difference. Lay (1990) provides a useful insight into the mechanisms which may be at work. Current research is concentrating on the subject of 'surface energy', a property of the aggregate surface similar in concept to the well-known 'surface tension' effect at a liquid surface.
81. Ethylenediamine, formaldehyde, heptaldehyde and phenol have all been found to enhance bitumen–aggregate adhesion in certain cases.

82. See Van der Poel (1954).
83. See Ullidtz (1979).
84. See Brown (1978).
85. Refer to note 80.
86. The problem with tension–compression testing is the need to glue the end platens. Even if the glue is effective, there will be a concentration of stress around the perimeter at the glue–specimen interface, potentially causing premature specimen failure. The only way to overcome this is to use a necked specimen, greatly adding to the complexity of specimen preparation.
87. One problem is that, in the formula quoted in Fig. 2.46 for stiffness derived from the indirect tensile test, the result is dependent on the value assumed for Poisson's ratio ν.
88. The Nottingham Asphalt Tester (NAT – Brown *et al.*, 1994) is one of the most commonly used pieces of asphalt testing equipment worldwide. It provides an industry-friendly indirect tensile test, as well as offering both fatigue and permanent deformation options.
89. The data shown are taken from Thom *et al.* (1997), Ibrahim (1998) and Sunarjono (2008). The equation shown is given in the UK Highways Agency design manual HD29 (Highways Agency, 2001).
90. The Paris law (Paris & Erdogan, 1963) relates the rate of crack propagation to a 'stress intensity factor' at the crack tip, a measure of stress concentration which takes account of the sharpness of the crack.
91. Maillard *et al.* (2004) describe tests which involve exactly this type of inter-particle fracture.
92. Data taken from Choi *et al.* (2005).
93. Despite the undoubted convenience of the indirect tensile fatigue test as a means of comparing the fatigue resistance of different materials, the significant permanent deformation induced means that the results should be treated with caution. For some materials, particularly low stiffness materials, the results may understate the true fatigue resistance.
94. This data, taken from Oliveira (2006), was actually obtained on a grouted macadam mixture, with 200 pen (i.e. very soft) binder. The use of this binder will have accentuated the healing effect, but the trends shown also apply to conventional asphalt mixtures.
95. A practical alternative to application of a confining pressure, is to use a top platen diameter smaller than the specimen diameter, allowing the outer part of the specimen to provide confinement to the inner part.

96. See Airey *et al.* (2004).
97. See for example CEN (2003b).
98. The Saturation Ageing Tensile Stiffness (SATS) test (Collop *et al.*, 2004; Highways Agency, 2007) allows simultaneous application of water and accelerated ageing due to a raised temperature and pressurised air.
99. Void content is deduced by comparing density (mass/volume; usually determined from a weight of water displaced by the specimen – wrapped in foil or film) of the compacted mixture with that of the component pieces (the so-called 'rice density'). An approximation of the density of the component pieces can be found by weighing the specimen in water unwrapped, allowing water to penetrate the voids, although it should be appreciated that enclosed voids will remain unfilled and that the estimate of void content which results will be lower than is actually the case.
100. See for example, CEN (2003a).
101. For research in this area, see Gubler *et al.* (2004).
102. See for example Phillips and Traxler (1963) and Pendrys (1989).
103. See Asphalt Institute (1996).
104. The distinctive grading curve for hot-rolled asphalt is not necessarily a problem. However, it means that great reliance is placed on the properties (principally shape) of the sand-size fraction, i.e. the critical size.
105. There is a limit to the thickness of binder film that can be expected to remain on an aggregate particle without draining off; if the binder is 'bulked out' by the addition of cellulose fibres, then this thickness increases significantly.
106. There are numerous variations on the Marshall design procedure given in specifications around the world. The most widely used is probably that given in MS-2 by the Asphalt Institute (1984).
107. See Asphalt Institute (1996).
108. Binder modifiers cannot work miracles. Styrene butadiene styrene (SBS) is among the most effective polymers; when blended with the right bitumen it is reported to extend the working temperature range by up to about 50°C (approximately +30°C and −20°C; see Read and Whiteoak, 2003).
109. Data taken from Ibrahim (1998) and Sunarjono (2008).
110. See Oliveira (2006).
111. See Thompson *et al.* (1999) for an evaluation of fibre-reinforced base materials.

112. See Thom (2003).
113. The data upon which this statement is based comes from beam tests. In fact, the full range of factors deduced for different types of reinforcing product was from 2 to 8.

Part 3
Design

3.1

Design principles

Design is a topic which is very hard to tie down. The problem is that there is never a unique solution to any given problem. When planning construction of a major pavement, there will always be a number of different options as to which combinations of materials to use. The surface can be either asphalt or concrete, and both options come in several varieties; asphalt surfaces need a base, which can also be asphalt, but which could equally well be hydraulically bound or even unbound. And when solutions such as cold-mix asphalt and grouted macadam are included, not to mention block paving, then it is clear that design is much more than the simple following of rules.

The pavement engineer has to be aware that no two design options will be truly identical in their performance – whatever any design chart may indicate. All pavements require maintenance as they deteriorate and the types of deterioration will differ from design option to design option. Thus, the *long-term characteristics* of a pavement have to be borne in mind as much as the day-one performance.

Therefore, up-front cost, maintenance cost and in-service ride quality all have to be considered. To this should be added *environmental costs*, such as the destruction caused by aggregate extraction, energy consumption in the manufacture of steel, concrete and asphalt, and emissions of harmful substances into air or water. There may be many reasons to prefer one solution over another, some of which have nothing to do with engineering, but the key skill which a pavement engineer has to bring to the table is the ability to produce a full range of designs, and to appreciate the true life-cycle costs, both economic and environmental.

3.1.1 Engineering principles

There are certain conceptually simple tasks which a pavement has to fulfil, which can be summarised as follows.

- *Protect the subgrade.* In general, the natural ground will not be strong enough to bear traffic load directly; it would deform and rut. The pavement must therefore be stiff enough and thick enough to distribute the load from the vehicle wheels over a wide enough area not to cause excessive subgrade deformation.
- *Guard against deformation in the pavement layers.* At every level in the structure of the pavement, the materials used must themselves be stable enough not to suffer deformation under the stresses experienced at that level.
- *Guard against break-up of the pavement layers.* Similarly, the internal strength of the pavement layers must be sufficient not to allow excessive cracking to develop under traffic loading.
- *Protect from environmental attack.* The materials used should be such that they do not lose their properties under attack from whatever the local climate throws at them; or with the passage of time. Drainage must be adequate to prevent excessive water build-up at any level in the pavement.
- *Provide a suitable surface.* Requirements of evenness, skid resistance, noise and/or spray suppression may vary, but the design has to be suited to the provision of an appropriate pavement surface.
- *Ensure 'maintainability'.* Accepting that no pavement lasts for ever, the design must ensure that it is possible to carry out necessary maintenance within acceptable limits of disruption and cost.

These six key tasks together define successful engineering design and much of this part of the book is devoted to the techniques by which such design can be achieved. However, design is also constrained by arguably equally important non-engineering principles. The following two subsections outline the concepts of 'whole-life cost' and 'sustainability', terms which may vary with time and geographic location but whose principles remain constant.

3.1.2 Whole-life cost

The concept of whole-life cost is simple enough; it is the true cost of a pavement over a long period of time, including both initial and ongoing costs. However, while the concept is simple, arguments rage as to which

Table 3.1 Highway pavement costing issues

Cost/benefit	Parties involved			
	Residents (local economy)	Pavement users	Highway authority	State
Direct construction cost			✓	
Indirect construction cost			✓	✓
Indirect construction benefit	✓			✓
Direct maintenance costs			✓	
Indirect maintenance costs		✓	✓	✓
Indirect maintenance benefit	✓			✓
Indirect cost due to pavement's presence	✓			
Indirect benefit due to pavement's presence	✓	✓		✓
Accident costs		✓		✓

costs should be included and how. Table 3.1 lists the key issues, taking the example of a highway project.

The problem is just where to draw the boundaries – and the answer may depend on just who is carrying out the calculation. A highway authority employee who has been allocated a budget and told to stretch it as far as possible will naturally only be looking at a single box in Table 3.1, namely the direct construction cost to the authority. And this attitude on the part of an individual cannot legitimately be criticised; it is not his/her job to second-guess on issues which should be sorted out as policy at a much more general level, however aware that individual may be regarding those issues.

However, what about the highway authority as a whole? The organisation should sensibly take into account every cost item which affects it, which means both construction and maintenance costs, plus the secondary costs of road damage due to site access, aggregate transport etc. – in fact the four ticked boxes in the Highway authority column in Table 3.1. But there is usually no incentive for the authority to draw the net wider and examine costs and benefits to the wider community. Perhaps that's slightly unfair and many highway authorities have an interest in issues affecting local residents – but they will not normally be concerned directly with road-user costs for example, i.e. travel time, fuel costs; even accident costs only impact indirectly. If these wider issues are to be included then this has to be either done or ordered at a more general level still, which means at local or national government level. Only those removed from the day-to-day need to control highway spending have the luxury of being able to take the bigger picture into account. Of course, day-to-day decision makers may be well aware of the issues – but they cannot be expected to take decisions which directly harm the finances of their own organisation, however great the benefit to the wider community may be.

Forgive this somewhat philosophical discussion. The aim is to get across the fact that there are wider issues which, in an ideal world, someone in local or national government should be tackling. Some of the most difficult problems are:

- putting an appropriate value on travel time
- assigning a 'discount rate' to future costs (i.e. £100 in five years' time might only be equivalent to £80 now if that £80 were invested wisely)
- taking road damage by construction vehicles into account
- costing of accidents, particularly injury and death
- disruption to business due to restrictions on highway usage
- benefits to business due to the highway being there – or being upgraded.

One could even add in such items as the cost due to increased flood risk, since pavements generally result in additional runoff to drains, sewers and rivers. The truth is that there is always a bigger picture however wide one draws the boundaries to the problem. However, the principle is that each of these costs and benefits have to be evaluated, and the easiest way to do that is to assign a monetary value to each. For example, the cost of a fatality in the UK is generally put at around £1 million (year 2007). There is obviously no single 'right answer' and many of the cost/benefit items will attract wildly differing estimates, particularly such items as the cost to business. However, this is no excuse for governments not to carry out such calculations – or insist that they be carried out by others. It is the only way to evaluate sensibly whether particular schemes should go ahead; it is also a logical input into the decision-making process as to just which pavement solution should be adopted in a particular case. It is not pavement engineering – but it may impact on engineering choices.

3.1.3 Sustainability

If whole-life costing is politically challenging, sustainability pushes the boundaries out further still. It is another subject which, though quite separate from engineering, should affect engineering choices. Like whole-life costing, it is a subject with which the pavement engineer should be familiar. As in whole-life costing, the calculations are not difficult in themselves; the difficulty lies in defining the boundaries to the problem.

First of all, what is meant by 'sustainability'? It is probably foolish to try to define it in anything other than the most general terms, but basically the word represents our aspirations not to destroy the planet, i.e. to make sure that our children and grandchildren actually have a reasonable future – a rather broader subject than pavement engineering! However, pavements: (1) use vast resources in terms of tonnages of bulk products; and (2) have a complex relationship with vehicle fuel consumption, noise, harmful emissions etc. They therefore have the potential to add significantly to the rate at which we bring about the destruction of our environment, and so are rightly attracting the attention of government authorities trying to minimise such destruction. The following subsections will outline key sustainability issues relating to pavements.

3.1.3.1 Material resource depletion

Traditionally, the principal component in road construction has been *rock*, and it is hard to argue that this resource is being significantly depleted. For instance, the entire volume of pavement in the UK (probably between 1 and 2 billion cubic metres) equates to a single 1000–1200 ft (300–400 m) high mountain with 1:4 side slopes. In the cold language of overall resource, this is negligible – and the same would be true for much of the world. Locally there may be a lack – for example in the Netherlands – but overall there is no global rock shortage. There may be a lack of very high-quality rock, such as stone for high skid-resistance surfacing, which may necessitate some relaxation in standards compared with what is ideal. Nevertheless, rock shortage is not a serious sustainability driver.

The other obvious resource demanded by pavements is *binder*, whether cementitious or bituminous. Taking cement first, there are serious sustainability issues – but not under this heading; there is no lack of limestone from which to manufacture cement. However, bitumen is another story. Most bitumen is derived from crude oil distillation and, while oil continues to be used as fuel and for other purposes, there will continue to be a supply of bitumen. It is, essentially, a by-product, but a by-product from a resource which is most definitely finite, namely oil. This puts it in a difficult category. As a by-product, its use fits in with sustainability goals since, if it were not used in pavements, oil companies would be desperately looking for alternative markets. However, in the long term, reliance on bitumen is *unsustainable* (something which is also true of many industrial by-products, since industrial processes and therefore their by-products are continually changing). The sensible approach therefore is to use it while it is there but to plan for a future in which it is less readily available.

3.1.3.2 Blight

The first point to make here is that the presence of a pavement implies that something else is no longer present. There is therefore a loss of agricultural productivity or of housing space or, simply, recreation space. This is not something which the pavement engineer can address of course, and it only affects the issue of new or widened pavements, but it is a subject which has to be at the heart of land-use planning. To carry out value calculations, land space has to be assigned a worth, according to its potential usefulness. Thus prime UK agricultural land has a typical (2007) value of around £1 per square metre, reducing to less than £0.50 for rough pasture land. In contrast, urban land in the UK, where permission for housing has been granted, is typically valued at around £250 per square metre. Of course this is an artificial figure, inflated by difficulties imposed by planning restrictions, but it provides a useful benchmark. On the other hand, if a site has been contaminated, usually due to past industrial activity, there may be a serious clean-up bill attached, effectively reducing the value to zero, even in a city environment. Compare these figures with the direct cost of a major new highway, around £40 per square metre, and the real value of land becomes a very significant factor indeed.

Of more direct concern to a pavement engineer is the issue of secondary blight; that is environmental destruction caused by the action of pavement construction. The obvious example is quarrying. There may be almost inexhaustible supplies of rock, but there are certainly not inexhaustible supplies of beautiful countryside – nor indeed of farm land. Thus, anything the pavement engineer can do to maximise use of recycled materials or industrial by-products and minimise extraction of virgin rock (or gravel) contributes to environmental sustainability. This calls for innovation. It is necessary to look beyond tried-and-tested products and to design pavements which are

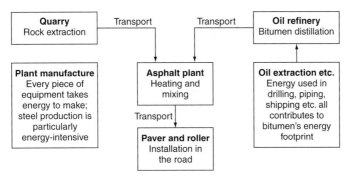

Fig. 3.1 The energy footprint of asphalt

able to accommodate materials that may have slightly different properties than those engineers have become used to over the years. In fact, this is one of the greatest challenges facing the pavement industry in many parts of the world.

3.1.3.3 Energy usage

Every component in a pavement apart from the natural subgrade has an energy associated with its production, transport, placement and compaction. For example, Fig. 3.1 illustrates the energy 'footprint' of asphalt pavement construction.

When the details are considered, such as the energy taken to produce steel – less the saving when that steel is reused at the end of the life of a particular piece of equipment – then the calculation is clearly complex. Fortunately researchers have painstakingly investigated these issues, narrowing down the uncertainty levels involved, so it is only necessary for those carrying out energy analyses to multiply the tonnage of each pavement material by the relevant figures for production, transportation etc. Part 1 (Section 1.1.5.2) has already listed approximate 'embedded' energies associated with different pavement materials, and it is worth recalling that both concrete and hot-mix asphalt score poorly, due to the high energy consumption in cement production and in heating the ingredients of asphalt. Even cold-mix bituminous products are not without their energy needs.

However, Part 1 made the point that there is a more significant energy issue, namely the energy consumed by vehicles driving on the pavement – and this will differ between pavement types. Unfortunately, it is not possible to report in a definitive manner at present, but it appears that the surface affects fuel consumption in two primary ways.

1. Surface deflection under (moving) load is equivalent to the vehicle continually having to travel uphill. Thus, a stiff pavement is beneficial.
2. Vibration induced in the tyre is a source of energy loss (and therefore fuel consumption). A smooth pavement is therefore beneficial.

The first point leads to the conclusion that a concrete pavement is the most fuel efficient – but not if it induces a rough ride and tyre vibration. The smoothest ride from the point of view of tyre vibration is given by small aggregate-size negative-textured asphalt surfaces (e.g. porous asphalt). Logically, therefore, the most efficient pavement of all may be one with a concrete structure but a thin asphalt surface (with appropriate texture). Research is ongoing, but claims and counterclaims sometimes speak in terms of differences in fuel consumption in the order of 10%. But how significant is this? On lane 1 of a busy highway, the traffic flow may be around 30 000 vehicles per day. If the average fuel consumption is 7 km per litre (assuming a high goods vehicle percentage), this equates to a fuel demand of around 4 litres per metre per day, approximately 140 MJ of energy per metre per day. Over an assumed lifetime for the surface course of ten years, this gives 500 GJ per metre, and a mere 1% change in fuel consumption would therefore involve 5 GJ per metre, equivalent to fuel costing about £50 in real terms (in 2007).

This can be compared with the embedded energy in the pavement. For example, a typical asphalt surface course with a 6% binder content might be valued at around 800 MJ per tonne, equivalent to about 300 MJ per metre of 3.65 m wide lane 40 mm thick. On this basis, therefore, the influence of surfacing type on fuel consumption looks to be very significant indeed. Even if the full pavement is considered, with a probable total embedded energy of something like 2 GJ per lane-metre, it is still well worth taking the effect on fuel consumption into account, particularly since the life of the structure as a whole is likely to be at least 20 years rather than the ten years assumed for a surface course. And in cold financial terms the issue is, if anything, even starker. A lane-metre of major highway costs about £150; if a £50 saving to the economy is on offer over ten years simply by designing for low fuel consumption, this is most definitely worth taking.

This issue has, frankly, been ignored for too long, and it is to be hoped that sufficient political will can be brought to bear such that the energy (and consequent financial) equation is allowed to influence spending policy.

3.1.3.4 Emissions

Many emissions can be tied directly to energy. The same litre of fuel which is approximately equivalent to 35 MJ of energy is also responsible for 2.3 kg of CO_2. When considering non-transport-related energy such as that needed to produce cement or run an asphalt plant, the quantity of emissions depends on the method of power generation, whether fossil fuel, hydroelectric, nuclear etc.; and every country will have a different and continually changing balance between different modes. Thus generalisation is impossible. The example in Calculation Sheet 3.1 uses Swedish data,[1] and therefore assumes a high proportion of hydroelectric and nuclear power, which makes asphalt appear less environmentally unfriendly than would be the case in many countries. But even in Sweden the quantities of CO_2 are significant when compared to the typical carbon footprint for an average UK citizen, currently about 11.8 t per year.

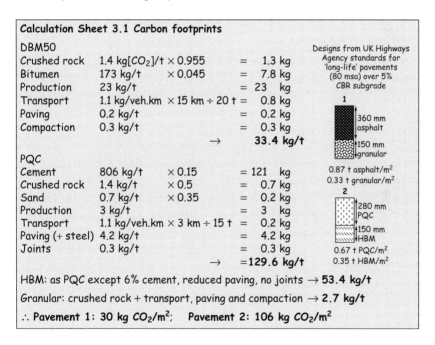

Calculation Sheet 3.1 Carbon footprints

DBM50 — Designs from UK Highways Agency standards for 'long-life' pavements (80 msa) over 5% CBR subgrade

Crushed rock	1.4 kg[CO_2]/t × 0.955	=	1.3 kg	
Bitumen	173 kg/t × 0.045	=	7.8 kg	
Production	23 kg/t	=	23 kg	
Transport	1.1 kg/veh.km × 15 km ÷ 20 t =		0.8 kg	
Paving	0.2 kg/t	=	0.2 kg	
Compaction	0.3 kg/t	=	0.3 kg	
		→	**33.4 kg/t**	

1: 360 mm asphalt / 150 mm granular — 0.87 t asphalt/m², 0.33 t granular/m²

PQC

Cement	806 kg/t × 0.15	=	121 kg	
Crushed rock	1.4 kg/t × 0.5	=	0.7 kg	
Sand	0.7 kg/t × 0.35	=	0.2 kg	
Production	3 kg/t	=	3 kg	
Transport	1.1 kg/veh.km × 3 km ÷ 15 t =		0.2 kg	
Paving (+ steel)	4.2 kg/t	=	4.2 kg	
Joints	0.3 kg/t	=	0.3 kg	
		→	**=129.6 kg/t**	

2: 280 mm PQC / 150 mm HBM — 0.67 t PQC/m², 0.35 t HBM/m²

HBM: as PQC except 6% cement, reduced paving, no joints → **53.4 kg/t**

Granular: crushed rock + transport, paving and compaction → **2.7 kg/t**

∴ **Pavement 1: 30 kg CO_2/m²;   Pavement 2: 106 kg CO_2/m²**

The reason why CO_2 is highlighted is because of its role in global warming, but many other emissions are also important in the sustainability equation. Nitrous oxide, sulphur dioxide, carbon monoxide and methane are all gases which in one way or another can damage either the environment or human health. They will not be discussed further here but the need to keep below dangerous limits affects the design of equipment such as asphalt batching plants and in situ recycling machines.

3.1.3.5 Groundwater issues

If a pavement is responsible for a loss of water resource due to harmful chemicals leaching into the groundwater, this clearly represents an unsustainable situation and must be avoided. Yet, the other side of the coin is that a pavement in itself generally diverts water into a drain rather than allowing it to percolate into the soil and replenish groundwater supplies. Thus, it depletes resources (and contributes to local flooding in storm conditions) just by its presence. There is therefore justifiable pressure to avoid this in some way, and Section 3.6.4 is included on the subject of 'drainage pavements'. Nevertheless, whether a pavement is specifically designed to allow water to percolate or not, there will always be the potential for harmful chemicals present on road surfaces to escape into groundwater, and various tests have been devised to combat this.

This is another area where significant disagreement is present. The problem is that, while tests can measure the presence of potentially harmful chemicals and can also measure the degree to which they escape into surrounding water, it is impossible to measure directly the degree to which they reach potential drinking water supplies.[2] In most cases, there is a long, slow process of percolation and the soil through which the water percolates tends to adsorb much (or even all) of the contaminant. Many engineers consider that rules such as are applied by environmental protection agencies have tended to be over-protective and may therefore be preventing optimised design. The point is that large stocks of waste materials have been and continue to be generated by industry and, as a planet, we need to treat this waste in a 'least worst' way; incorporation into pavement construction may just be that least worst solution.

3.1.4 Summary

The majority of this book is concerned with what might be described as engineering principles, the sphere of expertise of the engineer. However, all engineers should have an awareness of the context in which their engineering designs are to be applied, and this section has highlighted both the economic context and the issues of sustainability. These are not issues with which an engineer will usually be directly concerned – any more than an economist or an environmental expert will usually concern themselves with the details of engineering. However, if optimised solutions are truly to be found then these three parties need to be able to communicate, to speak each other's technical language. It is hoped that this section has provided the pavement engineer with some of the appropriate communication tools.

The rest of this part of the book is concerned with engineering design, commencing in the next section with a key design input, namely traffic. The following two sections cover design against the two principal structural failure modes, namely rutting and cracking, together lying right at the heart of pavement design. Most of the rest of Part 3 could be seen as a tying up of loose ends, dealing with durability, with non-standard pavements and surfacing design. Each is important, but none is central to pavement engineering. However, Section 3.8 is certainly much more than a loose end; it presents the concept of design reliability, i.e. the level of confidence which one can have that a given design will reach its intended life, and this is an area which pavement engineers should take a lot more seriously than is usual at present.

3.2

Traffic loading

The nature of the traffic using a pavement is the primary design input. Naturally, an airport runway taking large aircraft will require a different design from a highway or a port pavement, because of the differences in load magnitude, number of load applications, speed of travel and also tyre pressure. Clearly, this subject has the potential to be very complicated indeed, since most pavements will have to cater for a wide variety of different vehicles travelling at different speeds, and it is therefore necessary first to understand the importance of all the different variables and second to develop a means of simplifying the problem to something manageable.

3.2.1 Traffic variables

3.2.1.1 Load magnitude

Very obviously, damage to a pavement occurs much more rapidly under heavy loads than under light loads since every part of the structure will experience higher stresses. The question is: how much more rapidly? One could reflect on the fatigue characteristics of both hydraulically-bound and bitumen-bound material introduced in Part 2. For bitumen-bound material (i.e. asphalt), the appropriate characteristic was seen to be a linear relationship in logarithmic space between tensile strain and material life; this represents a power law equation. The exponent of that power law, being the slope of the characteristic in logarithmic space, is typically between 4 and 5 (or 0.2–0.25 depending on which way the equation is written). In the case of hydraulically-bound materials, the characteristic is a straight line in semi-logarithmic space, which is less convenient to interpret. However, in the range

210

typically applying in the pavement, with a computed tensile stress between about 0.3 and 0.4 of the flexural strength, the characteristic is approximately equivalent to a power law with an exponent of about 12.

The other principal mode of pavement deterioration, namely permanent deformation, is even harder to express mathematically. The equation for permanent deformation in unbound material introduced in Part 2, for example, suggests to a first approximation that an increase in applied stress will give an inversely proportional decrease in the logarithm of number of load applications (to reach a given level of permanent strain). In the normal operating range for highways, subject to between 10^7 and 10^8 load applications, this is equivalent to a power law with an exponent of 7; for airfields, with lower traffic numbers, the exponent would be nearer 4.

More complicated still is the problem of deformation in asphalt, for which no equation was offered in Part 2. The first problem is that an asphalt's resistance to rutting is derived in part from the aggregate skeleton but also from the binder. If the binder effect dominates, and if bitumen is considered as a linear viscous material, then a linear power law (i.e. exponent = 1) is appropriate; if the aggregate dominates then the power will rise to be closer to that for deformation of unbound material. But even these deductions only apply if the contact stress rises with increasing load, since stress within the asphalt will principally be a function of contact stress. If there is no increase in stress (i.e. same tyre pressure; larger contact area), there will be little increase in deformation.

The reader should by now be getting an impression of a quite impractical level of complexity. It is important to be aware of these points, but it is also important to move forward. If a theoretical approach presents such difficulties, what about an empirical one? In the late 1950s, the American Association of State Highway Officials (AASHO) undertook an extensive series of pavement trials using controlled trafficking with known loads.[3] Their conclusion was that, despite considerable scatter in the data, use of a fourth power relationship between load level and number of load applications needed to cause failure was appropriate – and most of the world has opted to take this approach ever since. So ingrained is this assumption that it is even known as the *Fourth Power Law* and may be expressed thus:

No. of equivalent design axles (N_{eq})

$$= [\text{axle load } (P)/\text{design axle load } (P_{des})]^4$$

Therefore, if P is twice the design axle load P_{des}, it will do 16 times the damage of a design axle.

Some organisations have considered they can do better – for example, an exponent of 4.5 is used in the UK Transport Research Laboratory design guide 'Road Note 31'.[4] It is clearly justifiable to take a different exponent for different types of pavement or for different distress modes. A low exponent is theoretically appropriate for asphalt rutting whereas the brittle behaviour of hydraulically-bound materials would theoretically demand a very high value. However, this is not a critical issue in most design approaches, since design standards will inevitably be calibrated to give an appropriate design when the specified exponent is used. It is also true that, when a typical set of axle loads found on a highway is converted to an equivalent number of design axle loads, the exponent actually matters remarkably little. Calculation Sheet 3.2 spells out the required computation and illustrates the sensitivity to overloading when a high exponent is used. In general, an exponent of 4 gives an approximate minimum number of equivalent design axles for highway traffic, but exponents within the range 2 to 6 give increases of no more than about 15%, which makes relatively little difference to pavement design. However, the reader is warned that the choice of exponent may be more significant for airfields or industrial pavements, or for calculations relating to occasional overloading.

In conclusion, therefore, the fourth power law appears to be a practical and sufficiently correct means of converting a real axle load spectrum to an equivalent number of design axles for highway pavements. However, the engineer should appreciate that the real effect of load variation will be quite different depending on which mode of damage is being considered, and fatigue of hydraulically-bound material is the most load-sensitive mode of all.

3.2.1.2 Contact pressure

The contact zone between a pneumatic rubber tyre and the road surface is by no means simple since both the tyre and the surface are 'textured', reducing the contact to a series of discontinuous areas. However, this is much too complex for practical pavement engineering, even though many researchers believe that this uneven distribution of stress is responsible for crack initiation at the road surface. Practical considerations dictate that a uniform pressure distribution is assumed, and it is logical to make the assumption that the contact pressure is equal to the internal pressure of the tyre.

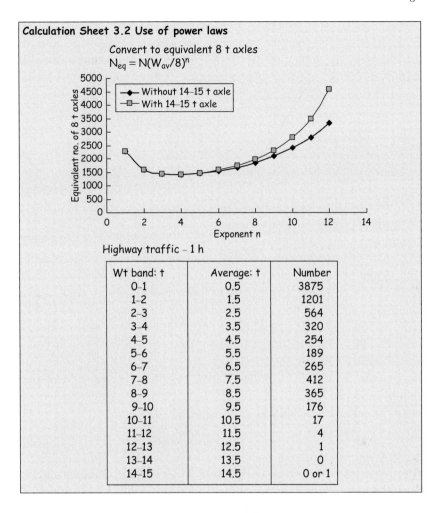

Calculation Sheet 3.2 Use of power laws

Convert to equivalent 8 t axles

$$N_{eq} = N(W_{av}/8)^n$$

Highway traffic – 1 h

Wt band: t	Average: t	Number
0–1	0.5	3875
1–2	1.5	1201
2–3	2.5	564
3–4	3.5	320
4–5	4.5	254
5–6	5.5	189
6–7	6.5	265
7–8	7.5	412
8–9	8.5	365
9–10	9.5	176
10–11	10.5	17
11–12	11.5	4
12–13	12.5	1
13–14	13.5	0
14–15	14.5	0 or 1

In fact, despite this being both logical and practical, it is far from being true. Tyre walls, reinforced with steel, are stiff enough to attract load, and the result is that the pressure is highest at the two edges of the contact zone and less in the middle[5] but, although this may well influence the development of surface distress, polishing of surface aggregate and noise generation, it is not generally considered significant for the deeper pavement structure and so is commonly ignored. In practice, the tyre pressure is usually assumed also to be the contact pressure, around 250 kPa for a car, 600 kPa for a large truck, 1000–1500 kPa for commercial aircraft and up to 3000 kPa for some military planes. The final simplification often made for purposes of pavement analysis is that the contact area is circular.

Pressure is not generally explicitly taken into account when converting a spectrum of load cases into an equivalent number of design axles or design wheel loads because of the complexity this would introduce, but it is very important that an appropriate contact pressure is assumed in pavement analysis.

3.2.1.3 Load groups

This is an important concept. Wheels often tend to be close enough together for there to be an interaction of effects in the pavement. The case of a dual tyre arrangement on a commercial truck is an extreme one, in which the loads are so close together that they almost act as if they were a single wheel carrying the combined load. Tandem and tridem axles on trucks tend to be spaced at least 1.3 m apart and, although adjacent wheels combine in their effect on the pavement, that combination does not usually add any significant stress at critical levels in the structure. In the case of dual, dual tandem or dual tridem wheel gear arrangements on aircraft however, the increased load magnitude means that the combination can, under some circumstances, comprise the critical design case. The same is true of certain port pavement loading equipment. The important issue for the designer is that the possibility that the combined load case may be the critical one should never be overlooked, even though it may often turn out not to be so. Figure 3.2 illustrates likely design cases conceptually.

3.2.1.4 Dynamic effects

No matter how efficient the suspension system fitted, all moving wheel loads fluctuate as the vehicle body oscillates vertically. Some suspension

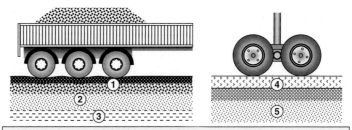

1. Asphalt layers unaffected by adjacent loads
2. Upper subgrade under asphalt also probably only influenced by individual loads
3. Lower subgrade affected by combined loads – but rarely a key design case
4. Concrete often affected by load combinations
5. Subgrade under aircraft loads usually affected by combined loads

Fig. 3.2 The effect of wheel load combinations

systems, notably air suspension, are more effective than others at avoiding high oscillating loads, but a certain level of dynamic load is inevitable. Furthermore, oscillation is unlikely to be purely vertical, and side-to-side oscillation results in a fluctuating imbalance between the loads on the left and right of the vehicle. When combined with cornering, particularly cornering where the radius is continually changing, the additional load on one side of the vehicle can be considerable; it is common to observe that road pavements suffer much greater damage on the outer wheel path of a curve compared to the inner wheel path. When considering the loading from certain industrial vehicles, such as reach-stackers, fork-lift trucks or rubber-tyred gantry cranes, the stop–start nature of the movements involved also tends to induce significant additional dynamic forces.

However, it is not the place of this book to discuss suspension systems or industrial plant operation. The pavement designer simply has to be able to estimate the degree of dynamic load to take into account. Some design approaches use a 'dynamic load factor', a multiplier used to convert the static load to a maximum likely dynamic load value. But the key question is just what the effect of this dynamic load is likely to be on pavement design and Calculation Sheet 3.3 presents an analysis assuming that the load variation is a sinusoidal one and referring back to the power laws introduced in Section 3.2.1.1. As may be observed, the effect of vertical oscillation is small enough on most highway pavements to be ignored, but becomes significant if a high exponent of damage is used or the dynamic load factor increases to 1.4 or more, something which could occur on roads with poor longitudinal profile.

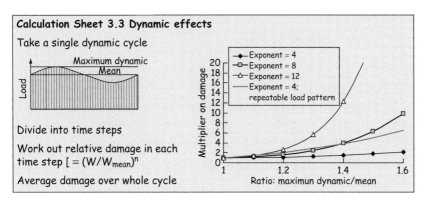

Calculation Sheet 3.3 Dynamic effects

Take a single dynamic cycle

Load — Maximum dynamic / Mean

Divide into time steps

Work out relative damage in each time step $[= (W/W_{mean})^n$

Average damage over whole cycle

Multiplier on damage vs Ratio: maximun dynamic/mean

Exponent = 4
Exponent = 8
Exponent = 12
Exponent = 4; repeatable load pattern

The first three curves in Calculation Sheet 3.3 make the assumption that the distribution of dynamic load is random. However, there is

215

plenty of evidence to show that this is often not the case and that similar vehicles, having similar suspension system characteristics, will tend to apply peak loads in roughly the same locations. The fourth curve shown makes the assumption that the loading pattern is perfectly repeatable, in which case the computed damage would occur at regular intervals along the pavement, corresponding with peak dynamic load locations. This effect is sometimes clearly visible in the form of regularly spaced areas of damage, particularly on relatively low-strength roads. On industrial pavements such as ports, dynamic load factors are sometimes applied generally in design in recognition of the fact that some peak dynamic loads reoccur at the same points, a function of the way the plant is operated.

Calculation Sheet 3.4 illustrates the imbalance in damage between the outer and inner wheel paths on a curve, a matter which should ideally be taken into account in design. However, it rarely is, on the principle that 'simplicity is elegance' – but it probably should be, especially at junctions and roundabouts, where maintenance nuisance is greatest.

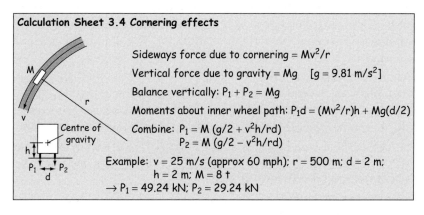

Calculation Sheet 3.4 Cornering effects

Sideways force due to cornering $= Mv^2/r$

Vertical force due to gravity $= Mg$ $[g = 9.81 \text{ m/s}^2]$

Balance vertically: $P_1 + P_2 = Mg$

Moments about inner wheel path: $P_1 d = (Mv^2/r)h + Mg(d/2)$

Combine: $P_1 = M (g/2 + v^2h/rd)$

$P_2 = M (g/2 - v^2h/rd)$

Example: $v = 25$ m/s (approx 60 mph); $r = 500$ m; $d = 2$ m; $h = 2$ m; $M = 8$ t

$\rightarrow P_1 = 49.24$ kN; $P_2 = 29.24$ kN

Centre of gravity

3.2.1.5 Loading speed

Vehicle speed is an important contributing factor to dynamic load; a slow rate of travel will not induce significant vertical oscillation. However, it is also an important input into design for two further reasons:

1. Asphalt is a loading-rate dependent material because of the viscous nature of bitumen.
2. Soils and granular materials at high levels of saturation may suffer from positive pore pressures (and therefore low strength and stiffness) at high loading rates.

Thus, an appreciation of the loading rate is essential if appropriate design stiffnesses are to be selected, both for asphalt and for certain unbound materials. The difference between the loading rate imposed by traffic and that generated during testing must also be taken into account when interpreting such test data.

3.2.1.6 *Lateral wander*
A final factor which is sometimes taken into account is the fact that not every wheel follows the same path. On highways, the distribution across a wheel path commonly has a standard deviation of around 150 mm; on airport runways this is likely to be a metre or more. It should therefore be permissible to apply a reduction factor to derive the actual number of load applications felt by an individual point on the pavement. On roads, this reduction factor is usually neglected as too small to worry about, although some design manuals apply factors of up to 2 depending on lane width.[6] For airfields the effect is much more significant, on runways at least, and a factor of 2 or more is sometimes applied.[7] Designers should beware of applying this to taxiways, however, which are much more like highways in terms of the spatial repeatability of the loads.

3.2.2 Determining design traffic
The simple, practical way to translate real traffic loads into a convenient input parameter for design (or evaluation) is to convert everything into equivalent numbers of a single *design load*. On a highway, it is common to speak of a *standard axle*, the design wheel load generally being one half of a standard axle load; on airfields, traffic is expressed in terms of a *design aircraft*. In some cases it may prove impossible to convert everything to a single design case because of the differences between different load types. Thus, port pavements are commonly checked for their resistance to container foot loading as well as vehicular traffic. Fork-lift trucks may have solid rubber tyres and thus may impose a quite different pressure to the surface compared to pneumatic-tyred vehicles; designs may have to be checked for both. However, the usual situation is for all traffic to be expressed in equivalent numbers of a design load case.

Since the damage done by a vehicle to the pavement is much more than linearly proportional to applied load, the design load case should logically be at the heavy end of the spectrum; in the case of airfields or industrial pavements it will commonly be the largest load case of

217

all. Typical design cases for highway traffic characterisation are 80 or 100 kN axle loads, 80 kN being in use in the UK (with approximately the same load – 18 kips – in the US).

Having determined the appropriate design load, the next step is to determine the expected spectrum of loads during the design life of the pavement. This is sometimes carried out by direct measurement of existing traffic loads using a weigh-in-motion device, but it would be more usual to count/predict the types and numbers of vehicles and to assume typical axle loads for each. These axle loads can then be converted into equivalent design load applications by means of the fourth power law, or such other power law as may be preferred – see earlier discussion in Section 3.2.1.1.

There are also many direct methods contained in design manuals which do not require any prediction of the full axle load spectrum. For example:

- The UK Highways Agency documentation gives multipliers, known as *damage factors* or *wear factors*,[8] to convert from projected numbers of commercial vehicles or, for existing roads, from counts of different types of commercial vehicle (number of axles, rigid or articulated) to a number of equivalent standard axles. Similar techniques can be found in the design advice of most other countries, differences reflecting the significantly different traffic characteristics (vehicle types, permitted and actual axle loads etc.).
- Airfield design methods such as that developed by the Federal Aviation Authority[9] in the US allow conversion based on the applied wheel load of each aircraft. The widely used Defence Estates guide,[10] issued in the UK, makes use of the International Civil Aviation Organisation (ICAO) method of classifying damaging power, namely the *Aircraft Classification Number*.[11]

Whichever method is used, the result will be an equivalent number of design load cases, for example 'equivalent standard axle loads' (otherwise known as *esals*). In many cases that will be sufficient, since empirical design methods then implicitly assume appropriate traffic speed, tyre pressure and dynamic effects. Thus, when using the 1993 AASHTO Design Guide, for example, it is sufficient to find a number of *esals*; the same is true of Highways Agency design documentation in the UK. It is only if an analytical design (or pavement evaluation) is to be attempted that it is necessary to consider anything further. However, as soon as computational analysis of a pavement is to be performed, then contact pressure, load enhancement due to dynamic effects, and lateral wander all have to be considered. Furthermore, loading speed, while it does not affect the design load itself, will certainly affect the stiffness moduli selected for some of the pavement layers.

3.2.3 Summary

Because of the very different nature of the loads experienced by different pavement types (highways, airfields, ports, footways, car parks etc.), it is not possible to give absolute general rules for the expression or prediction of traffic. However, the goal is to determine: (1) a design load case and; (2) a number of load applications. It should always be remembered that expression of traffic in this way is approximate and that predictions are fraught with uncertainty. For these reasons a practical approach is urged, erring on the side of caution but not being over-concerned to generate precise predictions. As will become apparent, even a significant error in predicted traffic numbers usually has only minor influence on pavement design thickness. Selection of an appropriate design load case is, however, much more critical.

3.3

Design against rutting

The formation of a rut along a wheel path is due to internal straining within one or more pavement layers. It is the most basic form of pavement distress. The primary reason for building a pavement structure on top of the natural subgrade is that it would otherwise not be able to withstand the applied load, i.e. it would rut. The first element of design is therefore to ensure that the pavement is thick enough, stiff enough and strong enough to give the subgrade the protection it needs.

3.3.1 Subgrade deformation

Permanent, plastic deformation under repeated load is a fact of life for all unbound materials. The trick is to make sure that the strains involved are small enough not to matter, and this means keeping the stresses well within the failure envelope. Part 2 introduced the typical forms of behaviour, including one possible equation (of many) for modelling permanent deformation, and for pavement design the key is to be able to relate the nearness to failure of the stresses within the subgrade to the rate of permanent strain (and therefore rut) accumulation. The following subsections will explore the art of the possible.

3.3.1.1 The real behaviour of soils

The first problem is that soils come in numerous different varieties and it is unrealistic to expect a clay, for example, to behave in exactly the same way as a sand. Figure 3.3 shows examples of laboratory tests carried out in the triaxial equipment on a soft clay and an angular sand, and the data are presented in the form of strain against number of load applications for different values of a *stress ratio*, representing

220

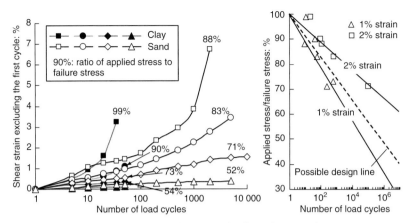

Fig. 3.3 Permanent deformation behaviour of unbound materials

closeness to failure. Naturally there are differences between the two materials, but it is perhaps surprising the degree to which the curves actually match when plotted in this way. In fact, for a given value of shear strain, it is quite feasible to produce a generalised plot of number of load applications against stress ratio, applicable to both the clay and the sand; this is shown on the right of Fig. 3.3, for strains of 1 and 2%.

Here, then, is a possible design approach. It requires a knowledge of the strength parameters of the soil (so that the stress ratio can be calculated) but, where these data are available, they provide a logical way forward. However, to put this approach into practice, the stress conditions within the subgrade must now be calculated.

3.3.1.2 Multi-layer linear elastic analysis

This method of analysis forms the backbone to analytical pavement design. However, this book will not delve into the actual techniques by which the analysis is performed – it is sufficient to be aware that there are a number of computer programs on the market, all of which are capable of solving the problem. The solutions are not exact, but they are close enough to be accepted as such for all practical purposes.

Multi-layer linear elastic analysis assumes the following:

- layers are composed of homogeneous linear elastic material
- horizontal extent is infinite
- layer thickness is uniform
- load of uniform pressure is applied over a circular contact area.

In most analyses perfect bond is assumed between layers, although some programs allow this to be varied. Similarly, most analyses consider only vertical load, but some programs give the option of horizontal load also. Since the system is purely linear elastic, it is always possible to superpose the effects of different loads, and this allows computation of behaviour under a wheel group, or to simulate a real non-circular load contact zone using a series of circular loads. In fact, so long as the idealised nature of the system is appreciated it is possible to model a pavement structure reasonably effectively. The input data required are:

- the magnitude and contact area of all applied loads
- the elastic modulus and Poisson's ratio of all layers
- the thickness of all layers
- the bond condition (slip stiffness) between layers – usually considered infinite.

Therefore, returning to the problem of predicting deformation behaviour in a subgrade, it is necessary to estimate elastic modulus and Poisson's ratio for all pavement layers including the subgrade itself and then to analyse under the action of a 'design load'. The program will calculate any desired stress, strain or deformation within the entire multi-layer structure, and for purposes of this design element, the stresses required are the maximum vertical and horizontal stresses and strains at the top of the subgrade.

3.3.1.3 Calculating closeness to failure

The traffic-imposed stresses calculated using multi-layer linear elastic analysis, together with any additional stress due to overburden, can be expressed as a Mohr circle, as shown in Fig. 3.4 for a structure representing a thinly surfaced road; σ_h is the computed horizontal stress, σ_v is the vertical stress. The designer's best estimate of the failure parameters for that particular subgrade material can then be added in the form of a failure line – as shown. Figure 3.4 also shows a second Mohr circle, representing the stress condition at failure.

In the example shown in Fig. 3.4, the stress ratio calculated at the top of the subgrade, 60%, can be compared with the examples of actual soil behaviour shown in Fig. 3.3. In the plot on the right of Fig. 3.3, it is necessary to choose a limiting strain value and, while it is impossible to give general rules, it is suggested here that 2% is reasonably conservative, i.e. it represents a suitably small rut depth. On that basis,

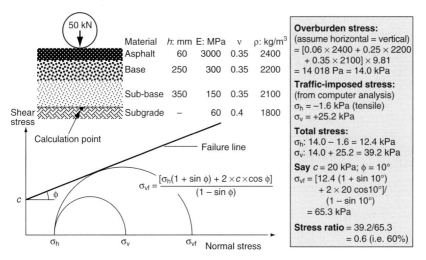

Fig. 3.4 Defining stress ratio at top of subgrade

the pavement structure shown in Fig. 3.4 could withstand about 10^7 applications of a 50 kN load.

This is a reasonable prediction – but it definitely does not represent a safe design. The consequences of subgrade failure are so serious that there has to be a significant factor of safety built in, covering the fact that not all soils will behave as the two shown in Fig. 3.3 and that estimation of soil strength parameters is not an exact science. A suggested safe design line is shown in Fig. 3.3, implying that the pavement in Fig. 3.4 should only actually be rated for around 10^4–10^5 load applications. A 10^7 load application design would need the stress ratio to be reduced to around 40% rather than 60%, requiring a significantly thicker structure.

It may appear that this method of prediction is both complex and fraught with uncertainty. However, multi-layer linear elastic analysis is a readily available and user-friendly method nowadays (2008). The chief difficulty undoubtedly lies in estimating the relevant soil parameters, particularly c and ϕ, making allowance for long-term condition.

3.3.1.4 The subgrade strain criterion

Recognising the difficulties involved in soil parameter estimation, most of the current analytical design methods use the so-called 'subgrade strain criterion'. This represents a massive simplification – and relies on a massive assumption. The assumption is that the strength of a soil is directly related to its stiffness. That this is not generally true has already been shown in Part 2, since strength depends principally on such parameters as particle shape and void content, whereas stiffness depends more on the frictional properties at particle contact points. Nevertheless, over a limited range of soils, for example UK heavy clays, it may be close enough to being true to be usable. The argument goes like this:

- life (to a limiting rut depth) = *fn* [stress/strength] – as in Fig. 3.3
- if: strength = *fn* [stiffness modulus] …
- … then: life = *fn* [stress/stiffness modulus] = *fn* [elastic strain].

The great advantage of this assumption is that it is only necessary to calculate the elastic strain value in the subgrade under load, i.e. the vertical elastic strain at the top of the subgrade.

Various relationships between subgrade elastic strain and life have been proposed in numerous different design manuals. In most cases they are based on real evidence of performance and so, within the range of subgrades and pavements encountered in gathering that evidence, they should prove to be practical. For example, the equation proposed by the UK Transport Research Laboratory in 1984[12] is likely to be approximately suitable for roads on UK clay soils. Similarly, the equation adopted by the National Association of Australian State Road Authorities[13] is likely to be suited to typical Australian soils and Australian pavement structures. When moving outside such experience however, for example as in the British Airports Authority design guide,[14] it is necessary to rethink – and to use different equations.

In this book the decision has been taken not to specifically recommend any of the many available equations; each is geared to the particular conditions applying over a range of pavements carrying specific types of traffic in a specific climate. It is a reasonable course of action to use them in design, but it is not a reasonable course of action to believe them unquestioningly. Thought should always be given to the actual type of soil applying. It should be appreciated, for example, that sandy soils will tend to have a quite different relationship between strength and stiffness modulus from that of clay soils, the effect of which is that they can carry many times the number of load applications – for a given level of computed elastic strain.[15]

3.3.1.5 Dealing with water

It is hard to overstate the importance of the water issue. One of the great unknowns in pavement design in many parts of the world is

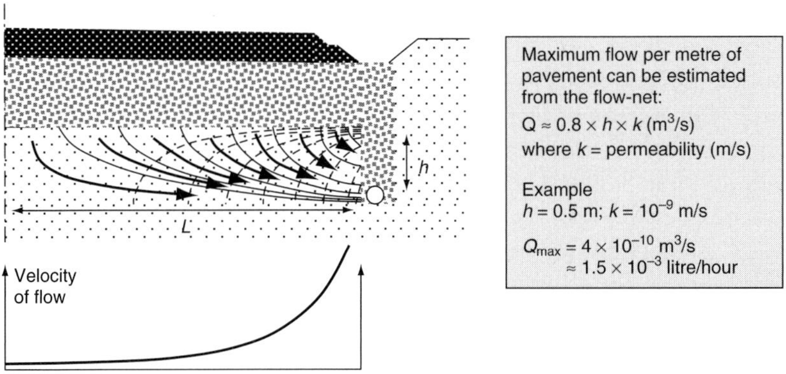
h
L
Velocity
of flow
Maximum flow per metre of
pavement can be estimated
from the flow-net:
Q ≈ 0.8 × h × k (m³/s)
where k = permeability (m/s)
Example
h = 0.5 m; k = 10⁻⁹ m/s
Qmax = 4 × 10⁻¹⁰ m³/s
≈ 1.5 × 10⁻³ litre/hour

Fig. 3.5 Estimated flow through the subgrade to a subsoil drain

the long-term equilibrium water content within a subgrade soil and the location of the water table. Good construction practice should minimise the damage done to the soil during construction, but long-term design depends on such matters as the effectiveness of pavement sealing and subsoil drainage. Of course, many designs have to be carried out in the full knowledge that the pavement will remain unsealed, or that no subsoil drain will be included, but the key point is that the pavement designer needs to be able to make appropriate assumptions for the long term. The principal pieces of information required are:

- the level of the water table
- the likely inflow of water through the pavement
- the permeability of the subgrade.

The *level of the water table* may be a function of natural ground conditions or it may be determined by the presence of a side drain. Figure 3.5 illustrates the effect of a drain. For details of calculations using a flow net, see specialist geotechnical texts.

The second piece of information required, the *inflow through the pavement*, cannot in practice be known. However, it should never be presumed to be zero. Joints and cracks are the main points of entry. Calculation Sheet 3.5 presents a prediction of the likely inflow through a crack under conditions of heavy rainfall, i.e. continuous water presence at the surface, and the conclusion is that a joint in a concrete pavement, with a width of 0.5 mm – typical of a cold day – will allow about 18 litres of water per metre length of joint per minute, assuming that the pavement foundation can accept such a large inflow. A narrow (say 0.2 mm) crack in a thick asphalt pavement would still let in 1.2 litres per metre per minute. Nor should the permeability of 'solid' asphalt be presumed to be zero; measurements are not commonly made, but a permeability of between 10^{-6} and 10^{-7} m/s is typical of a dense asphalt,[16] increasing by an order of magnitude for every 3% additional air voids. This means that even a dense crack-free asphalt pavement will allow some 6 ml of water to pass through each square metre every minute during heavy rain. A cracked pavement may allow several litres per square metre per minute. This is a significant volume of water and is certainly likely to cause subgrade softening.

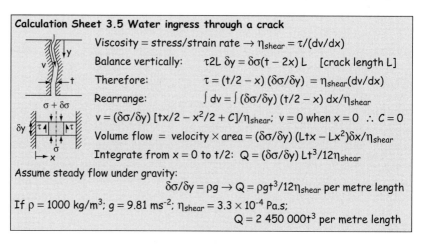

Calculation Sheet 3.5 Water ingress through a crack

Viscosity = stress/strain rate $\rightarrow \eta_{shear} = \tau/(dv/dx)$

Balance vertically: $\quad \tau 2L\,\delta y = \delta\sigma(t - 2x)\,L \quad$ [crack length L]

Therefore: $\quad \tau = (t/2 - x)\,(\delta\sigma/\delta y) = \eta_{shear}(dv/dx)$

Rearrange: $\quad \int dv = \int (\delta\sigma/\delta y)\,(t/2 - x)\,dx/\eta_{shear}$

$v = (\delta\sigma/\delta y)\,[tx/2 - x^2/2 + C]/\eta_{shear};\ v = 0$ when $x = 0 \ \therefore C = 0$

Volume flow $=$ velocity $\times$ area $= (\delta\sigma/\delta y)\,(Ltx - Lx^2)\delta x/\eta_{shear}$

Integrate from $x = 0$ to $t/2$: $\quad Q = (\delta\sigma/\delta y)\,Lt^3/12\eta_{shear}$

Assume steady flow under gravity:
$$\delta\sigma/\delta y = \rho g \rightarrow Q = \rho g t^3/12\eta_{shear} \text{ per metre length}$$

If $\rho = 1000$ kg/m^3; $g = 9.81$ ms^{-2}; $\eta_{shear} = 3.3 \times 10^{-4}$ Pa.s;
$$Q = 2\,450\,000t^3 \text{ per metre length}$$

The third piece of input information needed, *subgrade permeability*, determines how rapidly water will be drained and so where the local water table is likely to be. Figure 3.5 illustrates the worst-case scenario of a subgrade surface which hasn't been shaped to encourage sideways runoff.

There is clearly the potential for the ingress of water through the surface to exceed the natural ability of the subgrade to 'process' it. Excess water should simply drain off through the granular sub-base or capping material, but it means that, during rain, there would be a continual supply of water covering the surface of the subgrade. The likelihood of material softening is obvious.

To summarise the implications from this subsection:

- A subsoil drain is vital in cases where water ingress is likely to exceed the drainage capacity of the subgrade.
- Even with a drain, it is likely that water will have access to the surface of the subgrade for long periods.

- Sealing of the pavement is enormously important in reducing water access to the subgrade.

However thorough the precautions taken, it is clear that a sensible designer should always make allowance for the likelihood that some long-term increase in subgrade water content will occur.

3.3.1.6 Subgrade softening

The concepts of plastic limit (PL) and liquid limit (LL) were introduced in Part 2, and the entirely different behaviour of soil at these two extremes is reflected in large differences in both stiffness and strength. Water content increase is therefore highly undesirable.

In many soils, the natural water content is around the PL, held at that level by the downward suction effect imposed by a water table at depth. When additional water is provided at the surface of the subgrade, this will immediately be subject to this suction effect and so will begin to be absorbed into the subgrade material. As it penetrates, the water content will increase, which has the effect of reducing the suction. This effect can be predicted so long as it is possible to assign a permeability and an initial water content, using the relationship between suction and water content introduced in Part 2 (Section 2.1.4.6). Calculation Sheet 3.6 outlines the procedure.

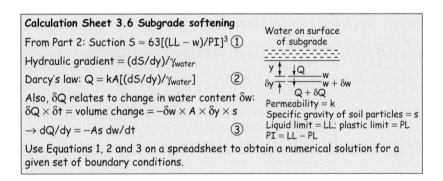

Calculation Sheet 3.6 Subgrade softening

From Part 2: Suction $S \approx 63[(LL - w)/PI]^3$ ①

Hydraulic gradient $= (dS/dy)/\gamma_{water}$

Darcy's law: $Q = kA[(dS/dy)/\gamma_{water}]$ ②

Also, δQ relates to change in water content δw:
$\delta Q \times \delta t = $ volume change $= -\delta w \times A \times \delta y \times s$

$\rightarrow dQ/dy = -As\, dw/dt$ ③

Water on surface of subgrade

Permeability $= k$
Specific gravity of soil particles $= s$
Liquid limit $= LL$; plastic limit $= PL$
$PI = LL - PL$

Use Equations 1, 2 and 3 on a spreadsheet to obtain a numerical solution for a given set of boundary conditions.

The result of carrying out such a calculation is that, even with a permeability of 10^{-9} m/s, it only takes a few days for a significantly wetted (and therefore weakened) zone to develop. If it is assumed that the water content remains constant at a certain depth (due to natural drainage), then a stable equilibrium soon develops, as illustrated in Fig. 3.6, an equilibrium which is independent of subgrade permeability.

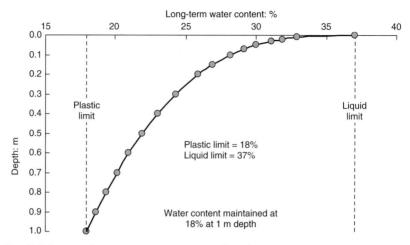

Fig. 3.6 *Increased water content in upper subgrade; continuous wetting*

In fact, if the water content scale in Fig. 3.6 were to be replaced by liquidity index $[= (w - PL)/PI]$, then the result would be general to all soils.

The actual equilibrium will be a rather unstable one, between periods of rain, during which softening progresses, and drier periods, during which it retreats. The observed practical outcome from this in many cases is for a zone of softened soil between 100 and 500 mm thick to form at the top of the subgrade, a thick enough zone to undergo permanent deformation and so to influence pavement design. The soil parameters appropriate to this zone will depend on the effectiveness of pavement sealing and of drainage, but a water content some 5% above the previous natural water content of the soil is common. Strength and stiffness measurements may give values much less than half those of the underlying, drier soil.

Although accurate prediction is virtually impossible, the issue simply cannot be avoided; whether design is to be based on equilibrium CBR, subgrade strain or a stress ratio, a best estimate of strength and/or stiffness must be selected. The uncertainty involved is a significant contributor to overall uncertainty in pavement performance, an issue which will be taken up in Section 3.8.

3.3.1.7 Stabilised subgrades
It is to be hoped that a properly designed stabilised subgrade will be a significantly better engineering material than the parent soil – which means it effectively becomes a pavement layer and that any computation or prediction relating to the subgrade applies to the material immediately

underlying the stabilised layer. This in turn means that it should be possible to be a little more 'optimistic' regarding the long-term state. Water will certainly be able to permeate through the stabilised layer, but the supply reaching the level of the untreated subgrade will be less than would have been the case without the protection of the stabilised layer. Details will vary greatly from case to case, but a sensible approximation would be to assume that the permeability of the stabilised layer is the same as that of the parent soil. The equations in Calculation Sheet 3.6 can therefore be applied, approximately, but at a depth corresponding to the stabilisation depth.

3.3.2 Deformation in granular layers

While protection of the subgrade is the most basic pavement design requirement, it is of course also necessary to ensure that the overlying pavement layers themselves are strong enough not to deform excessively under load. It is not an aspect of design that is often explicitly taken into consideration, it being more usual to rely on material specifications for base and sub-base layers. Specifications in their turn are generally based on decades of experience and tend to be expressed in terms of general description ('crushed rock', 'crushed gravel', 'uncrushed gravel' etc.), sometimes including a required percentage of crushed faces and always including grading limits and density or compaction requirements. The unstated (and usually unappreciated) aim of such a specification is to ensure a suitably high angle of internal friction, giving a suitably high shear strength.

In most practical design cases, it is sufficient to assume that the specification is appropriate and not to calculate anything in more detail. However, this is not necessarily true of unbound or very thinly surfaced pavements. Also, questions sometimes arise such as: is it permissible to use an alternative material source, for example an industrial by-product? Or: can a particular pavement withstand a certain abnormal load? In such cases, the specification cannot be relied upon since the design has to deal with areas outside the experience upon which the specification is based. It is principally with these issues in mind that this section of the book is included.

3.3.2.1 *The elastic analysis approach*

So long as the granular layers are separated from the load by a respectable thickness of asphalt or concrete, it is not unreasonable to assume linear elastic material properties in the same way as has just been

229

suggested for subgrade stress or strain calculation. *Multi-layer linear elastic* analysis can then be used, assigning an elastic modulus and Poisson's ratio to each layer, and stresses and strains calculated under the design load.

The next step is to adapt one of the design approaches introduced in relation to subgrade deformation, much the simplest of which was the 'subgrade strain criterion'. Vertical strains can be computed at the top of each unbound layer in exactly the same way as for the subgrade, and an appropriate relationship used between strain and life. No rules can be given for this other than the general guidance that the relationship used should suit a granular rather than a clayey material.[17]

In theory, it would be possible to look at 'closeness to failure', as illustrated for the subgrade in Fig. 3.4. However, this is not advised for anything higher in the pavement structure than the subgrade. The assumption of linear elasticity leads to highly untrustworthy (often tensile) values of horizontal stress being calculated within the granular layers.

3.3.2.2 The plastic analysis approach

The term 'plastic analysis' means that a large-strain failure mechanism is analysed rather than a small-strain elastic mechanism. An alternative description commonly applied in structural design is 'limit state' analysis.

The philosophy behind this approach is that it is not really correct to consider a pavement one element at a time. The subgrade cannot deform without the sub-base and base deforming also; the combination of layers forms a single 'mechanism'. The situation is analogous to a strip of plywood. Some of the internal elements within the plywood may be weak and may easily reach their theoretical ultimate load, but the material will remain intact until the overall load is sufficient to break all the elements at the same time. Thus, a weak sub-base might, according to an elastic analysis, fail after a certain relatively low number of load applications – but in reality it can't if it is protected by a strong base; it will simply demand that an increasing level of stress is taken by the base.

Since the problem is one of a failure mechanism, it becomes effectively a *bearing capacity* calculation, as for building foundations etc. The bearing capacity formula under a circular load is very well known and widely used and is as follows:[18]

$$q_f = 1.3cN_c + 1.2p_oN_q + 0.3\gamma dN_\gamma$$

The parameters N_c, N_ϕ and N_γ are all functions of angle of internal friction ϕ and the following are the author's digitised versions of the curves first determined by Karl Terzaghi[19] (ϕ in degrees).

$$N_c = 5.5 + 0.32\phi + 3 \times 10^{-5}\phi^4$$

$$N_\phi = 1.0 + 0.12\phi + 9 \times 10^{-3}\phi^2 + 9 \times 10^{-12}\phi^8$$

$$N_\gamma = 6 \times 10^{-4}\phi^3 + 2.33 \times 10^{-21}\phi^{14}$$

The other parameters in the bearing capacity equation are the overburden stress p_o, the cohesion c, material unit weight γ and the diameter of the loaded area d. Thus, in the case of an unbound pavement consisting of uniform material, the equation can be used directly to estimate a failure stress q_f. The number of load repetitions can then be brought in by assuming that the whole system behaves in the same way as the two soils under triaxial conditions shown in Fig. 3.3. Thus, a reasonable design for 10^6 load applications would be to restrict the applied pressure to about 50% of q_f.

3.3.2.3 Plastic analysis of multi-layer structures

The relatively simple procedure outlined in the previous section can be applied to direct trafficking of a subgrade soil, but not for the more likely case of a multi-layer pavement. For this it is necessary to draw out a proposed failure mechanism consisting of slip planes within the various pavement layers and to calculate the shear and normal forces acting on those planes. The bearing capacity equation can only be applied to the lowest, semi-infinite layer. This is not straightforward. There is an infinite variety of possible failure plane combinations and, though the pavement will always take the easiest one, i.e. the path of least resistance, it is not obvious to the designer just where that path is. For this reason, the advice here is to restrict such analysis to a two-layer problem, combining layers of different material where necessary, and not to try to use it where bound materials (other than very thin asphalt) are involved. Figure 3.7 illustrates the two-layer case. The simplifying assumption is made that the failure planes will be at sufficient angle to ensure that normal stress R is zero; this means that θ is equal to the dilation angle, and a default value of $15°$ is suggested.[20]

Many of the assumptions made in Fig. 3.7 are debatable, and the result will clearly depend significantly on choice of angle θ. However, the procedure is certainly simple enough to be carried out on a

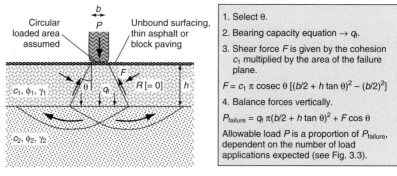

1. Select θ.
2. Bearing capacity equation $\rightarrow q_f$.
3. Shear force F is given by the cohesion c_1 multiplied by the area of the failure plane.

$$F = c_1 \pi \operatorname{cosec} \theta [(b/2 + h \tan \theta)^2 - (b/2)^2]$$

4. Balance forces vertically.

$$P_{\text{failure}} = q_f \pi (b/2 + h \tan \theta)^2 + F \cos \theta$$

Allowable load P is a proportion of P_{failure}, dependent on the number of load applications expected (see Fig. 3.3).

Fig. 3.7 Analysis of two-layer plastic failure

design spreadsheet. As in the previous section, the actual allowable load can be estimated with reference to the repeated load information given in Fig. 3.3.

Yet another alternative, readily achievable on a spreadsheet, is to divide the pavement into sub-layers, to derive an estimate for the stress conditions in each sub-layer and to compute the plastic strain in each sub-layer individually using an equation such as that given in Part 2 (Section 2.1.3.2). The overall deformation is then obtained by summing the plastic strains in each sub-layer. This approach is just about the only one which can actually give an estimate of the magnitude of rutting in a granular pavement. It will never be a confident estimate – that has to be appreciated – but it opens the door to a rational method of design when straying beyond the limits of past experience.

3.3.2.4 The effect of reinforcement

Plastic analysis also opens the door to design using reinforcement. There are essentially two mechanisms which have to be taken into account: first a redistribution of stress due to the tensile force taken by the reinforcement; and second a slowing of the rate of permanent strain under given stress conditions because of the interlock between the reinforcement and surrounding pavement material.

A means of estimating stress redistribution in an unbound pavement is presented in Calculation Sheet 3.7. The reduction in rate of accumulation of permanent strain under a given set of stress conditions is much harder to predict and is still subject to ongoing research; however, it may well be the more significant of the two mechanisms. It will depend on the details of reinforcement aperture size, shape and rib bending stiffness, as well as, probably, the unbound material itself. It is also yet to be established to what distance above or below the reinforcement this effect should be applied. With the current level of knowledge, a reasonable estimate for a high-quality reinforcing product might be a reduction factor of at least 4 on strain accumulation rate,[21] extending to a distance of at least 200 mm – but the reader should not be tempted to apply this in earnest without further evidence.

Calculation Sheet 3.7 Geogrid reinforcement of unbound pavements

Load spreading

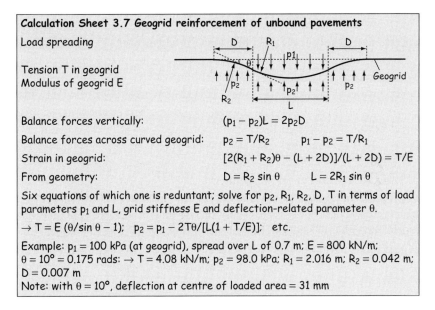

Tension T in geogrid
Modulus of geogrid E

Balance forces vertically:	$(p_1 - p_2)L = 2p_2D$	
Balance forces across curved geogrid:	$p_2 = T/R_2$	$p_1 - p_2 = T/R_1$
Strain in geogrid:	$[2(R_1 + R_2)\theta - (L + 2D)]/(L + 2D) = T/E$	
From geometry:	$D = R_2 \sin \theta$	$L = 2R_1 \sin \theta$

Six equations of which one is reduntant; solve for p_2, R_1, R_2, D, T in terms of load parameters p_1 and L, grid stiffness E and deflection-related parameter θ.

$\rightarrow T = E\ (\theta/\sin\theta - 1)$; $p_2 = p_1 - 2T\theta/[L(1 + T/E)]$;   etc.

Example: $p_1 = 100$ kPa (at geogrid), spread over L of 0.7 m; $E = 800$ kN/m;
$\theta = 10° = 0.175$ rads: $\rightarrow T = 4.08$ kN/m; $p_2 = 98.0$ kPa; $R_1 = 2.016$ m; $R_2 = 0.042$ m;
$D = 0.007$ m
Note: with $\theta = 10°$, deflection at centre of loaded area = 31 mm

---

3.3.2.5 The shakedown approach

The 'shakedown' concept is now applied to a wide variety of engineering problems, although not usually pavements.[22] The concept is that there exists a stress state below which deformation increment per cycle of load will become progressively smaller, leading to stable equilibrium rather than failure. Above this stress level, the deformation increments are large enough to produce failure at some point. Neither the actual magnitude of deformation nor the number of load applications to failure are defined using this approach; it is simply a safe-or-unsafe prediction.

Two different types of calculation can be carried out to determine 'shakedown limits', termed 'upper bound' and 'lower bound'. The lower bound calculation is an elastic one (usually linear elastic, with all the uncertainties which that can bring for unbound materials) and the aim is to check whether there is any point in the structure with a stress condition above failure.

233

The upper bound calculation involves an energy balance, and so is harder for most engineers to carry out. Basically, the work done by the load as it 'indents' a certain distance into the pavement (force × distance) is compared to the energy taken to cause slip along a defined set of failure planes within the pavement (shear stress × slip distance × area of plane). If the work done exceeds the energy absorbed, then the load is above the upper bound for shakedown.

Studies so far have shown that the lower bound load predicted in this way should be genuinely safe and that the upper bound load should be genuinely unsafe, but there remains a large area of unknown performance in the middle. Shakedown theory on its own will therefore never give real performance prediction, but it may well be a sensible approach to layer thickness design. A thickness equivalent to the lower bound shakedown limit should provide a good, safe solution.

3.3.3 Deformation in asphalt

If prediction of deformation in granular materials is fraught with uncertainty then it will come as no surprise to learn that asphalt opens the door to similar difficulties. After all, an asphalt is basically a granular material with an additional layer of complication, the binder. The usual procedure is therefore not to even try to estimate the rate of rut development in an asphalt layer but to concentrate on mixture design and to aim for a notionally deformation-resistant mix, the principles of which have already been outlined in Part 2. On the other hand, asphalt frequently forms ruts, and it would be useful to be able to make a prediction in advance based on measurable material properties. The following subsections outline one such approximate technique.

3.3.3.1 Assigning a mixture viscosity

Just as multi-layer linear elastic analysis can be used to calculate elastic strains within a pavement, so *multi-layer linear viscous* analysis can be used to calculate viscous strains. In fact, the same programs can be used, replacing the elastic modulus with a viscosity; computed strain is replaced by strain rate and deformation by deformation rate. The computation can readily be carried out by engineers – so long as they can assign appropriate viscosities. But is such an approach valid?

Evidence from actual rut development in roads is that it does indeed often tend to accumulate approximately linearly with time, with the

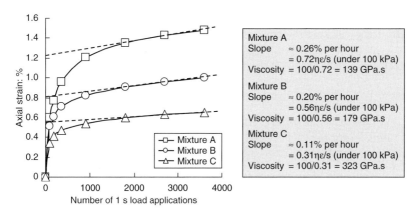

Fig. 3.8 Derivation of mixture viscosity from RLAT, 100 kPa at 40°C

exception of an initial period of more rapid development. And linear development implies that it is not unreasonable to assume a constant mixture viscosity; but on what basis can values of viscosity be chosen?

There are two main approaches. The first is to carry out static creep tests – the standard type of test for viscous materials – but the problem is that the resulting strain is often far from linear with time. The second approach, which is definitely recommended here, is to carry out repeated load tests such as the *repeated load axial test (RLAT)* introduced in Part 2 (Section 2.3.5.2). The growth of strain is not linear in this test either, particularly at the beginning of the test, but it becomes much closer to being linear later in the test. The recommended approach is therefore to use the slope of the strain against number of load applications plot towards the end of the test; in UK practice, this means over the last few hundred load applications out of a total of 3600, each of which lasts 1 s. Figure 3.8 shows three typical sets of data, and the viscosities determined from them.

3.3.3.2 Carrying out an analysis

The problem being evaluated here is not a whole-pavement problem; it is restricted to the asphalt. The procedure is therefore to run a multi-layer linear viscous analysis by inputting data for the asphalt layers, substituting viscosity for elastic modulus, and assigning a very high viscosity to the infinite layer beneath the asphalt. The design wheel load is applied and the deformation (actually deformation rate) is calculated under the centre of the load. For example, if the three materials shown in Fig. 3.8 are used, with 40 mm of Mixture A in the surface course, 60 mm of Mixture B in the binder course, and 180 mm of Mixture C in the base, and a 40 kN standard wheel load is applied over a circular area of radius 150 mm, then the following result is obtained:

- surface deformation of 1.809×10^{-7} m/s
- deformation at top of binder course of 1.454×10^{-7} m/s
- deformation at top of base of 0.880×10^{-7} m/s.

Thus, it may be observed that, in this case, the largest component of deformation per millimetre of thickness occurs within the binder course. This is actually quite common, and reflects the fact that the largest shear stresses commonly occur at a depth of around 50 mm.

The next step is to convert from seconds to numbers of load applications. This is achieved by working out the length of time taken for a vehicle travelling at design speed to cover a distance slightly greater than the length of a single tyre contact patch. For example, for a heavy goods vehicle the distance is about 400 mm and, at 60 mph (about 25 m/s), this will be covered in 16 ms. Thus, one second of load in the calculation is equivalent to about 60 load applications, and if a limiting rut value of 10 mm is adopted for design, then this implies that the pavement is suitable for about 4.0×10^6 load applications, equivalent to around two million goods vehicles.

3.3.3.3 Accounting for temperature variation

The final problem is that the RLAT data in Fig. 3.8 were obtained at a temperature of 40°C, and asphalt viscosity is heavily temperature dependent. A reasonable assumption for this dependency is that a 10°C decrease in temperature causes a *threefold* increase in viscosity,[23] and this provides a basis for converting a total annual traffic load into an equivalent number of vehicles at 40°C. Calculation Sheet 3.8 presents such a conversion, using temperature data obtained from the surface course of a pavement in the UK.[24] In this case, the result is a factor of 6.4 between total traffic numbers and equivalent 40°C load applications, and the pavement analysed in the previous section can therefore take rather more traffic than it first appeared, about 25 million standard 40 kN wheel load applications.

The reader is cautioned against taking the absolute magnitude of the prediction too literally; however, the method is a relatively easy one and is very useful for interpreting RLAT data.

236

Calculation Sheet 3.8 Converting traffic for pavement temperature

If a 10°C temperature change produces a threefold viscosity change:

$$\eta_T = \eta_{40c} \times 3^{(4-0.1T)}$$

Suggest using average noon temperatures since most traffic occurs during the day, giving the following monthly factors based on pavement temperatures in **Nottingham UK.**

			Viscosity	Strain
January	+3°C	$\rightarrow$	× 58.3 by	× 0.017
February	+7°C	$\rightarrow$	× 37.5 by	× 0.027
March	+13°C	$\rightarrow$	× 19.4 by	× 0.052
April	+21°C	$\rightarrow$	× 8.1 by	× 0.123
May	+25°C	$\rightarrow$	× 5.2 by	× 0.192
June	+30°C	$\rightarrow$	× 3.0 by	× 0.333
July	+32°C	$\rightarrow$	× 2.4 by	× 0.417
August	+33°C	$\rightarrow$	× 2.2 by	× 0.455
September	+24°C	$\rightarrow$	× 5.8 by	× 0.172
October	+14°C	$\rightarrow$	× 17.4 by	× 0.057
November	+5°C	$\rightarrow$	× 46.8 by	× 0.021
December	+3°C	$\rightarrow$	× 58.3 by	× 0.017

Average through the year
$\rightarrow$ × 0.157 on strain
$\rightarrow$ × 6.4 on viscosity
i.e. $\eta_{design} = \eta_{40c} \times 6.4$

3.3.3.4 Other factors affecting rut development

The following two factors also have a significant bearing on rutting.

Ageing

Unless RLAT data have been obtained from specimens recovered from an existing road, it is likely that a calculation such as that given above relates to new, unaged material. However, during the course of its life, bitumen will age significantly, resulting in an increase in viscosity. This increase may reach 400% in a dense mix in a climate such as the UK, and could be more like 5000% (a factor of 50)[25] in a tropical or desert climate – even more if an open-graded mixture is used. In rough terms, this viscosity increase may be translated directly to a decrease in rutting rate. In the UK, therefore, this will make a significant difference, and in many climates ageing demands a large decrease in predicted asphalt rutting.

Binder saturation

Part 2 has made the point that mixes which are overfilled with binder are some of the poorest performing, because the excess binder acts to reduce particle-to-particle contact forces and so renders inter-particle slip much easier. However, this effect only becomes apparent under high stress and especially under high loading rate, and these are not the conditions present in a RLAT test, nor in any other commonly used creep or repeated load creep test. Laboratory testing cannot therefore be expected to reveal this problem fully (though some increased deformation is usually observed). Furthermore, this is a problem which may not be apparent in early life but which becomes evident after trafficking has compacted the asphalt, reducing the void space available for the binder. The conclusion, therefore, is that no amount of simulative testing and analysis removes the need for sensible mix design, ensuring that the void content is kept well above 2%.

3.3.4 Summary

Conceptually, design against rutting is not hard to understand. It is simply the need to ensure that the stress level, specifically the shear stress level, at any point in the pavement is never sufficient to cause excessively rapid straining. This means:

- the subgrade must be adequately protected by overlying pavement layers
- any granular materials placed above the subgrade must themselves be protected by overlying bound materials
- asphalt mix design must give a sufficiently deformation-resistant mixture in order to avoid rutting within the asphalt.

The total rut, of course, is the sum of components from the different layers. The overall design has to be such that the cumulative rut during the design life is not excessive.

No mention has been made here of hydraulically-bound materials and that is because hydraulically-bound materials are rigid solids; they simply do not have the capacity to deform in the way that unbound and bitumen-bound materials can. A foundation beneath a strong hydraulically-bound material is absolutely safe, and deformation design need therefore not even be considered, until the point that the hydraulically-bound layer itself undergoes catastrophic failure – cracking – the subject of the next section.

3.4

Design against cracking

Having overcome the rutting problem and generated a sound, rut-resistant design, it is time to consider what else can go wrong. Inevitably, overcoming one problem only leads to the possibility of another, and cracking, though not immediately fatal, certainly represents a type of distress which is always likely when stiff materials such as concrete and asphalt are introduced.

3.4.1 Cracking of hydraulically-bound materials

Part 2 has introduced the fracture behaviour of hydraulically-bound materials and the different ways in which it is measured, and the point was made that the fundamental mode of failure is in *tension*. Every such material has a tensile strength and, if that is exceeded, then the material will fail. A hydraulically-bound layer is therefore in danger from the moment it sets as a solid. For many of the weaker materials this is accepted and such materials are designed to crack into small sections and to act as ultra-high-quality granular materials; but for others, those which are designed to withstand cracking, danger lurks around every corner. First, and most obviously, it is necessary to consider cracking due to imposed traffic load.[26]

3.4.1.1 Pavement quality concrete – Westergaard analysis

Since the 1920s, the equations developed by H.M. Westergaard[27] have represented the most widely used approach to analysis of concrete pavements under load. The original equations were derived assuming a concrete pavement to act as a slab in pure bending, and several subsequent modifications have been made over the years to increase the accuracy with which a real pavement can be modelled. The equations are in terms of the maximum tensile stress in the concrete due to slab bending and they are for three load locations: (1) *internal* (i.e. distant from a joint); (2) *edge*; and (3) *corner*. The load is assumed to consist of a uniformly stressed circular area. Commonly applied versions of the equations are shown in the box below.[28]

> ## Westergaard equations for stress in a concrete slab
>
> Internal loading; stress at base of slab
>
> $$\sigma_{Tensile} = (0.275p/h^2)(1 + \nu)$$
> $$\times \{4\log_{10}(L_s/b) + \log_{10}[12(1 - \nu^2)] - 0.436\}$$
>
> Edge loading; stress at base of slab
>
> $$\sigma_{Tensile} = [0.529p/h^2][1 + 0.54\nu][4\log_{10}(L_s/b) + 0.359]$$
>
> Corner loading; stress at top of slab
>
> $$\sigma_{Tensile} = [3p/h^2][1 - (\sqrt{2a/L_s})^{1.2}]$$
>
> where: p = load; a = radius of loaded area; h = slab thickness; ν = Poisson's ratio; L_s = 'radius of relative stiffness' = $\{Eh^3/[12k(1 - \nu^2)]\}^{0.25}$; E = concrete stiffness modulus; k = 'modulus of subgrade reaction'; b = 'radius of equivalent pressure distribution' = $\sqrt{(1.6a^2 + h^2)} - 0.675h$, if $a > 0.72h$; = a, if $a < 0.72h$.

A few words of explanation are required here. The 'radius of relative stiffness' is a convenient parameter expressing the ease with which the slab bends. It has no fundamental meaning on its own but depends on other quantities. The 'modulus of subgrade reaction', however, is a fundamental input to the equations. It is defined as the pressure required to cause unit distance of vertical deflection and it represents a computationally convenient way of expressing foundation stiffness. Traditionally, it is measured using a large (762 mm diameter) plate loading test – see Part 2 (Section 2.1.1.10). It can also be estimated from the combination of foundation layer stiffness moduli expected – see Part 1 (Section 1.4.2.5) – but the problem is that no Poisson's ratio effect is present when a modulus of subgrade reaction is used and so direct conversion from E and ν values is impossible.

Clearly, once the tensile stress has been calculated, it can be compared with the tensile strength, preferably derived from a flexure test. If the computed stress is lower than the strength then the slab should survive loading; if not it will crack.

This simplistic evaluation can then be extended for cyclic loading with reference to the typical fatigue behaviour of hydraulically-bound material, illustrated in Part 2 (Section 2.2.2). The following equation was given, derived from laboratory fatigue testing of various concretes and other hydraulically bound materials.

$$\sigma/\sigma_f = 1.064 - 0.064\log_{10}(N)$$

where:

σ = tensile stress due to load

σ_f = flexural strength

N = number of load applications to failure.

The slope of this fatigue characteristic is a shallow one, which means that a small increase in stress can lead to a large reduction in life. Designs should therefore be appropriately conservative, bearing in mind the effect of locally reduced concrete thickness or loss of slab support – see Section 3.8 for further advice on this.

A common problem however is the difference between the idealised load cases covered by the Westergaard equations and real life. In a concrete highway pavement for example, the joints represent points of weakness and therefore locations of increased stress. But a joint is not the same as an edge. Dowel bars are generally used to ensure a degree of load transfer; but on the other hand, the situation is definitely worse than the internal load case. This is a real dilemma, and it limits the usefulness of the equations. A common approach would be to calculate both the Westergaard internal and edge load cases and then to make a judgement, depending on the type of joint present, as to just how much better than a free edge a real joint is likely to be. It always has to be appreciated that joint efficiency changes with temperature as concrete expands and contracts, so a conservative, low-temperature, case should be taken. In the case of an existing pavement, it may even be possible to measure joint quality using the falling weight deflectometer (see Part 4), but it is still not straightforward to determine from such a measurement how best to apply the Westergaard equations. The author's experience is that a multiplier between 1.2 and 1.5 times the stress from the internal load case is usually appropriate, whereas the edge loading stress typically works out at about 1.8 times the internal stress.

241

A particular issue is how much attention should be paid to the corner loading case, since this is always the most critical in terms of the predicted stress. However, free corners do not occur. Even at joint intersections, there is always a degree of load transfer to adjacent slab sections. It should also be borne in mind: (1) that joint intersections are not generally in the wheel paths on highways (although they may be for airfields or industrial areas); and (2) that corner cracking is a much less serious phenomenon than other forms of cracking since a corner crack is of limited extent. Once again, engineering judgement is needed, supported by approximate analysis.

And a final problem lies in the lack of flexibility in load position. Most real load situations involve interacting effects from more than one wheel, for example aircraft wheel gears, and the Westergaard equations make no allowance for this. They can still be used, of course, but only as approximate guides.

3.4.1.2 Pavement quality concrete – multi-layer linear elastic analysis

Multi-layer linear elastic analysis, introduced already in calculations for pavement rutting, represents an alternative to Westergaard analysis. As in the Westergaard approach, the output from the analysis is the maximum tensile stress in the concrete. However, this type of analysis has one major advantage over Westergaard and that is that load combinations can be included, such as dual tandem or dual tridem wheel sets. Unfortunately it also has a major disadvantage and that is that all layers have to be infinite in extent; there is no way of analysing an edge or corner situation.

A reasonable compromise, attempting to extract the best from each method, is to combine the two approaches. The Westergaard equations give the relative effect of an edge or a corner compared to the internal case, and this can be translated into a multiplier on the stress derived from multi-layer linear elastic analysis – which always relates to the internal case. This is a sound, common-sense, approach and is to be recommended. The value of the multiplier should be around 1.2 for the case of joints with good load transfer, becoming as much as 1.5 for poor joints.

3.4.1.3 Pavement quality concrete – limit state analysis

A conceptual problem with a purely elastic analysis such as Westergaard's, or layered elastic theory, is that concrete simply cannot crack at a single

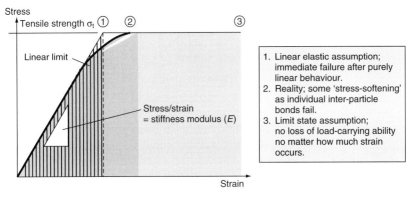

Fig. 3.9 Idealisations of stress–strain behaviour

point. If cracking is to occur, then this will involve a 'mechanism' of cracks. Thus, even if, in theory, the stress at a particular point is sufficient to induce a crack after a certain number of load applications, the reality is that this cannot occur until adjacent sections of concrete are also ready to crack. What will actually happen is that the point of theoretical failure will simply reduce in stiffness locally as the first inter-particle fractures begin to occur (refer back to explanations in Part 2, Section 2.2.1.1), shedding stress onto neighbouring regions. The upshot of this is that conclusions based on an elastic analysis will generally be *conservative*. The alternative form of analysis is termed 'limit state'. It is a plastic analysis rather than elastic and the different way in which stress–strain behaviour is idealised is shown in Fig. 3.9.[29]

It is clear from Fig. 3.9 that, while the linear elastic assumption may be conservative, the limit state assumption is *optimistic*. Only in the particular case of fibre-reinforced concrete, for which the stress–strain behaviour genuinely does include a large post-peak stress-carrying capacity, can it be considered as realistic.

Nevertheless, the limit state approach opens the door to solving problems that would otherwise be intractable. No matter how complex the interaction between load locations and joints, all that is required is that a crack mechanism is postulated and an energy balance carried out. The relevant equation is as follows:

Work done by loads = energy absorbed by foundation

+ energy dissipated at cracks.

The crack mechanism (see Fig. 3.10 for examples) is assumed to move by a small amount (δ vertically in Fig. 3.10). The *work done by*

243

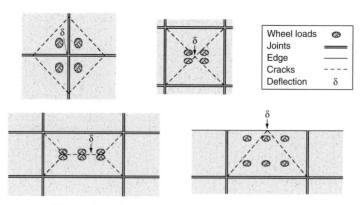

Fig. 3.10 Possible crack mechanisms for use in limit state analysis

the loads is then given by the magnitude of each load multiplied by the vertical movement, which is related to δ. The *energy absorbed by the foundation* has to be estimated; it is the product of stress and deflection, summed over the entire deflected area. The *energy dissipated at cracks* is the bending moment at failure multiplied by the imposed angle of rotation, summed over all lengths of all cracks. It is the *bending moment at failure* per linear metre of crack, M_f, that is the desired output of this equation. The *tensile stress at failure*, σ_f, is then given as follows (see Part 2, Section 2.2.1.2):

$$M_f = \sigma_f h^2 / 6$$

where $h =$ slab thickness.

Once a mechanism has been postulated, it is relatively simple to work out the deflection at each load location and the rotation angle (in radians remember) at each crack. The uncertain element is always the distribution of foundation stress. In some cases it is worth carrying out a multi-layer linear elastic calculation in advance to predict this; however, a reasonable assumption would be that the sum of all the applied wheel loads is distributed over the deflected area in proportion to the magnitude of deflection. A simpler and very conservative assumption would be to assume a uniform distribution over the deflected area. An example of the use of limit state analysis is given in Calculation Sheet 3.9.

Limit state analysis is less frequently carried out for pavements than elastic analysis, but the advice here is not to ignore it. The technique can be used to address specific cases such as the effect of a joint with no load transfer, unusual jointing patterns, or load arrangments such as those from specialist pieces of industrial equipment or aircraft wheel

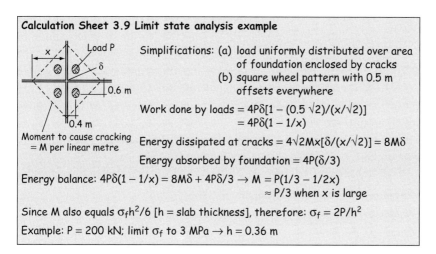

Calculation Sheet 3.9 Limit state analysis example

Simplifications: (a) load uniformly distributed over area of foundation enclosed by cracks
(b) square wheel pattern with 0.5 m offsets everywhere

Work done by loads $= 4P\delta[1 - (0.5\sqrt{2})/(x/\sqrt{2})]$
$= 4P\delta(1 - 1/x)$

Moment to cause cracking = M per linear metre

Energy dissipated at cracks $= 4\sqrt{2}Mx[\delta/(x/\sqrt{2})] = 8M\delta$

Energy absorbed by foundation $= 4P(\delta/3)$

Energy balance: $4P\delta(1 - 1/x) = 8M\delta + 4P\delta/3 \rightarrow M = P(1/3 - 1/2x)$
$\approx P/3$ when x is large

Since M also equals $\sigma_f h^2/6$ [h = slab thickness], therefore: $\sigma_f = 2P/h^2$

Example: $P = 200$ kN; limit σ_f to 3 MPa $\rightarrow h = 0.36$ m

gears. However, it must be remembered that the method is inherently 'unsafe' in that the assumption made regarding stress–strain behaviour is optimistic unless designing with fibre-reinforced concrete.

3.4.1.4 Pavement quality concrete – warping stress analysis

Thermally-induced warping stresses, resulting from a temperature difference between the top and the bottom of a slab, can be highly significant. In most design methods they are not explicitly taken into consideration, but the calibration upon which the method is based implicitly takes them into account. If using an analytical approach, one technique is to build in extra conservatism when considering stresses due to traffic, and an example of this is the use of the so-called 'Packard line'[30] for fatigue assessment, an ultra-conservative fatigue characteristic commonly used by designers. The equation of the Packard line is as follows:

$$\sigma/\sigma_f = 0.96 - 0.0799\log_{10}(N)$$

where:

σ = tensile stress due to load

σ_f = flexural strength

N = number of load applications to failure.

But, while this may be satisfactory for standard cases it is not recommended for non-standard applications other than as a rough check. For such cases, it is appropriate to attempt a thermal stress prediction, which may either be carried out from first principles or use may be made of the predictive method developed by R. D. Bradbury.[31] The Bradbury approach can be summarised in the two equations shown in the box below, one for internal stress and the other for edge stress, mirroring the conditions covered by the Westergaard equations.

Bradbury equations for maximum warping stress in a concrete slab

Internal loading; stress at base of slab

$$\sigma_{Tensile} = \tfrac{1}{2} E \alpha T (C_x + \nu C_y)/(1 - \nu^2)$$

Edge loading; stress at base of slab

$$\sigma_{Tensile} = \tfrac{1}{2} E \alpha T C_x \ (\text{or } C_y)$$

$x/L_s = 0, \quad C_x \approx 0; \qquad x/L_s = 2, \quad C_x \approx 0.05;$

$x/L_s = 3, \quad C_x \approx 0.18; \quad x/L_s = 4, \quad C_x \approx 0.50;$

$x/L_s = 5, \quad C_x \approx 0.73; \quad x/L_s = 6, \quad C_x \approx 0.89;$

$x/L_s \geq 7, \quad C_x \approx 1$

where: E = stiffness modulus; α = coefficient of thermal expansion; T = temperature difference top–bottom; C_x, C_y depend on the ratio of slab dimensions x and y respectively to radius of relative stiffness L_s; $L_s = \{Eh^3/[12k(1 - \nu^2)]\}^{0.25}$; h = slab thickness; k = modulus of subgrade reaction; ν = Poisson's ratio.

Approximate analysis from first principles is also possible, simplifying the situation to just two dimensions rather than three. Figure 3.11 illustrates the basis of the computation and presents theoretical solutions for the idealised case where a concrete slab is founded on a fully rigid support.

Putting typical numbers to the symbols in Fig. 3.11, the length of the unsupported section of slab is likely to be between 1 and 2 m under night-time conditions (say 5°C temperature difference), and potentially up to around 3 m under the most severe daytime conditions (say 8°C temperature difference). This gives worst-case stresses of around 1 MPa at night and nearly 2 MPa during the day – depending on slab thickness etc. However, the most serious problem comes when a vehicle passes over the unsupported section of slab, leading to an overall stress

246

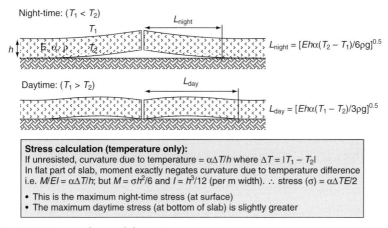

Night-time: $(T_1 < T_2)$

L_{night}

T_1

h E, α, ρ T_2

$L_{night} = [Eh\alpha(T_2 - T_1)/6\rho g]^{0.5}$

Daytime: $(T_1 > T_2)$

L_{day}

$L_{day} = [Eh\alpha(T_1 - T_2)/3\rho g]^{0.5}$

Stress calculation (temperature only):
If unresisted, curvature due to temperature = $\alpha\Delta T/h$ where $\Delta T = |T_1 - T_2|$
In flat part of slab, moment exactly negates curvature due to temperature difference
i.e. $M/EI = \alpha\Delta T/h$; but $M = \sigma h^2/6$ and $I = h^3/12$ (per m width). $\therefore$ stress $(\sigma) = \alpha\Delta TE/2$
- This is the maximum night-time stress (at surface)
- The maximum daytime stress (at bottom of slab) is slightly greater

Fig. 3.11 Stresses due to slab warping

significantly higher than would have been predicted under wheel loading with full support conditions. The interaction is complex; simply summing the maximum thermally-induced and (internal) load-induced stresses will give an exaggerated estimate of the real worst case.

This is not the end of the story however; for a start, the hardness of support is clearly a major issue, particularly in the case of the daytime state. It would only require a fraction of a millimetre of foundation deflection to dramatically reduce the unsupported length. Some design methods therefore recognise that use of an unbound sub-base layer beneath the concrete reduces thermally-induced stresses. On the other hand, a reduced foundation stiffness increases traffic-induced stresses, and many authorities nowadays take the view that a hydraulically-bound sub-base is actually the safest option (see also Section 3.5.2.3). This is an area of continuing debate and this book cannot advise strongly one way or the other.

The final point to bear in mind if an analytical assessment of thermally-induced warping stresses is carried out is that the worst-case scenario does not happen very often. Reference to the fatigue characteristic for concrete means that it is theoretically possible to convert a small number of severe stress applications (i.e. combination of full traffic load and unfavourable thermal conditions) to a much larger number of 'standard' stress applications – or vice versa. Although any such conversion can only result in an estimate for the number of design traffic loads since temperature variation within the slab will not be known with any certainty, it at least represents a rational approach to solving the problem. Calculation Sheet 3.10 presents an example computation.

Calculation Sheet 3.10 Combining traffic and thermal stresses

Say: (a) maximum stress due to traffic loading = 1.7 MPa
    (b) design traffic = 150 000 load applications
    (c) maximum additional stress due to thermal effects = 0.9 MPa
    (d) thermal stress has equal probability of being anywhere in the range
       0–0.9 MPa

Question: how many equivalent load applications at full thermal stress?

Replace fatigue characteristic such as Fig. 2.29 by a power law with exponent 12.

$\therefore$ Damage $= k\sigma^{12}$ where k is a constant

Integrate between 1.7 and 2.6 MPa for **average damage**: $\int k\sigma^{12} \, d\sigma/(2.6-1.7)$

$$= k(2.6^{13} - 1.7^{13})/(13 \times 0.9) \quad = 21\,122k$$

Equivalent damage due to N_{eq} load applications at 2.6 MPa $= N_{eq}\, k \times 2.6^{12}$

$\therefore N_{eq} = 21\,122/2.6^{12} = 0.221;$

i.e. take $0.221 \times 150\,000 = 33\,150$ at full thermal stress

---

3.4.1.5 Pavement quality concrete – joint spacing

Part 1 has already introduced the need for joints and it will have become obvious from the foregoing sections that joint detailing is inseparably linked to slab strength and thickness design. While joint details are routinely ignored by users of elastic analysis, the section on limit state analysis has demonstrated that load-carrying capacity is integrally tied to the pattern of joints present. And although joint separation was not explicitly mentioned under 'warping analysis', it may have been noted that the length of unsupported slab introduced in Fig. 3.11 supposes a semi-infinite slab length; if the actual joint spacing is less than twice the calculated unsupported length then the warping stress will clearly be reduced.

However, the primary reason for choice of joint spacing is related to none of these; it is a simple function of linear thermal contraction – ignoring warping. In many climates there is likely to be at least a 20°C difference in concrete temperature between the time of initial set and the coldest time of year, leading to a strain of at least 2×10^{-4}, and this is a little over the failure strain for most cement-bound materials. The concrete will therefore crack unless joints are included (or unless heavy reinforcement is provided).

However, having established a need for joints, the question of joint spacing remains, and the key argument relates to *load transfer efficiency*.

The assumption has been made in previous sections that this will be high, allowing a joint to act as a hinge but not allowing any significant differential vertical movement under load, thus avoiding the damaging 'edge load' condition. Though joints may be equipped with dowels (see Part 1, Section 1.3.2.8) to assist in carrying the load from one side to the other, these will only be of limited use unless there is a considerable degree of *interlock* across the joint between the two concrete faces – and this presumes that joints will never open excessively. Studies have shown that, once an opening exceeds around 1 mm, interlock across the joint becomes minimal, and it is the need to control joint opening which really controls spacing. With a 20°C temperature reduction and a strain of 2×10^{-4}, a 5 m joint spacing would give a 1 mm opening. In fact, experience suggests that, for most climates, joint spacings *between 3.5 and 6 m* represent the range of reasonable compromise between the cost and nuisance of joint construction and maintenance and the need to maintain load transfer efficiency. Less and the cost becomes too great; more and joint problems become increasingly likely.

3.4.1.6 Pavement quality concrete – joint deterioration

Whatever the joint spacing, load transfer efficiency will deteriorate under repeated load. Figure 3.12 presents best-fit lines from data obtained from a series of beam tests on cement-bound base quality material in which the rate of reduction in load transfer efficiency (expressed as a stiffness – shear stress/differential vertical movement)

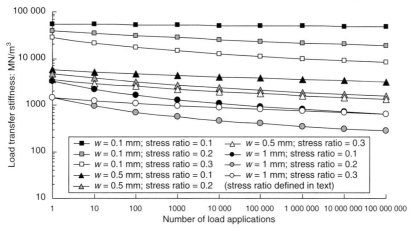

Fig. 3.12 Crack deterioration under repeated shear load[32]

was measured during multiple application of shear stress across a crack in the beam. Crack opening w was varied up to a maximum of 1 mm and the influence of this parameter is clear. Unsurprisingly, the other key factor is stress, expressed as the ratio of shear stress across the joint to flexural strength.

This is not an area which lends itself to confident modelling or prediction. The data in Fig. 3.12, combined with experience from various sites, suggests that deterioration rate is, like fatigue, a function of the ratio of stress to material strength. However, it is also clear that, so long as the stress ratio is kept to 0.1 or less, the rate of joint deterioration will be relatively small. In the case of a PQC pavement with a flexural strength of 4 MPa, this equates to a shear stress of 400 kPa, which would demand a slab thickness of around 120 mm for highway traffic (always exceeded in practice), and more like 400 mm for heavy aircraft loading (not necessarily exceeded). The shear stress acting in individual cases may be calculated approximately using multi-layer linear elastic analysis, assuming a continuum (with the stiffness expected from intact concrete) in place of a joint; this will slightly overstate the real value of shear stress.

3.4.1.7 Pavement quality concrete – joint type

The question as to which type of joint to use (refer to Part 1, Section 1.3.2.8) is another with no simple answer. Dowelled transverse joints are common in highway pavements and dowels are often used for all joints in a large expanse of concrete pavement such as an airfield apron. In most cases these are 'contraction joints', allowing the concrete to contract relative to its dimension at the time of set – but not to expand. However, if construction takes place in cool weather, then it may be necessary to include 'expansion joints' at intervals, for example every fourth joint or so. This avoids the possibility of blow-up failures in very hot weather, when slabs in compression literally buckle under pressure. The problem with expansion joints, though, is that they can never achieve interlock; they rely solely on dowels for load transfer. An expansion joint is therefore a point of weakness, a step nearer to the 'edge loading' condition. Expansion joints present two choices: either ignore the weakness and accept an accelerated failure locally; or strengthen (usually thicken) the pavement locally. The first option is the more common, but serious consideration should really be given to the second.

Note that joints do not have to be dowelled. Some organisations have taken the view that dowels are a nuisance and a likely source of future trouble and that a pavement is safer without them! They accept that load transfer efficiency is reduced and use designs which recognise this by increasing slab thickness accordingly. And even where the assistance of a dowel would be normally worthwhile, if the total linear extent of the pavement is no more than about 20 m (notably transversely across a highway) then freedom for expansion and contraction is not really required. In such cases, the dowel should be replaced by a tie-bar, thus ensuring good interlock across the joint under all circumstances, but at the same time allowing a degree of rotation at the joint. This allows slab warping and so limits the resulting stresses. This type of joint is known as a 'warping joint'.

3.4.1.8 Reinforced concrete

It is common knowledge that reinforcement has to be added to structural concrete (for example in a bridge or a building) to enable it to take significant tensile stress without breaking, so it might be supposed that the same approach should be taken in pavement engineering. However, the cost–benefit equation is very different in the case of a pavement compared to most structures. If a concrete bridge span 'breaks', that is a very serious matter; if a pavement 'breaks', hardly anyone notices. A pavement is continuously supported by its foundation, and so can operate quite effectively in a 'broken' state. The inclusion of joints is simply a method of controlling the nature of those breaks such that they can readily be managed. Thus, while reinforcement has the potential to limit or even eliminate such breakage, the benefit is not particularly dramatic.

Nevertheless, reinforcement is reasonably common in PQC. In many cases, a light reinforcement mesh is included near the top of the slab as a means of controlling shrinkage cracking. It is also used to cut back significantly on the number of joints. The argument goes like this:

- joints are a nuisance and the number should therefore be minimised;
- with greater joint spacing, warping stresses increase and load transfer at joints decreases;
- therefore there is a much greater likelihood of cracking;
- but, if reinforcement is present, cracks are 'controlled'; they will remain narrow and the slab will not break up.

Basically, in this sort of pavement, with intermediate levels of reinforcement, 'hairline' cracking is accepted; but there is sufficient reinforcement to hold the slab together, ensuring excellent 'interlock' across each hairline crack and therefore no significant loss of performance. And such pavements work. They are particularly common in industrial applications where a slight loss of ride quality due to cracking is unimportant. Many road authorities, including the UK Highways Agency, have also permitted jointed reinforced pavements, although maintenance difficulties (see Part 4) mean that they have now become less popular on highways.

Thickness design is an interesting issue here. In a pavement that is designed to crack, it is unclear how the thickness is to be selected. Logically, while stresses sufficient to cause cracking are acceptable, crack deterioration is not. Once cracks begin to spall, load transfer efficiency will be lost no matter how strong the reinforcement, and this type of deterioration will then accelerate. Unfortunately, however, this type of distress is hard to model, and current practice, perhaps wisely, is to base thickness selection on experience. For example, standard practice in the US[33] is to adopt the same thicknesses as for unreinforced concrete, while in the UK a slightly decreased thickness is permitted.[34]

The next question is the degree to which joint spacing can be opened up. There is still a limit to the length of unjointed pavement possible, and this stems from the tensile stress induced in the slab due to contraction (during cooling) and the frictional restraint provided by the pavement foundation. Figure 3.13 illustrates the situation and outlines the analysis involved. For example, with an angle of friction between the concrete slab and the foundation of 30°, an intact 4 MPa tensile strength concrete could sustain a length of about 540 m between joints – a massive distance. However, there will almost certainly already be shrinkage cracks, and at these locations the entire tensile force has to be taken by the steel reinforcement. Thus, with 12 mm diameter bars at

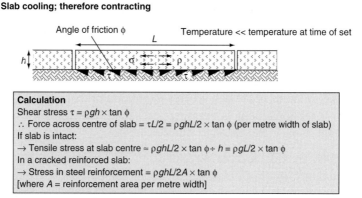

Slab cooling; therefore contracting

Angle of friction ϕ L Temperature << temperature at time of set

Calculation
Shear stress $\tau = \rho gh \times \tan \phi$
$\therefore$ Force across centre of slab $= \tau L/2 = \rho ghL/2 \times \tan \phi$ (per metre width of slab)
If slab is intact:
$\rightarrow$ Tensile stress at slab centre $= \rho ghL/2 \times \tan \phi \div h = \rho gL/2 \times \tan \phi$
In a cracked reinforced slab:
$\rightarrow$ Stress in steel reinforcement $= \rho ghL/2A \times \tan \phi$
[where A = reinforcement area per metre width]

Fig. 3.13 Tensile stresses due to slab shrinkage

252

250 mm spacing for example, giving 4.5 cm^2 of steel per metre width, and assuming high-yield steel with a strength of 450 MPa, the maximum sustainable tensile force would be just over 200 kN/m. In a 250 mm thick pavement of density 2500 kg/m^3, and with a 30° friction angle, the limiting length reduces to 114 m. Anything more and the reinforcement would fracture.

In practice, the angle of friction between the slab and the foundation is hard to predict. It also has to be remembered that steel is subject to fatigue failure under repeated loading at stress less than its ultimate strength. For these reasons it is prudent to impose a factor of safety of at least 3, and in fact joint separation distances of between 15 and 30 m are commonly used when greater separation joint sealing becomes very difficult due to the magnitude of daily joint opening and closing.

3.4.1.9 Continuously reinforced concrete (CRC)

CRC is the ultimate concrete pavement. The principle is simple. The reinforcement has to be strong enough to resist concrete contraction due to cooling, giving reinforcement quantities typically between 0.7% and 1% of the concrete area. Calculation Sheet 3.11 explains the theoretical basis for these percentages, although the real justification is practical experience. Notice that the concrete tensile strength limit (3 MPa in the example in Calculation Sheet 3.11) is less than the true

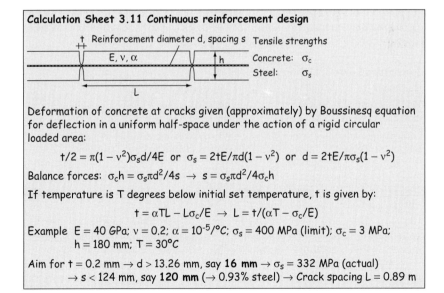

Calculation Sheet 3.11 Continuous reinforcement design

Reinforcement diameter d, spacing s   Tensile strengths

E, ν, α   h   Concrete: σ_c Steel: σ_s

L

Deformation of concrete at cracks given (approximately) by Boussinesq equation for deflection in a uniform half-space under the action of a rigid circular loaded area:

$$t/2 = \pi(1 - v^2)\sigma_s d/4E \quad \text{or} \quad \sigma_s = 2tE/\pi d(1 - v^2) \quad \text{or} \quad d = 2tE/\pi\sigma_s(1 - v^2)$$

Balance forces: $\sigma_c h = \sigma_s \pi d^2/4s \rightarrow s = \sigma_s \pi d^2/4\sigma_c h$

If temperature is T degrees below initial set temperature, t is given by:

$$t = \alpha TL - L\sigma_c/E \rightarrow L = t/(\alpha T - \sigma_c/E)$$

Example E = 40 GPa; ν = 0.2; α = 10^{-5}/°C; σ_s = 400 MPa (limit); σ_c = 3 MPa; h = 180 mm; T = 30°C

Aim for t = 0.2 mm → d > 13.26 mm, say **16 mm** → σ_s = 332 MPa (actual) → s < 124 mm, say **120 mm** (→ 0.93% steel) → Crack spacing L = 0.89 m

tensile strength because of the inevitability of locked-in longitudinal stress. This may be partly due to differential set of the concrete but will also be caused by a temperature differential through the slab.

Thickness design of CRC is not straightforward. Cracking is accepted; indeed it is inevitable, with a typical spacing of around 1 m. This means that the pavement is relatively flexible since each crack acts as a hinge, allowing a small degree of rotation. Yet the pavement must be thick enough to prevent excessive crack deterioration, and the balance is not an easy one to achieve. Where crack deterioration is excessive, ride quality is severely compromised and maintenance is very difficult indeed. Reference back to Section 3.4.1.6 suggests that, with a crack opening of no more than 0.5 mm and a concrete flexural strength of 4 MPa, the shear stress across each crack should be kept to less than about 400 kPa if significant crack deterioration is to be avoided. Under commercial truck loading, this typically demands a slab thickness of at least 120 mm.

One of the key requirements for CRC pavement is that the concrete has to be restrained in order to avoid large movements at each end. Restraint is provided by *anchorages* at either end of a length of CRC pavement, details for which can be found in standard designs produced by a number of highway authorities. An anchorage is basically a plug of concrete (or steel) set into the ground, and it has to be deep enough for the ground to be able to prevent movement under the full tensile force generated by thermal contraction. As in the case of reinforcement quantity and slab thickness, the real justification for anchorage designs is successful experience; Calculation Sheet 3.12 provides theoretical backup – to be used cautiously!

Calculation Sheet 3.12 Anchorage design

Say tensile force in concrete pavement is sufficient to cause cracking, i.e. tensile strength (with allowance for locked-in stress) × area: $F = \sigma_{tc}h_c$ per metre.

Strength parameters c and ϕ define a limiting relationship between horizontal and vertical stress in the foundation material, as explained in Part 2 (Section 2.1.1.4):

$\sigma_h = [2c \cos \phi + \sigma_v (1 + \sin \phi)]/(1 - \sin \phi)$

Average σ_v at anchorage $= h_c\gamma_c + 0.5h_a\gamma_s$

∴ F to cause anchorage failure $= h_a\sigma_h$

$= h_a[2c \cos \phi + (h_c\gamma_c + 0.5h_a\gamma_s)(1 + \sin \phi)]/(1 - \sin \phi)$

Example: $c = 10$ kPa; $\phi = 50°$; $\gamma_c = 24$ kN/m^2; $\gamma_s = 18$ kN/m^2; $h_c = 0.2$ m; $\sigma_{tc} = 3$ MPa
→ $F = 600$ kN/m; requires 1 anchorage with $h_a = 2.4$ m;
2 anchorages with $h_a = 1.5$ m; 3 anchorages with $h_a = 1.2$ m;
4 anchorages with $h_a = 1.0$ m; etc.

3.4.1.10 *Rapid-setting hydraulically-bound layers – thermal stress analysis*

As has become clear, it is impossible to design any hydraulically-bound pavement layer not to crack. Every 1°C drop in temperature induces enough tensile stress to resist a strain of around 10^{-5} – depending on the aggregate used. If, for example, the stiffness modulus of the material was 10 GPa, the induced stress would be 100 kPa per 1°C temperature drop. Since the tensile strength of such a material is unlikely to be much more than 1 MPa, cracking would occur with a temperature drop of 10°C.

In a relatively rapid-setting cement-bound material, what actually happens in practice is critically dependent on the weather during the first few days after placement. Figure 3.14 illustrates the point conceptually.

Crack spacing will influence performance considerably. A spacing of 50 m will give 49 m of excellent pavement base (or sub-base) – followed by a serious crack, with virtually zero load transfer in cold weather. This may not matter too much if the layer is to be overlaid with either a concrete pavement or block paving, but it certainly places a heavy burden on an overlying asphalt, and so-called 'reflective cracks' are certain to appear at the surface. On the other hand, a crack spacing of 5 m will ensure reasonable load transfer most of the year but, if and when reflective cracking does appear, the number of such cracks will be much higher. Either way there is likely to be problem – it is just that the problems will be different.

The answer is an obvious one: to create joints, similar to those in PQC pavements. This is not difficult. It is simply necessary to create

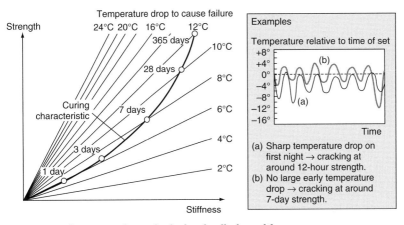

Fig. 3.14 Early-age cracking of a hydraulically-bound layer

a plane of weakness in the layer, and this is usually achieved by cutting a slot (typically to one-third depth) in the wet material and inserting either a thin polythene strip or a spray of bitumen emulsion. This is followed by compaction of the material, closing the slot but leaving the weakness. Subsequent thermal, and later traffic-induced, stresses will ensure that the weakness becomes a crack – and a crack in a pre-determined location is a joint. In the context of a hydraulically-bound base the term used is '*pre-cracking*'[35] – but what spacing should be used?

The first constraint is that excellent interlock across the crack is essential, and even a spacing of 5 m is too much for this. In a jointed concrete pavement, with dowels across the joints, it may be acceptable to allow up to 1 mm of joint opening, but not in the case of a weaker material without any assistance from dowels; 0.5 mm is much more satisfactory and would give a much enhanced load transfer efficiency. However, this demands a crack spacing of no more than about 2.5 m. Against this must be set the fact that the effective stiffness of the layer as a whole will decrease at such low crack spacing, as explained in Part 2 (Section 2.2.5.5), reducing its effectiveness as a protection to foundation layers; it will become slightly 'flexible' in nature, allowing local deformation of the foundation to take place. The accepted compromise nowadays is a spacing of 3 m, although a good case could be made for reducing this. The resulting effective modulus of the layer should be at least 40% of the value for intact material. Figure 3.15 shows an example prediction, computed for the case of a 150 mm thick layer of strong lean concrete, and assuming a relationship between crack width and load transfer stiffness based on Fig. 3.12.

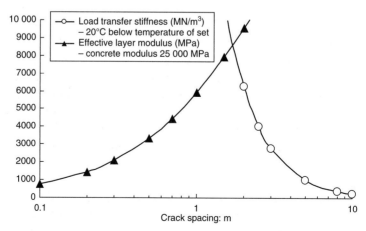

Fig. 3.15 The effect of crack spacing in a lean concrete layer

Difficult though this aspect of design is, it is important. Load transfer efficiency has a significant effect on the time before a crack 'reflects' through an asphalt surface, and reflective cracking is a serious maintenance headache. If unchecked, water will enter the crack, accelerating deterioration of the crack faces as well as potentially softening the pavement foundation. Thus, it is worth trying to ensure that material of the right strength is used and that cracks are kept narrow (generally by pre-cracking).[36]

3.4.1.11 *Slow-setting hydraulically-bound layers – thermal stress analysis*

The preceding section has been directed at the case of a material with a relatively rapid-setting binder, which generally means a binder with a high Portland cement content. Slower-setting materials are conceptually similar and, in principle, can be treated in the same way. However, the proportion of strength achieved during the first night after placement will be lower, which means that cracking is almost certain to occur during that night, and that crack spacing is likely to be very low. For example, if the strength gain was delayed by a factor of 4 relative to cement-bound material, the strength achieved after 12 h would be almost negligible, perhaps 1% of the design value, and a very modest temperature drop would ensure crack development. The equation in Fig. 3.13 would then suggest a crack spacing of 1–2 m. It has to be admitted that this is a highly theoretical computation since continuing chemical reaction will partially reinstate the integrity of the layer during the warmer temperatures of the day, only to see cracks redeveloping during subsequent nights. This is a complex, weather-dependent phenomenon and impossible to predict with certainty, but the eventual result appears, from experience, to be a layer with zero visible cracking but a significantly reduced effective stiffness compared to a laboratory-prepared specimen. The inference is that there are numerous minute (and therefore invisible) cracks, all with excellent load transfer, giving a layer which is, in practice, flexible rather than rigid. The effective layer modulus will typically be around 10–20% of that displayed by an intact laboratory specimen.[37] Pre-cracking is not required for such a material.

3.4.1.12 *Strong hydraulically-bound layers – traffic loading*

Although it is accepted that even the strongest hydraulically-bound layer will crack due to temperature changes, such cracks are almost always transverse in direction. They represent points of weakness but, so long as longitudinal wheel-path cracking is avoided, the layer still forms an excellent support to overlying materials and gives excellent protection to an underlying subgrade. That all changes as soon as a longitudinal wheel-path crack forms.

The usual way to design against such longitudinal cracking is to carry out a multi-layer linear elastic analysis and to compute the tensile stress at the base of the layer under a design load application. This can then be divided by the tensile strength expected from the material to give a stress ratio, and a number of load applications to failure determined using a fatigue characteristic such as that introduced above for PQC pavements. For heavily trafficked highways, this stress ratio should be maintained at no more than about 40%.

However, it is important that the computation is: (1) carried out using appropriate input parameters, and (2) adjusted appropriately. The stiffness used for the hydraulically-bound layer should be the value for *fully intact material*, *not* the effective modulus of the layer (see also the statistical advice in Section 3.8). This is because the effective layer modulus does not represent a real material stiffness but a composite including the effects of cracks, whereas it is the response of intact lengths of material which is needed here. However, the transverse thermally-induced cracks are real enough, and the computed stress must therefore be increased by a factor to take account of the increased layer bending which occurs near a crack due to loss of continuity. This factor may be as little as 1.2 for cracks with excellent interlock but as high as 1.5 for wide cracks (see Sections 3.4.1.1 and 3.4.1.2); unfortunately there is no substitute for experience when making this assessment.

Most strong hydraulically-bound materials are designed not to crack longitudinally and a pavement incorporating such a layer has exhausted 'phase 1' of its life as soon as longitudinal cracks occur. However, slow-setting materials are different. They will already include minute longitudinal cracks as well as transverse ones but, because there will be numerous such cracks, lying at many different orientations, the effect on overlying asphalt or underlying subgrade will be much less significant. The material is already in effect acting as an outstandingly effective unbound layer and, because the long-term intrinsic strength is high, little further damage is likely. The load transfer across cracks should be highly efficient and should not deteriorate appreciably.

Because of the numerous pitfalls possible when designing with strong hydraulically-bound layers, Fig. 3.16 is included as a guide. Notice that

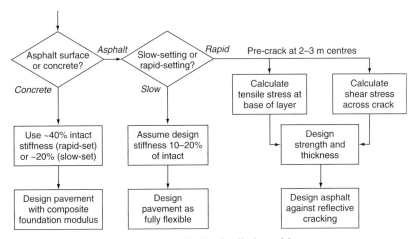

Fig. 3.16 Design guidance – strong hydraulically-bound layers

the figure includes a shear stress check for rapid-setting mixtures. This can be computed, approximately, using multi-layer linear elastic analysis and, based on the data in Fig. 3.12, should be kept to less than 10% of the design flexural strength.

3.4.1.13 Weak hydraulically-bound layers

This design case is a trivial one. The description 'weak' here means that the strength is not intended to be sufficient to prevent cracking under traffic loading. Actual compressive strengths will generally be well under 10 MPa on highways, but stronger materials could still fall under the classification 'weak' on airfields and industrial pavements where load levels are much higher.

Since cracking is expected, no design against cracking is possible. The only task is to assign a realistic long-term stiffness modulus to the layer so that overlying layers can be designed correctly. The stiffness computation for a discontinuous layer introduced in Part 2 (Section 2.2.5.5) can be used, but this depends on sensible inputs to the calculation. These are:

- *Crack spacing.* It is reasonable to assume that a layer subject to stresses sufficient to break it will, eventually, reach a state where cracks are separated by about two to three times the layer thickness – see Calculation Sheet 3.13.
- *Slip stiffness at cracks.* A value of $5000 \, \mathrm{MN/m^3}$ represents a crack with good interlock, probably including angular crushed rock

259

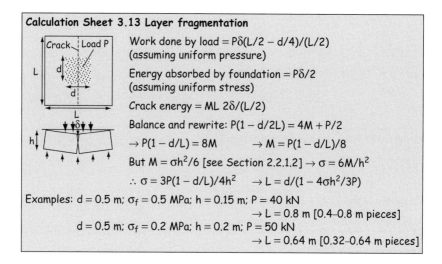

Calculation Sheet 3.13 Layer fragmentation

Work done by load $= P\delta(L/2 - d/4)/(L/2)$
(assuming uniform pressure)

Energy absorbed by foundation $= P\delta/2$
(assuming uniform stress)

Crack energy $= ML\, 2\delta/(L/2)$

Balance and rewrite: $P(1 - d/2L) = 4M + P/2$

$\rightarrow P(1 - d/L) = 8M \qquad \rightarrow M = P(1 - d/L)/8$

But $M = \sigma h^2/6$ [see Section 2.2.1.2] $\rightarrow \sigma = 6M/h^2$

$\therefore \sigma = 3P(1 - d/L)/4h^2 \qquad \rightarrow L = d/(1 - 4\sigma h^2/3P)$

Examples: $d = 0.5$ m; $\sigma_f = 0.5$ MPa; $h = 0.15$ m; $P = 40$ kN
$\rightarrow L = 0.8$ m [0.4–0.8 m pieces]

$d = 0.5$ m; $\sigma_f = 0.2$ MPa; $h = 0.2$ m; $P = 50$ kN
$\rightarrow L = 0.64$ m [0.32–0.64 m pieces]

aggregate, whereas a value of 500 MN/m^3 represents a material with poor interlock, for example having a very small particle size or very low material strength.

- *Intrinsic material modulus.* Base on material strength (see Part 2, Section 2.2.5.4).

Applying the discontinuous layer computation from Part 2 (Section 2.2.5.5) to the two examples in Calculation Sheet 3.13, with a material modulus of 10 GPa and a slip stiffness of 1000 MN/m^3, gives effective layer moduli ranges of 730–1790 and 330–1030 MPa respectively. These are typical values for such materials.

3.4.2 Cracking of asphalt

Asphalt has the dubious distinction of being able to crack as well as rut. It 'fatigues', like hydraulically-bound material, and Part 2 has presented a detailed discussion on the subject, concluding with the development of a fatigue characteristic based on laboratory test data. The following subsections introduce the ways in which pavement design takes account of asphalt fracture and fatigue.

3.4.2.1 Low-temperature cracking

This phenomenon manifests itself in the form of transverse cracks across the full width of a pavement and, as stated in Part 2, susceptibility to this type of cracking is generally related to empirical tests on bitumen; analysis is rarely carried out. In point of fact, such analysis is not difficult – Calculation Sheet 3.14 outlines what is involved – but the problem is that one of the key inputs to the analysis, asphalt viscosity, is not easy to estimate accurately. However, taking as an example a viscosity at $0°C$ of $30\,000\,GPa.s$ (binder penetration around 50), and assuming a factor of 3 increase for every $10°C$ temperature drop (as suggested in Section 3.3.3.3), then, with an asphalt fracture strength of 5 MPa (refer to Part 2, Section 2.3.1.5), the following are examples of daily surface temperature variations (assumed to be sinusoidal) which would be predicted to cause fracture:

- -10 to $-28°C$
- -15 to $-30°C$
- -20 to $-31°C$

Calculation Sheet 3.14 Low-temperature cracking

Assumption: Uniform temperature within the asphalt

As the asphalt cools at night, the contractive strain due to temperature loss ΔT is matched by an extensive strain due to tensile stress θ and viscosity η.

Thermal shrinkage: $\varepsilon_{contraction} = \alpha \Delta T$
Viscous flow: $d\varepsilon_{extension}/dt = \sigma/\eta$ $\Bigg\}$ $\varepsilon_{contraction} = \varepsilon_{extension} = \varepsilon$

Differentiate 1st equation: $d\varepsilon/dt = \alpha\, dT/dt = \sigma/\eta$ $\rightarrow \eta = \sigma/(\alpha\, dT/dt)$

Example: $\alpha = 1.8 \times 10^{-5}$; $dT/dt = 1°C/h$; $\sigma_{fracture} = 5$ MPa $\rightarrow \eta_{fracture} = 10^{15}$ Pa.s
If $\eta = 3 \times 10^{15}$ Pa.s at $0°C$, increasing by $\times 3$ every $10°C$, η reaches 10^{15} Pa.s at $-32°C$

However, low-temperature cracking is actually a repeated loading phenomenon, and the fracture strength should therefore be adjusted using a fatigue characteristic. For example, if the slope of the fatigue characteristic is 4 (or -0.25) on a log [strain]–log [load cycles] scale, the daily temperature ranges to cause failure after 50 cycles become:

- zero to $-20°C$
- -10 to $-23°C$
- -15 to $-25°C$

Therefore, supposing that 50 cycles represented a winter season, low-temperature cracking could be expected to occur, in this example, in a climate where pavement temperatures commonly fall below $-20°C$. (It is assumed that summer temperatures allow partially fatigued asphalt to make a full recovery.)

Clearly, viscosity is the key parameter. In the example in Calculation Sheet 3.14 a factor of 2 decrease in viscosity would allow around $5°C$

lower temperatures before the onset of cracking; hence the use of low viscosity binder in cold climates. In a desert climate, where binder penetration frequently reaches single figures, viscosity may be at least ten times that of a new 50 penetration grade mixture, in which case it is predicted that 50 cycles between +20 and 0°C would be sufficient to cause fracture.

Since viscosity is the critical parameter and bitumen is the viscous element in asphalt, design against low-temperature cracking can only be achieved by appropriate *binder selection*. In moderate climates this is not difficult and standard penetration grades are suitable, but in climates with very low winter temperatures or in hot climates with large day–night temperature variation, where binders are likely to age rapidly, modified binder may be the only answer – if indeed an answer can be found at all. Even advanced binder technology cannot work miracles and in certain climates low-temperature cracking simply has to be accepted as a fact of life and annual maintenance budgeted accordingly.

3.4.2.2 An overview of wheel-path cracking

It is, of course, commonly observed that cracks occur predominantly in wheel-paths, which means they are clearly due to repeated wheel loading – perhaps assisted by climatic factors such as low-temperature stresses. Part 2 (Section 2.3.4.4) has presented the fact that a relationship is generally found between tensile strain under load in a test such as the four-point bending test and the number of load applications until failure occurs; it is therefore quite logical that tensile strain due to bending of the asphalt layers in a pavement under a wheel load should also be related to cracking. Figure 3.17 illustrates the situation conceptually.

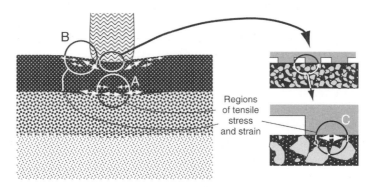

Fig. 3.17 Tensile strains in asphalt under wheel loading

Cracking can occur anywhere where tensile strain is present and Fig. 3.17 indicates three such areas:

- A: at the bottom of the asphalt immediately under the load
- B: near the surface just outside the loaded area
- C: at the surface in the tyre tread contact zone.

The first of these is generally (but often incorrectly) assumed to be dominant. Numerous so-called 'analytical pavement design' methods all over the world are based on this assumption and it is fair to say that this approach has stood the test of time. It has the advantage of simplicity since the strain at the bottom of the asphalt can be calculated unambiguously using multi-layer linear elastic analysis.

However, engineers can't help noticing that many, perhaps the majority, of the cracks they see have clearly originated at the surface. It is common, particularly in thick asphalt pavements, to find that a visually wide and dangerous-looking crack in a wheel-path actually only extends a centimetre or two in depth, and it is therefore natural to want to explain this and to build a top-down cracking prediction into pavement design. Unfortunately there is still considerable disagreement as to the cause of top-down cracking. Analysis clearly predicts that the immediate contact zone beneath the tyre tread will be extended horizontally by the mechanics of the tyre rubber,[38] making this a likely reason for crack initiation, although the depth of this high strain region is very shallow indeed. Immediately to the side of the tyre is a deeper-reaching region of high shear, leading to a tensile strain in a direction at an angle to the horizontal. The magnitude is not usually calculated to be as high as at the bottom of the asphalt, but this is compensated by the fact that bitumen commonly ages more at the surface than at the base of the layer.

Conceptually, therefore, top-down cracking is not difficult to explain – but it is far from easy to predict. So it is unsurprising that the great majority of analytical pavement design methods still concentrate on the strain at the *bottom* of the asphalt layer.

3.4.2.3 Design temperature

The point has been made many times that asphalt is a temperature-sensitive material. Its stiffness changes by a factor of about 3 for every 10°C temperature change, and stiffness is a key input to any calculation of tensile strain, wherever that strain may be. The truth is that temperature also affects fatigue behaviour. Perhaps fortunately, this effect is masked by the accelerated way in which laboratory fatigue testing is carried out, so test data are not usually particularly sensitive to temperature; but in real pavements fatigue cracking certainly is. Experience in temperate climates is that most wheel-path cracking damage takes place in the winter, when the stiffness is highest and computed strain is lowest, and some design procedures recognise this by building in a stiffness-dependent element to the fatigue characteristic; i.e. predicted fatigue life (at a given strain level) reduces as stiffness becomes higher.

The main reason for this temperature dependence lies in the property known as *healing*. Even after cracking, a bitumen is still a liquid and, given sufficient time and warmth, a crack will eventually self-heal. Time is available in a real pavement in a way not possible under laboratory constraints; warmth is available in summer. The result is that, despite the higher elastic strains in the summer because of reduced asphalt stiffness, and therefore the larger number of fractures of inter-particle bonds occurring, this is more than offset by healing.

So what are the implications? A rigorous analysis would have to take account of the contributions to cracking at all temperatures and then to sum them over a year, and this is hard to do with confidence. The latest US design guide actually does take this computationally-intensive approach, using an equation (see next section) for the rate of fatigue damage that depends on asphalt stiffness and therefore temperature.[39]

For most designers, however, the only practical approach is to admit that the problem is far too complex to analyse in such a rigorous way. They therefore select a design temperature – not quite at random, but the value selected is certainly not critical – and carry out the analysis with stiffnesses appropriate to that temperature. In the UK, the temperature usually selected is 20°C; in France it is 15°C. In reality, fatigue damage probably occurs at lower temperatures in both countries. But this is not really relevant. It is accepted that the computation carried out will only be indicative; there will have to be a significant *calibration factor* between any prediction of life based on laboratory fatigue data and life expected in reality.

3.4.2.4 Traditional analytical pavement design

The principal enabling task which has to be undertaken is the development of a *fatigue characteristic* for use in design, and this can only be achieved by calibrating against observed pavement performance. Any relationship between strain and asphalt fatigue life found from laboratory testing will require calibration before it can be trusted for real, partly due to the lack of realism present in all laboratory test set-ups and procedures, but also a function of the lack of realism inherent in traditional pavement analysis (relying on calculation of the tensile strain at the bottom of the asphalt layer ε_t). Such calibrations have been carried out by a number of organisations since the 1970s, notably the Shell oil company, the Asphalt Institute in the US, and the Transport Research Laboratory in the UK.[40] For example, the main Transport Research Laboratory equation for the number of load applications to fatigue failure of asphalt N_f, derived from experience of dense asphalt mixtures on typical UK roads, can be expressed as follows:

$$N_f = 4.17 \times 10^{-10}(1/\varepsilon_t)^{4.16}$$

In the US, the AASHTO mechanistic design procedure[41] makes use of the following stiffness-dependent formula:

$$N_f = 0.00432k_1'C(1/\varepsilon_t)^{3.9492}(1/E)^{1.281}$$

where $k_1' = \mathrm{fn}(h)$; $C = \mathrm{fn}(\text{mixture volumetrics})$; $E =$ asphalt stiffness modulus; $h =$ asphalt thickness.

An approach which is both sensible and practical is to adjust the actual equation applying in a particular case by treating laboratory testing as a purely comparative exercise. Thus, any proposed new asphalt material could be tested using a selected fatigue test and the results compared to a data set determined for a standard material of known properties. This would give a shift factor to be applied to the standard fatigue characteristic, i.e. a multiplication factor on predicted pavement life.

Once an appropriate fatigue characteristic has been selected, design is simple. Figure 3.18 illustrates the procedure. Naturally, the result depends on all the inputs to the procedure, not only the fatigue characteristic, and the advice given in Section 3.8 is relevant here.

Use of this type of design approach is widespread and, in the main, successful. It is often criticised for an underlying assumption that cracking starts at the bottom of the asphalt, something which is not always supported by observation, but this is a flawed argument since these methods do not rely on fundamentally correct modelling but on calibration against reality. However, there are genuine limitations of which users should be aware. Most importantly, the calibrated fatigue characteristic cannot be assumed to apply outside the climatic region for which it was developed. Nor can it be applied with any real

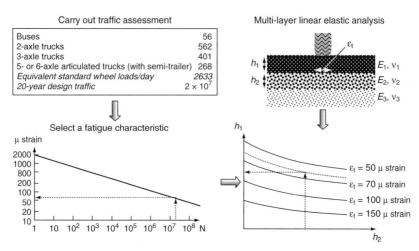

Fig. 3.18 An example of the traditional analytical design process

confidence to significantly non-standard asphalts, design loads, traffic numbers, pavement foundation materials etc. In such cases, the message is: handle with care!

3.4.2.5 Pavements with a thin asphalt layer

A particular problem with this type of analysis occurs with thin asphalt layers, as illustrated in Fig. 3.19. The problem is that deformation (and

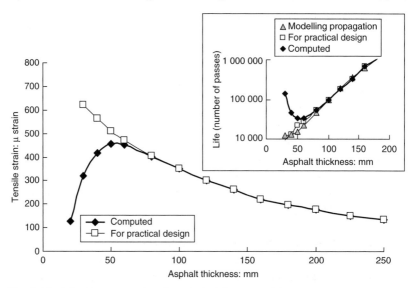

Fig. 3.19 Adapting conventional analytical design to thin pavements

therefore curvature) of pavements with thin asphalt layers is dominated by the stiffness of underlying support, which means that it only increases relatively slightly as asphalt thickness reduces; and strain, which is proportional to curvature but inversely proportional to thickness, actually starts to reduce again. However, while this may be theoretically true, it results in a highly unrealistic prediction of pavement life, and a practical approach (shown in Fig. 3.19) is simply to fit a characteristic curve to points with greater thickness and to project this characteristic into the low-thickness region. Also shown in the insert to Fig. 3.19 is a comparison of pavement life determined in this way with a prediction using the crack propagation modelling approach outlined in the next two sections, and the match is seen to be reasonably good down to a thickness of 30 mm. So, although this construction cannot easily be justified theoretically, it generates realistic solutions.

3.4.2.6 *Predicting crack propagation*
Most traditional design approaches make no attempt to model the progression of a crack. The result is simply the number of load applications until the 'state of cracking' has reached some defined condition, such as the first appearance of cracking on the surface. This has the clear advantage of simplicity but does not really have logic on its side. For instance two pavements may have the same calculated tensile strain, but one has twice the asphalt thickness of the other (due to dramatically different foundation stiffnesses for example). With traditional design, the predicted life would be the same, despite cracks having to propagate through twice the distance in one case compared to the other.[42]

To tackle this anomaly, and potentially develop an improved predictive technique, it is possible to interpret fatigue test data somewhat differently and to postulate a *crack propagation law*. The obvious choice here would be the so-called 'Paris law',[43] developed to model crack growth in metals, which relies on the calculation of a 'stress intensity factor' at the tip of a crack, and there are researchers who do indeed make use of this model for asphalt also. However, the differences between asphalt and metal are highly significant, and Part 2 has made the point that cracking in asphalt actually consists of the progressive breakage of bonds between individual aggregate particles rather than the propagation of a discrete crack. For this reason, the Paris Law is not recommended here. However, there is no reason why the observed relationship (from laboratory tests) between strain and number of load applications to failure cannot be re-expressed as a relationship between strain and crack propagation rate, always accepting that 'damage progression' may be a better description in reality than crack propagation. The suggested equation is of the form:

$$dc/dN = A\varepsilon_{crack}^{n}$$

where c is crack length; A and n are constants.
Or:

$$\int \varepsilon_{crack}^{-n}\, dc = AN \text{ [integrating over the propagation length C]}$$

The parameters A and n have to be determined from laboratory testing, and Calculation Sheet 3.15 suggests how this might be achieved. The details are open to debate, and Calculation Sheet 3.15 certainly represents a highly simplified understanding of the stress distributions applying under conditions of tension and flexure. The equations shown are, it should be noted, applicable only to tests carried out under *strain control*, although it would be equally possible to formulate parallel equations to derive A and n from stress-controlled tests.

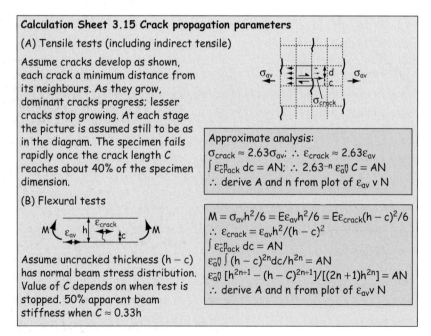

Calculation Sheet 3.15 Crack propagation parameters

(A) Tensile tests (including indirect tensile)

Assume cracks develop as shown, each crack a minimum distance from its neighbours. As they grow, dominant cracks progress; lesser cracks stop growing. At each stage the picture is assumed still to be as in the diagram. The specimen fails rapidly once the crack length C reaches about 40% of the specimen dimension.

Approximate analysis:
$\sigma_{crack} \approx 2.63\sigma_{av}$; ∴ $\varepsilon_{crack} \approx 2.63\varepsilon_{av}$
$\int \varepsilon_{crack}^{-n}\, dc = AN$; ∴ $2.63^{-n}\, \varepsilon_{av}^{-n}\, C = AN$
∴ derive A and n from plot of ε_{av} v N

(B) Flexural tests

Assume uncracked thickness $(h - c)$ has normal beam stress distribution. Value of C depends on when test is stopped. 50% apparent beam stiffness when $C \approx 0.33h$

$M = \sigma_{av}h^2/6 = E\varepsilon_{av}h^2/6 = E\varepsilon_{crack}(h - c)^2/6$
∴ $\varepsilon_{crack} = \varepsilon_{av}h^2/(h - c)^2$
$\int \varepsilon_{crack}^{-n}\, dc = AN$
$\varepsilon_{av}^{-n} \int (h - c)^{2n}dc/h^{2n} = AN$
$\varepsilon_{av}^{-n}\, [h^{2n+1} - (h - C)^{2n+1}]/[(2n +1)h^{2n}] = AN$
∴ derive A and n from plot of ε_{av} v N

A particular issue is selection of an appropriate value for the final crack propagation length C, representing the end of the test. Under stress control, the test ends when the specimen fails. In the case of a tensile (or indirect tensile) test, Calculation Sheet 3.15 implies that when a crack extends across about 40% of the specimen width then the assumed crack pattern breaks down and failure will occur rapidly; under flexure, with cracks developing from both top and bottom of the beam, rapid failure will occur (under stress control) once C reaches approximately one third of beam thickness h.

Having determined parameters A and n, the crack propagation equation can then, in theory, be applied to a pavement, although it is necessary to develop a method of pavement analysis that allows calculation of the strain in the region of a crack tip. This could be a finite-element analysis, but it could also be a simpler evaluation of asphalt bending (and shear), making an allowance for the reduction in effective stiffness as cracks develop. One such simplified form of analysis, suitable for spreadsheet work, is the so-called 'method of equivalent thicknesses'.[44] This method is based on the assumption that the stresses, strains and displacements beneath a surface layer (e.g. asphalt) are solely a function of the bending stiffness of that layer and the properties of the underlying material. Thus, a thickness h_1 of an upper layer of stiffness modulus E_1 and Poisson's Ratio ν_1 is assumed to be equivalent to a layer of thickness h_{eq2} of modulus E_2 and Poisson's ratio ν_2, E_2 and ν_2 being the properties of the underlying material. Stresses, strains and displacements can then be calculated using Boussinesq's half-space equations.[45] Calculation Sheet 3.16 outlines the necessary steps.

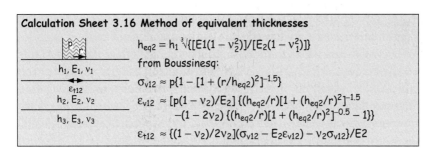

Calculation Sheet 3.16 Method of equivalent thicknesses

$h_{eq2} = h_1 \sqrt[3]{\{[E1(1 - \nu_2^2)]/[E_2(1 - \nu_1^2)]\}}$

from Boussinesq:

$\sigma_{v12} \approx p\{1 - [1 + (r/h_{eq2})^2]^{-1.5}\}$

$\varepsilon_{v12} \approx [p(1 - \nu_2)/E_2] \{(h_{eq2}/r)[1 + (h_{eq2}/r)^2]^{-1.5}$
$\qquad -(1 - 2\nu_2) \{(h_{eq2}/r)[1 + (h_{eq2}/r)^2]^{-0.5} - 1\}\}$

$\varepsilon_{t12} \approx \{(1 - \nu_2)/2\nu_2](\sigma_{v12} - E_2\varepsilon_{v12}) - \nu_2\sigma_{v12}\}/E2$

h_1, E_1, ν_1

ε_{t12}

h_2, E_2, ν_2

h_3, E_3, ν_3

The method of equivalent thicknesses generates reasonably accurate answers so long as each layer is significantly stiffer than the one beneath. In the case of a partially cracked asphalt layer, the value of E_1 used should be reduced to take account of the cracking present – see Fig. 3.20; the computed strain is then converted to a bending moment, from which the strain in the region of the crack tip can be determined (following the principle shown in Calculation Sheet 3.15

269

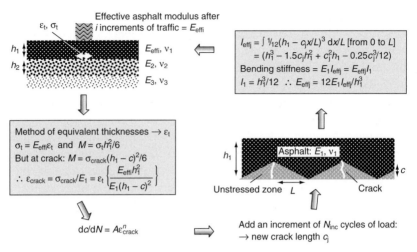

Fig. 3.20 Calculation of a crack propagation increment

for flexure). Note that the expression 'in the region of the crack tip' is appropriate here because the 'crack' is, in reality, not continuous, but represents a region of concentrated damage, i.e. broken bonds between particles.

The procedure is incremental. For each increment of a certain number of load applications (logically related to a certain growth in crack length), a new effective asphalt layer modulus is calculated, from which, using the method of equivalent thicknesses, the strain in the region of the crack is determined. This leads to the calculation of a crack growth rate, followed by a revised crack length, etc.

A sensible procedure for determining an equivalent stiffness modulus for the combined asphalt layers is needed and this might reasonably be taken as a weighted average, weighted according to the relative thickness of each sub-layer. It has to be remembered that this is an approximate calculation method, but it lends itself readily to spreadsheet work, which is an appreciable advantage. It also allows different asphalt layers of differing properties to be taken into consideration, for example the effect of use of a modified binder in one of the layers.

However, despite this approach taking crack propagation into account, *calibration* against known performance will still be required. This is partly due to the fact that different types of fatigue test tend to produce differing fatigue characteristics, but is also due to the inevitable differences between laboratory and site in loading rate, pattern of loading and temperature.

3.4.2.7 Top-down cracking

The problem with this sort of realistic modelling of crack propagation is that the issue of top-down cracking raises its head once more. It is no good carefully predicting the course of cracks from the bottom of an asphalt layer if the true mode of deterioration is by surface-originating cracking! Logically, therefore, it is necessary to develop a calculation technique for strain at the surface, and this is shown in Fig. 3.21. Admittedly, this is an area where there is no consensus as yet, and the equation shown in Fig. 3.21 is nothing more than a useful working approximation; the key assumption made is that surface strain is primarily a function of asphalt compression – and different researchers and practitioners may have differing views as to the most appropriate assumptions to make.

If using this computational method for crack propagation prediction, the equation for shear strain should change as the crack progresses. The simplest approach is to assume that the pressure due to wheel loading dissipates with depth into the pavement; the value of p in Fig. 3.21 should therefore be reduced as the crack grows, assuming a load spread angle (e.g. $35°$) acting in the longitudinal direction (i.e. along the crack).

Note that the equation in Fig. 3.21 is for shear strain and that the direction of maximum tensile strain is at $45°$ to the horizontal, which would logically produce an inclined crack. However, the *lateral distribution of tyre paths* across the pavement surface means that different load applications produce different maximum stress points and directions and the effect will be for inclined increments of crack growth to cancel each other out, leading to a near vertical crack. In fact, an

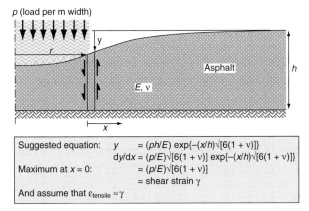

Suggested equation: $y = (ph/E) \exp\{-(x/h)\sqrt{[6(1 + v)]}\}$
$dy/dx = (p/E)\sqrt{[6(1 + v)]} \exp\{-(x/h)\sqrt{[6(1 + v)]}\}$

Maximum at $x = 0$: $= (p/E)\sqrt{[6(1 + v)]}$
$= \text{shear strain } \gamma$

And assume that $\varepsilon_{tensile} \approx \gamma$

Fig. 3.21 Surface strain computation

271

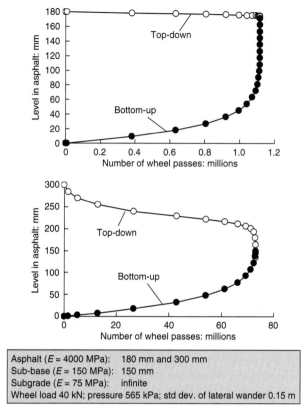

Fig. 3.22 *Predictions of crack propagation in asphalt pavements*

adjustment for the lateral distribution of wheel loads, often around ±0.15 m on highways but considerably more on most airfield pavements, can also be built into a spreadsheet-based prediction.

A point to emphasise is that the designer must never be afraid of approximation. The nature of pavement performance prediction will always be approximate because of the inherently uncertain materials involved and the unfathomable complexities of temperature effects. Thus there is little real value in precise analysis – only in taking a fundamentally correct approach.

Figure 3.22 shows predictions for both bottom-up and top-down cracking, carried out using the simplified techniques described above,[46] for two conventional asphalt pavements with identical granular pavement foundations, but with different asphalt thicknesses. Whether accurate or not, the predictions clearly match the observed fact that top-down cracking tends to predominate on thick pavements

272

but that bottom-up cracking is dominant for thin pavements. For the thick pavement, top-down cracking is predicted to occur relatively rapidly but then to slow at a depth of around 50 mm, which matches what is typically observed and gives a degree of confidence that the assumptions made are sensible. Notice that further rapid crack propagation only occurs after the bottom-up crack finally starts to make significant progress.

3.4.2.8 Pavement edge design

The difference between edge and internal loading has already been emphasised when considering concrete pavements – and it also applies to asphalt. However, because asphalt pavements are generally less stiff, the zone of flexure is concentrated within a fairly short distance of the point of load application, which means that, so long as the wheels are a metre or more from a pavement edge, the influence of that edge will be small enough to ignore. Problems generally only arise on minor roads, with insufficient width to accommodate two heavy goods vehicles without encroaching close to the edge. Most of the time, vehicles will maintain a position well away from the edge, but encroachment will occur when vehicles pass each other. Thus, although the edge loading case is a severe one, the number of load applications to be withstood is usually low.

The ratio between edge and internal loading cases introduced already in the Westergaard analysis of concrete pavements (Section 3.4.1.1) can be assumed to apply to asphalt pavements also, which means that the stress and strain in the asphalt would typically reach about 80% higher values at the edge than in the wheel path. Assuming an asphalt fatigue characteristic with a slope of 4 (or -0.25 depending on how the equation is formulated), this means that each edge load application induces about ten times the damage caused by a normal wheel path load application. Thus, if heavy vehicles keep well away from the edge 90% of the time or more, then edge loading is not critical; if, on the other hand, over 10% of passes are at or near the edge, then this becomes the critical design case (i.e. a reduced number of load applications but an increased asphalt tensile strain) and the pavement should be thickened accordingly, at least locally.

3.4.2.9 Reflective cracking – thermally-induced

Reflective cracking occurs when a cracked pavement is overlaid with fresh asphalt; it is also likely to occur when asphalt is placed over all but the weakest hydraulically-bound bases, since all hydraulically-bound materials inevitably crack, either naturally or at predetermined locations, i.e. joints. It is in this second case, where asphalt overlies hydraulically-bound material, that thermally-induced reflective cracking can occur.

Each intact piece of hydraulically-bound material will undergo a daily thermal cycle, and this will cause each crack to open and close. There may also be effects from warping. The layer of asphalt above the crack therefore has to accommodate this opening and closing movement and clearly the degree to which it is able to do this will depend on its viscosity, its fracture resistance, the magnitude of crack opening and, most of all, its thickness. It is not a particularly simple situation to model accurately and, for this reason, it is common to adopt an experience-based design. In the UK, the current official view is that an asphalt thickness of 180 mm is sufficient so long as the underlying hydraulically-bound layer is cracked at no more than 3 m centres; 200 mm is a figure sometimes quoted for a more general situation. Some design methods include simple predictive equations. However, they will not usually be based on sophisticated modelling. Even the otherwise frighteningly sophisticated AASHTO mechanistic design procedure in the US includes nothing more than the following rather crude formula:

$$\% \text{ cracking} = 100/(1 + e^{a+bt})$$

where t = time (years); $a = 3.5 + 0.75(h + f)$; $b = 0.688584 - 3.37302(h + f)^{0.915469}$; h = asphalt thickness (inches); $f = 0$ for asphalt underlay, 1 for concrete underlay in good condition, 3 for concrete underlay in poor condition.

However, there is an alternative. Mechanically, the problem is not an impossible one, although a degree of approximation is required to solve the equations resulting from balancing forces and from viscous flow. Calculation Sheet 3.17 details a solution.

The analysis summarised in Calculation Sheet 3.17 is admittedly simplified, and depends greatly on the assumptions made for the thickness and viscosity of the bond coat between the asphalt and the base. Nevertheless, it is realistic enough to allow the relative effect of different variables to be explored and is well suited to spreadsheet work, in which the viscosities of both asphalt and bond coat can be varied as the temperature changes. Once calibrated against experience, the model should be capable of generating satisfactory predictions for a wide range of cases.[47]

274

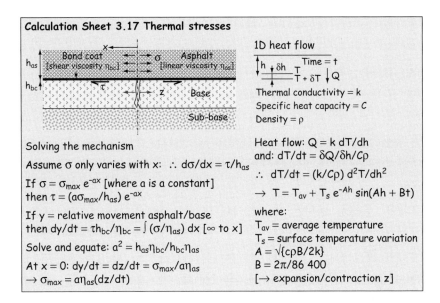

Calculation Sheet 3.17 Thermal stresses

1D heat flow

Thermal conductivity = k
Specific heat capacity = C
Density = ρ

Solving the mechanism

Assume σ only varies with x: ∴ $d\sigma/dx = \tau/h_{as}$

If $\sigma = \sigma_{max}\,e^{-ax}$ [where a is a constant]
then $\tau = (a\sigma_{max}/h_{as})\,e^{-ax}$

If y = relative movement asphalt/base
then $dy/dt = \tau h_{bc}/\eta_{bc} = \int (\sigma/\eta_{as})\,dx$ [∞ to x]

Solve and equate: $a^2 = h_{as}\eta_{bc}/h_{bc}\eta_{as}$

At x = 0: $dy/dt = dz/dt = \sigma_{max}/a\eta_{as}$
→ $\sigma_{max} = a\eta_{as}(dz/dt)$

Heat flow: $Q = k\,dT/dh$
and: $dT/dt = \delta Q/\delta h/C\rho$

∴ $dT/dt = (k/C\rho)\,d^2T/dh^2$

→ $T = T_{av} + T_s\,e^{-Ah}\sin(Ah + Bt)$

where:
T_{av} = average temperature
T_s = surface temperature variation
$A = \sqrt{\{c\rho B/2k\}}$
$B = 2\pi/86\,400$
[→ expansion/contraction z]

As in the case of low-temperature cracking, it should be remembered that the problem is really one of fatigue. Thus, it is reasonable to postulate a fatigue characteristic for the asphalt, assuming a slope of 4 (or −0.25) on a $\log_e(\sigma)$–$\log_e(N)$ plot, and to consider the build-up of fatigue damage to occur during the course of a winter season. During the summer, although the opening and closing of the underlying cracks may be just as great or greater, the ability of the bitumen to self-heal will effectively repair the damage. Thus, for example, if a total of ten worst-case thermal cycles are expected during a winter, the permissible stress should be taken as around 0.55 times the ultimate tensile fracture strength.

One of the key inputs is, of course, the worst-case daily temperature cycle, and this is not easily determined. Records of air temperature are readily available – but pavement temperature is not usually recorded. However, as an example, measurements carried out in the grounds of the University of Nottingham gave a variation at about 25 mm depth of around −2 to +8°C on just four days throughout the winter of 1997/8; on most days the day–night pavement temperature difference was in the range +2 to +5°C.

3.4.2.10 Reflective cracking – traffic-induced

In the minds of many engineers, all reflective cracking is thermally induced. This is certainly not true. There are numerous examples of two-lane carriageways with considerably more reflective cracking in the more heavily trafficked lane. And this is entirely logical. If nothing else, a crack in an underlying layer represents a local reduction in support stiffness. But the truth is that such a crack can represent much more than this. If the crack develops even the smallest 'step' (i.e. relative vertical movement) under the passage of a load then the overlying asphalt has to accommodate a serious strain. Experience has suggested to many researchers that a practical way of predicting this strain is to take an artificially low stiffness for the underlying cracked material, 500 MPa being commonly quoted and used. This is usually much lower than the 'effective layer modulus', the average flexural stiffness taking rotation and vertical displacement at cracks into account; it is a purely artificial value with no other justification than that of experience. However, several researchers and practitioners have come to the conclusion that the figure of 500 MPa is a sensible conservative value to use, and a standard analytical pavement design computation can then be carried out to determine life before traffic-induced reflective cracking occurs. Where a designer has confidence in the integrity of joints and cracks in the underlying materials, then a higher (but still artificial) stiffness may be justifiable, but no figure of greater than 1000 MPa can be recommended here.

For those who wish to look beyond this simple estimate however, it is necessary to think in more detail about the actual mechanisms involved in the production of traffic-induced reflective cracking. These are illustrated in Fig. 3.23.

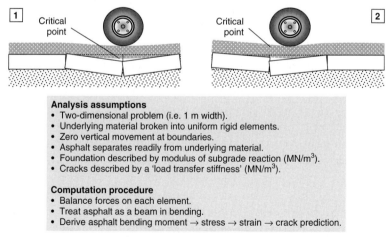

Fig. 3.23 Traffic-induced reflective cracking mechanisms

Notice the assumption that the adhesion between the cracked layer and the overlying asphalt is insufficient to prevent separation. It is not too difficult to demonstrate that this assumption is justified. If full bond is assumed, then the stresses both within the asphalt and at the interface with the underlying layer become extremely large, demanding failure somewhere in the system; since the bond is the weak link in the chain, significantly weaker than the asphalt itself, that is where the failure will take place. Besides, there is anecdotal evidence from sites where 'debonding' either side of a reflective crack has been noted.

Once debonding is allowed, the analysis illustrated in Fig. 3.23 is relatively straightforward; however, implementation is much more problematic. It is necessary to make several engineering approximations in order to generate a meaningful prediction of cracking. The key points which have to be addressed are as follows.

- The analysis is two-dimensional; the calculated asphalt bending moment (and therefore strain) must be adjusted to reflect real three-dimensional life.
- If crack propagation calculation is to be attempted, the local reduction in effective asphalt layer stiffness (due to a crack) has to be taken into account.
- Allowance should also be made for bending of the individual elements in the cracked supporting layer.
- Mode 2 in Fig. 3.23 occurs twice during every passage of a wheel – both before and after the crack. The second occurrence is the mirror image of the first and will generate an identical surface (or top-down crack tip) strain.
- One of the key inputs to the analysis is the load transfer stiffness, and this cannot easily be assigned, particularly since it will vary with crack width (and therefore with temperature in a hydraulically-bound layer). Experience[48] suggests that $5000\,MN/m^3$ represents an excellent condition whereas $500\,MN/m^3$ is extremely poor, but the real state can only be estimated approximately.

The truth is that this approach, like all pavement design, requires calibration. However, since it genuinely addresses the mechanisms that produce reflective cracking, it is inherently likely to give realistic predictions, even outside any directly calibrated range. On that basis, it is therefore recommended to the reader as a sensible method for reflective cracking analysis.[49] It also enables the engineer to appreciate the relative importance of different variables, including asphalt stiffness and thickness, but most particularly the load transfer efficiency across a crack. Where Mode 1 (bottom-up) is dominant, the load transfer is irrelevant; if Mode 2 is dominant, it is of critical importance.

3.4.2.11 Reinforced asphalt

The type of mechanistic analysis described in Sections 3.4.2.6–3.4.2.10 is well suited to non-standard designs, one of the most difficult of which is the use of reinforcement. It was suggested in Part 2 (Section 2.4.3.2) that the effect of reinforcement was to slow down the rate of crack propagation by a factor of up to around 4 in a zone – perhaps 100 mm thick – immediately above and below the reinforcing layer. The question as to exactly what factor is appropriate for what type of product, and indeed the extent of the effect above and below the reinforcement, cannot be answered here, but at least the use of a system for prediction of crack growth means that this slowing effect can be readily incorporated.

A more sophisticated analysis could also take account of the effect of a reinforcing grid in 'stitching' a crack, effectively preventing the crack from opening at the location of each reinforcing strand – although not between strands. This is a more complex computation, more difficult to include in a spreadsheet, but undoubtedly an important component in asphalt reinforcement. Figure 3.24 illustrates the concept.

It is simply not possible to generalise regarding the effect of reinforcement, since every design case is different. Predictions using the crack-propagation approach described above often suggest that a layer of

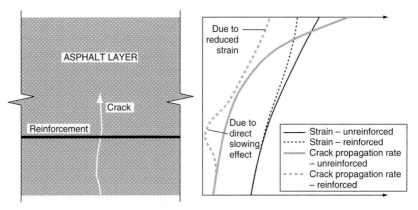

Fig. 3.24 The effect of grid reinforcement

reinforcing grid may be equivalent to around 30–50 mm of asphalt in a conventional asphalt pavement in terms of its effect in delaying crack development; in some reflective cracking cases, the predicted benefit is much greater than this, but this depends on the details of spacing and severity of underlying cracks.

It is even harder to estimate the benefit in the later stages of pavement life, when reinforcement may be expected to have the effect of holding an asphalt layer together, preventing narrow cracks from developing into larger failures. However, if pavement serviceability is to be allowed to deteriorate post cracking, there will certainly be a benefit.

3.4.3 Summary

Design against cracking depends on limiting the stress or the strain in a bound layer, whether hydraulically-bound or asphaltic, to an acceptable value. In the case of thermally-induced cracking, the limit is likely to be close to the tensile strength of the material since relatively few load applications are expected; in the case of traffic-induced cracking, the large number of load applications implies a much reduced stress or strain limit. The key points to bear in mind when designing against cracking are as follows.

- For *hydraulically-bound materials*, a realistic measure of *tensile* (or *flexural*) *strength* is required, and this will depend on the age of the material.
- For *thermally-induced cracking of asphalt*, the *low-temperature strength* is needed.
- For *traffic-induced cracking of asphalt*, a *tensile strain* must be calculated and used in conjunction with a fatigue characteristic.
- Improved life can be obtained by improving the crack-resisting properties of the materials concerned, including by means of reinforcement.
- Improved life can also be obtained by altering the design to reduce the value of the critical stress or strain in the pavement. In hydraulically-bound materials (and for reflective cracking in an overlying asphalt), reducing crack spacing and/or improving load transfer give significant benefit. For all designs against traffic-induced cracking, foundation stiffness has a large influence.

One question which has not really been addressed here is the degree to which cracking actually matters. On its own, a crack does not

interfere with pavement usage at all; it is only when that crack deteriorates and leads to more general break-up of the pavement that it
becomes a real problem. And that brings in a further very important
topic, namely that of pavement durability.

3.5

Design for durability

The term 'durability' is used here in the sense of durability of the pavement system as a whole. Some of this will be provided by durability of individual components; some will depend on overall pavement design. Any issue which has the potential to result in progressive loss of load-bearing capacity other than that anticipated due to cracking comes under the heading of 'durability'. This section will identify the various different issues that can apply.

3.5.1 The effect of time

While a well-constructed concrete may remain in a more or less 'as-new' condition for many decades, and an unbound material may remain unchanged for millennia, the one thing which is certain about an asphalt is that it will change its properties significantly over the years. This may not be a bad thing, but it is a fact which has to be recognised and which should be taken into account in design.

Part 2 has already made the point that bitumen ages with time, resulting in an increasingly stiff asphalt mixture. In itself this is no problem at all. Studies of UK highways constructed during the 1960s and 1970s have shown that the properties of many of the asphalt materials used are better now (2007) than they have ever been. The mixtures are stiffer, which means the strains due to traffic load are lower, yet the fatigue characteristic is almost unaltered. If this were a universal truth then ageing would be welcomed unequivocally.

Unfortunately, ageing is not always such a benign phenomenon. Ageing of bitumen is the observed consequence of loss of some of the lighter fractions either by oxidation, the effect of which is to tie molecules together, or by absorption into the aggregate. And it is the lighter fractions which give a bitumen its elasticity, its ability to flow and, perhaps of greatest significance, its adhesive quality; a hardened binder finds it difficult to 'bind'. In the first instance this is often seen in a loss of bond between individual asphalt layers and, once that bond is lost, it becomes much easier for water to find its way along the debonded interface. The next manifestation will be a tendency for the asphalt to become brittle. While confined in its layer and surrounded by other material, this may not cause any noticeable problem, but once deterioration commences, perhaps due to continuing water ingress, it can spread rapidly and result in the asphalt becoming little more than a heap of blackened stones. This is an extreme case, but experience shows that it can happen, especially where too hard a grade of binder has been used, or where high void content allows a ready passage of oxygen into the material, and most particularly where water is able to gain access.

The lessons for designers are clear. Appropriate binder grade, adequate binder content and good compaction all contribute to limiting the progress of bitumen ageing.

3.5.2 The effect of water

Despite the usefulness of water when compacting unbound or hydraulically-bound layers and the vital role of water in all hydraulic binding actions, during the life of a pavement water is often public enemy number one. The influence of water content on the deformation likely in an unbound material has already been emphasised, but the potential destructive role of water is actually much broader than that.

3.5.2.1 *Water in asphalt*

Bitumen is an excellent waterproofing agent. It therefore has excellent intrinsic water-resistant properties. However, an asphalt mixture has a weak link, namely the interface between the aggregate particles and the bitumen. During hot-mix asphalt production every effort is made to dry the aggregate and thus to ensure excellent binder adhesion and there is good reason for this; bitumen simply will not stick to wet aggregate. Thus, if water finds its way into the void spaces within an asphalt, there is a real danger that it will penetrate the bitumen coating and start to be absorbed by the aggregate particles themselves, starting an inexorable process of weakening the bitumen–aggregate bond.

Part 2 (Section 2.3.6.2) has introduced the various tests that have been formulated to check to what extent an asphalt is affected by water. Generally they involve soaking specimens at an elevated temperature for a period of days, sometimes interspersed with freezing cycles, and then testing for either strength or stiffness. The ratio of the strength or stiffness before and after this 'conditioning' is recorded, with ratios greater than 80% typically being accepted as proving suitability.[50] However, there is real doubt as to whether such an accelerated test can really guard against an effect which takes many years in practice. In the end, the design measures which are most likely to result in a water-resistant asphalt pavement are similar to those most likely to inhibit undue ageing, namely:

- Try to keep the water out.
- Make sure there is enough bitumen to coat the aggregate properly.
- Compact the layer well, thus limiting permeability to water.

All of these are important, but the second point is easy to get wrong accidentally. The effectiveness with which the larger aggregate particles are coated is very sensitive to the amount of bitumen soaked up by the filler fraction. Excessive filler content will allow insufficient bitumen for the larger particles, resulting in weaker bonds between these particles and an increased likelihood of water damage. But be warned; this may not show up in standard tests on new material.

One point which emerges from this discussion is that there is a very real need for a trustworthy test for water susceptibility of an asphalt and that, despite there being a large number of alternatives on offer, none has yet reached anything like full acceptance.

3.5.2.2 The effect of traffic on saturated bound material

An important issue which should not be overlooked is that a water-filled asphalt layer is not just in danger from accelerated ageing or from water damage to the bitumen–aggregate bond. Application of a high-pressure tyre will induce pore water pressures and rapid local flows of water between voids, particularly at the base of a poorly compacted layer, and this effect can wash binder clean off the aggregate. It can also destroy bonds in hydraulically-bound materials. It is common to find that the greatest water-related damage has taken place in a wheel path, strongly suggesting that these pore pressure effects make a significant contribution. Water damage is not likely in a PQC, but it is certainly possible in a weaker base or sub-base quality hydraulically-bound material, and it is equally possible in an asphalt.

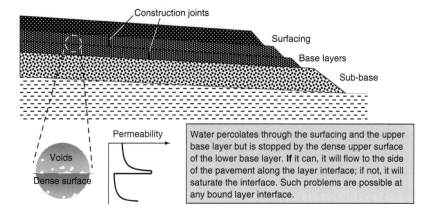

Fig. 3.25 *The problem of water trapped in bound layers*

In a well-designed pavement, the idea is that the surface is almost impermeable and that any water which does find its way through is readily able to escape. Problems only occur when water is blocked and is unable to escape from a particular location. And the worst problems are almost always to be found at layer interfaces. Figure 3.25 illustrates the design challenge.

This is not straightforward to model. However, design advice to protect against this effect is as follows:

- Do not place layers in excessively thick lifts, such that compaction is poor at the base of the layer.
- Use a generous bituminous tack coat between bound layers (except between two hydraulically-bound materials).
- Take care at construction joints not to leave a high void region (and never place a longitudinal construction joint in a wheel path).
- Ensure that water can escape to the side of the road.

The issue of a high void region is worth highlighting. It is not uncommon to find that damage has taken place adjacent to a construction joint, where compaction was poor, principally due to water becoming trapped. The result will be high pore water pressure under traffic loading, rapid water movement, binder erosion, bond fracture etc., and in a matter of a few weeks a seemingly strong layer of hydraulically-bound or asphalt base can be transformed into little more than an unbound material.

There is also sometimes pressure to forget the last of the above points, piling relatively impermeable soil against the side faces of the pavement; the use of granular fill is strongly preferred.

3.5.2.3 *Water in joints*

Joint sealing represents a whole technology in itself. Most fundamentally, it must be realised that no joint sealant can work miracles.
Modern sealants can accommodate amazing amounts of movement
over an enormous range of temperatures while continuing to adhere
to the surrounding asphalt or concrete, but they still have finite life
and the greater the stresses and strains they are asked to withstand
the shorter that life will be.

Even the best joint will eventually leak. In both asphalt and hydraulically-bound layers, where it is impossible to avoid longitudinal
construction joints between one laying operation and the adjacent
one, this means that water will potentially gain access to vulnerable
layer interfaces and also to the pavement foundation. Resealing of
construction joints is a maintenance nuisance but can be important
to maintain pavement durability.

In concrete pavements, the likelihood of water penetration through
joints is even greater due to the movement expected at such joints and
the consequent difficulty in maintaining an effective seal. As soon as
the seal begins to fail, rainwater will be able to make its way to the location of any dowel or tie-bar connecting adjacent slabs of concrete and,
given the chance, it will certainly initiate corrosion. A durable jointed
concrete pavement will therefore:

- have joints that are not too far apart, thus limiting movement at
  each joint
- include corrosion protection to dowels and tie-bars where they cross
  the joint
- utilise a bound sub-base.

The last of these may be hard to justify from the standpoint of pure
design theory, but organisations such as the UK Highways Agency and
several airport authorities have reached the conclusion that the long-
term pavement durability benefits outweigh the cost.

3.5.2.4 *Water in pavement foundations*

The issue of water in the subgrade has already been highlighted and
suggestions made as to the appropriate assumptions for long-term
design (see Section 3.3.1.6). It was proposed that a softening of the
upper 100–500 mm of any low-permeability soil beneath a granular
foundation should be accepted as inevitable, the actual degree of softening being seasonal as more or less water makes its way through the

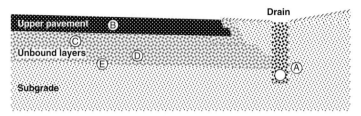

Fig. 3.26 Methods of limiting water susceptibility

pavement and into the foundation. This loss of performance will continue to worsen unless side drains continue to function properly. If the drainage fails, then matters will generally become much, much more serious. The question, therefore, is whether the pavement designer can do anything to limit the danger.

Clearly the drainage has to be suitably designed, constructed and maintained – that goes without saying. However, the pavement designer may also consider the following possible measures, illustrated in Fig. 3.26:

- A. Connect unbound layers to the drain.
- B. Include a highly impermeable layer within the upper pavement, such as a bitumen-impregnated geotextile.
- C. Ensure that the granular layer immediately above the subgrade is sufficiently permeable to shed water quickly to the sides.
- D. Limit the fines content of all unbound layers, thereby reducing their moisture sensitivity.
- E. Use an impermeable membrane immediately above the subgrade.

Apart from option A, these options should not be adopted thoughtlessly. Option B may have side-effects within the asphalt itself; option C should not lead to use of excessively open-graded materials or intermixing of soil and aggregate may occur; option D risks losing the benefits of suction at low moisture contents; and option E may cause more problems than it solves if the membrane leaks, allowing water to penetrate to the subgrade but never to evaporate from it. Thus, there are very real risks to offset against the benefits, risks which are not easy to quantify. Experience certainly supports the importance of maintaining the relative impermeability of the upper pavement – but the other 'solutions' are more questionable. In some cases, where a granular base forms the principal structural layer, it would be foolish in the extreme to reduce the fines content too much since performance is strongly dependent on a high suction within the material – but this means that it becomes even more crucial to maintain the surfacing in an impermeable state.

3.5.3 The effect of frost

Many of the issues relating to frost are the same as those relating to water since, if saturation with water can be avoided, then there can be no frost problem. The following paragraphs spell out the principal points.

3.5.3.1 Frost damage in bound material

Any free water within a pavement material is always susceptible to freezing if the climate allows. Ice occupies some 8% more volume than water, which means that water within an enclosed void will swell when it turns to ice and potentially cause fracture in the surrounding material. In the case of asphalt mixtures, frost damage is relatively rare since even the limited viscosity of bitumen at low temperatures is generally sufficient to allow local deformation around any ice-filled void. After all, freezing never occurs suddenly. In hydraulically-bound materials on the other hand there is no viscous element to material behaviour and local fracture is a strong possibility. However, this sort of frost damage will only occur under conditions of near saturation. Where there is sufficient free air this will readily compress, allowing the water to expand harmlessly. The solution therefore lies in making sure saturated conditions *never* arise at potentially frost-susceptible depths.

For PQC, where frost damage shows itself as surface spalling, Part 2 (Section 2.2.3.2) has identified two practical approaches to frost protection. The first is to ensure that the concrete is of such high strength (>5 MPa flexural) that it is capable of withstanding pressure from minute ice particles. The second approach is to use the technique known as air entrainment. A foaming additive is used in the concrete which generates large numbers of very small air bubbles, typically around 5% by volume. These allow sufficient flexibility throughout the concrete for strain due to expanding ice droplets to be accommodated.

However, in base concrete and other hydraulically-bound materials, which are less strong and therefore potentially more vulnerable, the most effective solution is definitely to design the pavement such that saturation never occurs.

287

3.5.3.2 Frost damage at interfaces

In climates where frosts occur, this issue is inseparable from that of water damage. When water gains access to an interface then it will start to attack the bond between bitumen and aggregate; when traffic load occurs, deterioration accelerates; when the water freezes it frequently becomes worse still, often destroying the inter-layer bond completely. This is most common near the surface of a pavement where regular freeze–thaw cycles occur, and the action of ice formation at an already damaged interface, where a relatively large volume of water is present, can contribute strongly to fracturing of an overlying asphalt layer – aided as always by traffic loading.

The solutions are the same as those given above in relation to water damage.

3.5.3.3 Frost damage to pavement foundations

Part 2 has already made the point that certain unbound materials are susceptible to frost as ice crystals form within and between particles. The *frost heave* test[51] has been widely used in the UK to give a measure of the way that frost formation destroys the structure of a material, following serious frost heave experienced on major roads in the 1960s, and it is usual to insist that all material within 450 mm of the surface has an appropriately low frost heave value. The depth can sometimes be reduced from 450 mm depending on local climate.

The immediate effect of frost heave is poor ride quality, although this is largely restored once the ice has melted. However, the legacy of a period of heave is cracking damage to the bound pavement layers and, sometimes, an irreversible softening of the unbound layers due to changes in soil structure. Additionally, if frost reaches a layer of stabilised subgrade, then this can dramatically affect the integrity of bonds between particles, and therefore the strength and stiffness of the layer.[52] If possible, therefore, frost-susceptible materials should be suitably protected.

The strategy inevitably has to be climate dependent. In the UK it is not difficult to prevent frost from reaching the soil; in continental Europe, the thickness of frost protection required is greater, reaching to almost a metre in eastern Europe. Switzerland is among countries which make use of an insulating layer at the base of the foundation. In countries such as Canada, however, there is no economically viable way that frost penetration through to the soil can be avoided. In this sort of case, since it is impossible to prevent freezing of soils, many of which will be frost susceptible, the only alternative is to deny the soil the water it needs in order for ice crystals to grow sufficiently to cause heave. Drainage, together with the prevention of water ingress through the surface, therefore becomes critical.

A final and quite acceptable strategy is simply to allow frost heave to happen. Use of a very soft binder in the surfacing layers provides sufficient flexibility to accommodate large strains, even at very low temperatures, and, though cracking will occur during the winter, healing will take place in the summer.[53] This strategy is obviously not suited to heavily trafficked highways, but it is quite acceptable on minor roads.

Although this section has been framed in terms of frost heave, with associated damage to materials, damage can still occur without any heave at all. Frost heave can be negated by choosing a relatively open grading, giving good drainage and therefore insufficient small water-filled voids – but freezing of the particles themselves can also inflict serious damage if those particles are porous. This danger is not normally checked directly and reliance is placed on general descriptors such as 'clean, hard and durable', but any aggregate with an absorption of more than about 0.5% should be considered potentially at risk.

3.5.4 Summary

Durability design is very largely concerned with problems caused by water, either as a liquid or in its solid form as ice. Basically, if water contents can be maintained at a low level, there are unlikely to be any pavement durability issues. The design will still have a finite life before cracking or rutting become excessive, but at least there should be no reduction in material properties during that lifetime. The economic importance of *drainage* should therefore never be underestimated.

Unfortunately, drainage is frequently neglected. The argument is sometimes heard that bases and sub-bases can never dry out because suction will always ensure that water is retained, and the value of drainage is therefore questioned. However, this misses the point that there is a massive difference between the performance of a material which is merely 'wet' and that of a saturated layer. A functioning drain can never remove water completely, but it will lower the water content until a balance is achieved between suction effects and those of gravity – and this state will be one of only *partial* saturation.

The message therefore is: try to stop the water getting in; make sure it can get out.

3.6

Non-standard pavements

For purposes of this book a 'standard' pavement consists of either unbound, PQC or hot-mix asphalt upper construction and a granular or hydraulically-bound foundation. Anything else is 'non-standard'. The various types of pavement grouped under this heading all demand either a slightly different design approach or else they have specific additional requirements.

3.6.1 Cold-mix asphalt pavements
A cold-mix asphalt is still an asphalt; that is to say it is still a mixture of aggregate particles and bitumen and the bitumen still acts to bind the particles together. However, as outlined in Part 2 (Section 2.3.7.5), the demands of cold-mix technology mean that:

- the material takes up to six months to achieve its design strength and stiffness;
- the void content will be higher than that of an equivalent hot-mix;
- the distribution of binder will be non-uniform, giving reasonable binding action among finer particles but reduced binding between larger particles;
- the resulting stiffness and deformation resistance will usually be lower than that of an equivalent hot-mix.

There are basically two approaches to pavement design where cold-mix asphalt is involved: either the material can be treated in the same way as a hot-mix, in which case the design principles already presented with respect to rutting, cracking and durability all apply, or it can be considered as an ultra-high-quality granular material. If considered in the same way as a hot-mix, then design against cracking is required

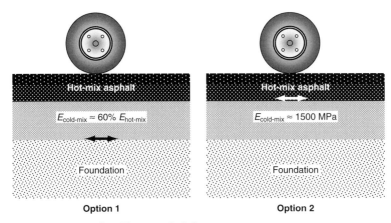

Option 1   Option 2

Fig. 3.27 Design with cold-mix asphalt base

and, since the stiffness will be lower than that of hot-mix while the fatigue resistance will probably be similar (at a given level of strain), this means that the design thickness will be greater. The advantage of treating cold-mix as a high-quality granular material is that no design against cracking is required. It is assumed, in effect, that cracking has taken place already. Figure 3.27 illustrates the two alternatives.

The actual numbers in Fig. 3.27 are indicative only, and the designer has to take account of the properties anticipated in each case. The estimate of 60% of the stiffness of an equivalent hot-mix, i.e. one with the same grading, binder content and grade, is based on the assumption that the void content of the cold-mix will be some 5% higher. With only 60% of the stiffness of hot-mix, the cold-mix design thickness in Option 1 will typically be some 25% greater than it would have been if hot-mix had been used.

The 1500 MPa shown in design Option 2 is intended to be a reasonable long-term value, accepting that trafficking during the first six months of life will limit the final stiffness achieved and that a significant number of micro-cracks or missing inter-particle bonds will be present. The figure is a little lower than would probably be found as an average for the layer since it is intended to represent the least intact locations.

Despite the understandable keenness of the cold-mix industry to promote full hot-mix equivalence, it is advised here that Option 2 is the safer and the more realistic. By nature, a cold-mix has discontinuities in it which are not present in a hot-mix, due to unequal distribution of binder, residual water films and early-life trafficking (discussed more fully in Part 4 (Section 4.5.5) under 'Cold in situ recycling'), and it seems sensible to acknowledge this in design. As it happens, the resulting design thickness is often no greater for Option 2 than for Option 1.

With respect to design against rutting however, it is advised that hot-mix principles are followed. Either a wheel-tracking test or a repeated load axial test will give a comparative measure of deformation resistance. It will usually be lower than for a hot-mix because of the higher void content, which may mean that a hot-mix surfacing is required; this will depend on traffic levels.

3.6.2 Grouted macadam pavements

Grouted macadam is another highly non-standard asphalt. As explained in Part 2 (Section 2.3.7.6), it is still basically an asphalt since it is temperature dependent and has an asphalt-like fatigue characteristic, but it is an unusually stiff asphalt with a near-zero susceptibility to deformation. So, while there is no radically different design technique involved, the secret is to use the material wisely – it is after all an expensive product.

It is generally used as a surfacing course for low-speed, heavy-duty applications, where PQC might otherwise be the natural choice. In many cases the advantages which make it attractive are the relative speed with which it can be constructed compared to concrete and the jointless finished product. The big question, however, is: what should the underlying pavement consist of? The options are asphalt (hot or cold), hydraulically-bound or unbound; and the chief design requirement is to avoid cracking. Figure 3.28 illustrates the most likely alternatives.

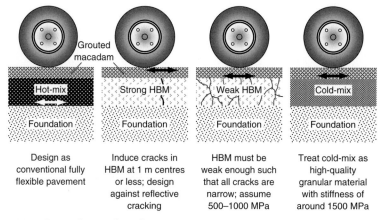

Fig. 3.28 Grouted macadam design options

All of these designs have been used successfully. The first is safe but expensive; the second two are less safe because of the slight uncertainty in hydraulically-bound material (HBM) properties, particularly the degree and nature of the cracking, but they may be economic. The fourth option appears to be an excellent compromise, accepting that there is always a degree of risk with cold-mix. Although not shown, an unbound base is in theory also an option; however, the susceptibility of grouted macadam to fatigue cracking means that it is not recommended except for very infrequently trafficked locations.

It should also be noted that geogrid reinforcement can be used at the bottom of a grouted macadam layer with a high level of assurance that full interlock will be achieved, since the grout will readily find its way around each strand of reinforcement. The additional degree of crack control offered by a geogrid is particularly useful where uncertainty in base properties exists. It can even be held in reserve as an emergency measure in any case where base construction does not quite go according to plan.

It is worth noting that grouted macadam is actually rather different from a conventional asphalt in its fatigue behaviour. In a standard fatigue test it appears to have a characteristic not unlike that of a dense-graded asphalt, but on closer examination there is an interesting and potentially valuable difference. Figure 3.29 illustrates the point.

The explanation for this behaviour is not straightforward but is likely to relate to the difference between discrete particle-to-particle bonds in a conventional asphalt and a continuous binder film between particles and grout in a grouted macadam. The implication is that a grouted macadam may be rather tougher than would appear from standard

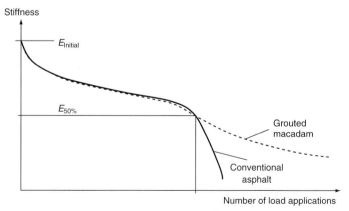

Fig. 3.29 Fatigue behaviour of grouted macadam[54]

fatigue tests, since these are generally stopped once the effective stiffness of the specimen has reduced to 50% of its initial value. This then raises the possibility of using grouted macadam other than as a surface course, for example as a very stiff, rut-resistant binder course. This is a potentially economic solution when rehabilitating an existing highway pavement by means of an inlay.

3.6.3 Sandwich construction

This term has been applied to many different types of construction by various authorities. However, here it refers to the inclusion of an unbound layer between two bound layers, a form of construction which has found frequent usage in South Africa[55] and which has now also been employed on several projects across the world. The particular design problem for which this type of pavement may be useful is as follows:

- High pavement temperatures mean that thick asphalt is likely to lead to rutting.
- Very heavy, slow-moving traffic also presents the danger of rutting but demands that a thick, strong pavement is used.
- Concrete is not considered a viable option (for example due to cost or equipment non-availability).

The combination of high temperature and heavy loading means that thick asphalt is not suitable. This means that a hydraulically-bound layer is definitely required. However, if the asphalt is placed directly over a hydraulically-bound base then reflective cracking is to be expected, unless a reasonable thickness (say 180 mm) is used – but this thickness is most undesirable due to the threat of rutting. A practical solution, shown in Fig. 3.30, is to separate the asphalt from the base by means of a granular interlayer, thick enough to prevent reflective cracking but not so thick as to lose the benefit of the high stiffness support provided by the hydraulically-bound base.

No design can work miracles. There are too many conflicting requirements here for complete comfort. Experience suggests that the granular interlayer must be at least 120 mm thick if reflective cracking is to be avoided, preferably 150 mm, yet the thicker it is the poorer the support to the asphalt and the greater the danger of fatigue cracking. The obvious response, i.e. thickening up the asphalt, then increases the danger of rutting. The design therefore has to be a practical compromise.

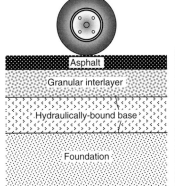

	1. Determine maximum permissible asphalt thickness to avoid excessive asphalt rutting – often around 100 mm.

Image labels: Asphalt / Granular interlayer / Hydraulically-bound base / Foundation

Box text:
1. Determine maximum permissible asphalt thickness to avoid excessive asphalt rutting – often around 100 mm.
2. Estimate 150 mm of granular material; take stiffness of around 300 MPa (due to confinement).
3. Design base thickness to avoid traffic-induced cracking by limiting tensile stress at bottom of layer.
4. Design sub-base and capping to avoid overstressing the subgrade (i.e. avoiding subgrade rutting).
5. Reduce thickness of granular interlayer if necessary to avoid fatigue cracking in the asphalt.

Fig. 3.30 Sandwich pavement design

There are one or two construction issues which should be mentioned. It is important to achieve good interlock between the hydraulically-bound base and the granular interlayer. If the hydraulically-bound material is dry and roller compacted this should present no difficulties; if it is laid wet then it is prudent to spread a layer of stones over the surface of the wet base before it sets.

Drainage can also be an issue. It is particularly important that water is not allowed to accumulate within the granular interlayer as this will rapidly destroy its properties and lead to asphalt fatigue. Therefore, since water will certainly penetrate the asphalt, it must be able to drain laterally through the granular layer and out at the sides.

3.6.4 Drainage pavements

Having stated that water is public enemy number one, here is a type of pavement which positively embraces the enemy. Pavements have a deserved reputation for increasing flood risk. They represent large areas from which water is generally led rapidly into drainage pipes and thence to a local water course, whereas rainwater would once have had to spend days soaking into the soil and slowly percolating through to reach a stream. This leads to more extreme peaks in river flow. It is therefore logical to try to do something about the problem at source, i.e. at the pavement.

3.6.4.1 The concept

Rather than being rapid shedders of water, drainage pavements are designed to act as reservoirs, holding onto rainwater and only slowly

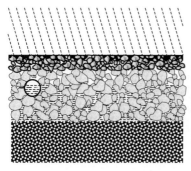

1. Rain soaks straight through the porous asphalt (or porous block) surfacing.
2. Water passes into the almost single-sized base material with around 30% voids. This is the 'reservoir'.
3. If appropriate, water is allowed to percolate slowly into the underlying soil.
4. Excess water is drained off via an overflow pipe.

Fig. 3.31 The drainage pavement concept

releasing it. They can even take water from elsewhere, thus going beyond flood-neutral status and becoming part of the solution. The pavement therefore becomes part of a 'Sustainable Urban Drainage System' (SUDS).[56] Figure 3.31 shows the concept.

There are different variations on the theme. If it is deemed unsuitable to allow the water to percolate straight into the subgrade because of contamination fears, then a separator membrane is used at the bottom of the reservoir and excess water is piped away – but much delayed compared to the case of a conventionally drained pavement. It is also possible to use artificial materials (plastics) to form the reservoir, the advantage being that the void content can rise from around 30% for an open-graded granular material to 90% or more, allowing a much shallower reservoir for the same capacity. The disadvantage may be cost and/or lack of structural strength. It is even possible to construct a drainage pavement on sloping ground by inserting internal 'weirs' within the reservoir material, dividing the area into separate 'ponds'. The particular design considerations in this type of pavement are outlined in the following sections.

3.6.4.2 Pavement thickness design

Reservoir design is not primarily a pavement engineering task. The capacity required for the reservoir depends on the role of the pavement in the overall drainage system. At 30% void content, the capacity equates to 3 cm of rainfall per 100 mm depth of material (counting only the rainfall landing directly onto the pavement). Design involves a knowledge of the relationship between likely rainfall events and the occurrence of flooding. In a small valley with a limited catchment area, flooding may occur within half an hour of a peak rainfall

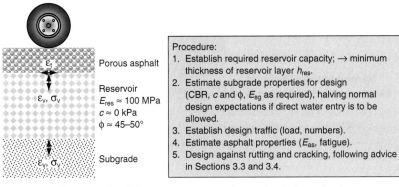

Porous asphalt

Reservoir
$E_{res} \approx 100$ MPa
$c \approx 0$ kPa
$\phi \approx 45\text{–}50°$

Subgrade

Procedure:
1. Establish required reservoir capacity; → minimum thickness of reservoir layer h_{res}.
2. Estimate subgrade properties for design (CBR, c and ϕ, E_{sg} as required), halving normal design expectations if direct water entry is to be allowed.
3. Establish design traffic (load, numbers).
4. Estimate asphalt properties (E_{as}, fatigue).
5. Design against rutting and cracking, following advice in Sections 3.3 and 3.4.

Fig. 3.32 The principle of drainage pavement design (asphalt surface)

event, and so a capacity equating to half an hour to an hour of rain may be sufficient. In larger catchments, the critical rainfall event is of longer duration and the required capacity may therefore be greater. The reader should refer to specialist guidance for further information.

However, pavement structural life is definitely the responsibility of the pavement engineer and Fig. 3.32 indicates the design issues involved. The reservoir layer is part of the structure, with a modulus and a potential to deform. Assuming that the material is a crushed rock, the modulus will usually be around 100 MPa under the stress conditions applying, compared to 150 MPa or more for a typical well-graded sub-base. The potential to deform is best related to strength parameters c and ϕ, and single-sized crushed rock tends to have a ϕ value of around 45–50° and a negligible value of c.

Thus, the reservoir modulus will affect design of the upper pavement, since it strongly influences the degree of pavement flexure which can take place. Similarly, the strength parameters should also influence upper pavement design since they dictate how much protection the reservoir material needs in order for it not to deform. Similarly, reservoir thickness, besides being a function of drainage design, is also constrained by the need to protect the underlying subgrade, and for this the strength of the subgrade itself has to be estimated.

The problem here is that, if water is to be allowed to drain directly into the ground beneath the pavement, this will greatly reduce the strength of that ground. Evidence from conventional pavements is that water entering a pavement through joints and cracks can already lead to a very significant softening, and this will clearly become worse in the case of a drainage pavement. Of course, the real value applying in the case of a drainage pavement will depend critically on soil permeability as well as the depth of the water table, but if an estimate is required, then a reduction factor of 2 on 'normal' design expectations appears sensible.

Once subgrade strength or stiffness (depending on the design method adopted) has been quantified, reservoir thickness design can be checked and if necessary modified in the same ways as for a conventional pavement.

3.6.4.3 Pavement surface

Drainage pavements are not generally high-speed highways and so neither ride quality nor skid resistance are likely to be significant issues. The key factors are that the materials used must be permeable and of adequate strength, and the usual candidates are porous asphalt or porous blocks. Block pavement design is covered in the next section, and the principles are exactly the same for drainage pavements as in any other case – although the block itself may be weaker due to the presence of vertical drainage holes. In the case of asphalt, the permeability requirement dictates a void content of around 20%, giving a likely design stiffness modulus at 20°C of about 1000 MPa. The fatigue characteristic may also be slightly poorer than for conventional dense asphalt, although this depends on the grade and quantity of binder used.[57]

3.6.5 Block paving

Block paving is a widely used surfacing type, being a modern continuation of a millennia-old paving technique. The blocks can be anything from small elements of rock, known as 'setts', to relatively large concrete paving flags. However a common standard size is a rectangular 200 mm × 100 mm concrete or baked clay element, with a usual thickness of 60 or 80 mm. Blocks are used for various reasons. In city centres, car parks etc., the primary reason is often aesthetics; however, maintainability is an older and still applicable justification. For industrial pavements, lorry parks, aircraft stands etc., the benefit lies in block paving's deformation resistance.

Whatever the justification for its use, block paving represents a quite different type of pavement from either asphalt or paved concrete, and it brings its own challenges to the pavement engineer.

3.6.5.1 *Structural pavement design*

Since they form a discontinuous layer, blocks add little to the structural strength of a pavement. If an analytical design is to be carried out, then a layer stiffness of 500 MPa is commonly used.[58] Structural strength has to be provided by whatever lies beneath the blocks.

Immediately beneath, there will be a 30–50 mm layer, either of bedding sand or of sand–cement mortar, and this may be considered part of the block layer for analysis purposes. However, the block layer will readily deform unless it is supported by a base of adequate strength. For lightly trafficked areas (pedestrian usage, light vehicles) this can be granular, in which case the mode of failure is deformation; see guidance in Sections 3.3.1 and 3.3.2.

Heavier-duty pavements will require a bound base, usually hydraulically-bound. The potential failure mode will be cracking, followed by disintegration and then deformation, and guidance has been given in Section 3.4.1. Note, however, that use of block paving means there is little benefit in controlling cracking in the hydraulically-bound base by means of joints.

Thus, structural design presents no more challenge than any other pavement type; the difficulties lie in the details, as described in the next two sections.

3.6.5.2 *Bedding and jointing*

Traditionally, blocks have been placed on *bedding sand*, and experience has led to the use of 30–50 mm. Sand is also used to fill the joints between blocks. This is a subject where engineering design achieves only so much; success depends critically on workmanship, i.e. ensuring a sound, even support to each block. However, that does not excuse the pavement engineer from rational thought. One of the most common forms of deterioration of block paving is settlement of individual blocks under repeated load, and an approximate analysis of the problem is certainly possible. The issue (Fig. 3.33) is one of failure within the layer of sand bedding, and this can only occur if the failure strength of the material is exceeded or, at least, closely approached. Obviously the quality of the sand in terms of its angle of internal friction is critical; so too the thickness of the blocks themselves; also the sand layer thickness – too thick and failure occurs more easily. However, one of the key influences is the effectiveness of joint filling and the block pattern used. The pattern shown in Fig. 3.33, known as 'herringbone', is one of the most effective at generating the required interlock.

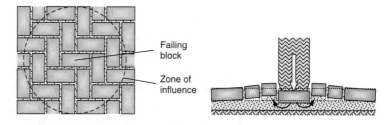

Fig. 3.33 Sand bedding failure

Failure within sand bedding has to be recognised as a potential mechanism and this places a limit on the tyre pressure which should be permitted on this sort of structure. In heavy-duty applications it is necessary to use something much stronger than sand if block settlement is to be avoided, namely cementitious mortar.

3.6.5.3 Avoiding block fracture

Blocks can fracture when a non-uniform stress distribution is applied, and this will occur where there are defects within the bedding. Naturally, this cannot be predicted with any confidence, but Calculation Sheet 3.18 gives examples of possible situations, with both sand and mortar bedding. And, despite the uncertainties involved, one factor emerges as of critical importance, namely the ratio of block length to block thickness.

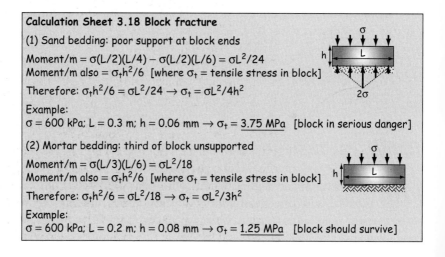

Calculation Sheet 3.18 Block fracture

(1) Sand bedding: poor support at block ends

Moment/m $= \sigma(L/2)(L/4) - \sigma(L/2)(L/6) = \sigma L^2/24$
Moment/m also $= \sigma_t h^2/6$ [where σ_t = tensile stress in block]
Therefore: $\sigma_t h^2/6 = \sigma L^2/24 \rightarrow \sigma_t = \sigma L^2/4h^2$

Example:
$\sigma = 600$ kPa; $L = 0.3$ m; $h = 0.06$ mm $\rightarrow \sigma_t = \underline{3.75\ MPa}$ [block in serious danger]

(2) Mortar bedding: third of block unsupported

Moment/m $= \sigma(L/3)(L/6) = \sigma L^2/18$
Moment/m also $= \sigma_t h^2/6$ [where σ_t = tensile stress in block]
Therefore: $\sigma_t h^2/6 = \sigma L^2/18 \rightarrow \sigma_t = \sigma L^2/3h^2$

Example:
$\sigma = 600$ kPa; $L = 0.2$ m; $h = 0.08$ mm $\rightarrow \sigma_t = \underline{1.25\ MPa}$ [block should survive]

One further point is that uneven support to a block on cementitious mortar will also tend to stress the adhesive bond between block and mortar. In the second example in Calculation Sheet 3.18, if the tyre load only covered the unsupported part of the block then the resulting bending moment would cause a tensile stress of 450 kPa at the block–mortar interface. This has to be resisted by means of a specialist bonding product; otherwise loose blocks will result, eventually leading to an uneven surface as detritus works its way in under the block.

3.6.6 Summary

Although this section of the book has tried to deal with all the different non-standard pavement types which are likely to be encountered, it has certainly not covered all possibilities. As alternatives to bitumen and cement are sought, then it is likely that materials with significantly different forms of behaviour may emerge, leading to significantly different modes of pavement deterioration. Pavement designs including products such as bio-binders, polyurethane and sulphur may need to be carried out.

Of more immediate concern are pavements which have grown into complex structures over the years as a result of multiple overlay treatments, for example where a concrete pavement has been constructed over an existing concrete slab, but with an asphalt interlayer in between. However, this is territory which will be tackled in Part 4.

3.7

Pavement surface design

Previous sections have concentrated on the structural strength of a pavement, ensuring that neither deformation nor cracking is excessive and that material properties do not deteriorate with time. However, the most sensitive element in a pavement from the point of view of a user is obviously the surface. Part 1 has outlined the different methods used to construct a surface, both in concrete and in asphalt; this section will treat surface design in rather more detail.

3.7.1 Achieving good ride quality

One must never forget that excellent ride quality is not always necessary; but on high-speed roads it most definitely is. Typical tolerance limits specified at the surface of such a road would be ± 3 mm in 3 m, and in order to achieve this an appropriate 'system design' is needed.

3.7.1.1 Wet-formed pavement quality concrete

There should be no problem achieving the required tolerance in a machine-laid wet-formed concrete pavement (although this is not true of hand-laid pavements). Therefore, concrete should logically be well suited to high-speed applications. Unfortunately, one of the few things that virtually all highway users can agree on is that it is not a pleasure driving on a concrete road. The problem however is not failure to achieve construction tolerance. It is the hard, unforgiving nature of concrete itself, unable to absorb much energy from the tyres. This results in high *tyre vibration*, which is felt within the vehicle as well as being associated with relatively high noise.[59] It is true that surface texture also plays a key role here and that certain grooving patterns have been found to make these vibrations worse, whereas an exposed aggregate finish (refer to Part 1, Section 1.3.2.9) is a much kinder surface to drive on – comparable to dense asphalt. Nevertheless, concrete suffers from a fundamental problem due to its lack of energy absorption. It is only a problem at high speed and only for road vehicles – aircraft noise drowns out anything due to the pavement.

A secondary problem is that of joints. Perhaps surprisingly, the 20 mm or so of gap between bays is readily felt as a mild impact despite the excellence of modern car suspension systems. The problem is that the frequency range of this impact is vastly higher than that for which the suspension (including car seat damping) is designed. It is not a major problem in reality, but it is a further perceived nuisance. Again, it is not a significant issue for airfield pavements or for low-speed applications.

Of course, concrete can still be used for high-speed roads, but this will depend on the relative importance assigned to ride quality against other issues, most notably economics.

3.7.1.2 Roller-compacted concrete

Unfortunately it is quite impossible to achieve the same tolerances in dry roller-compacted mixtures as in wet-formed concrete, which effectively rules out such materials as surface layers on major roads. The problem is that layer thickness would generally be at least 150 mm and this is much too thick for tight level control. As a surface material, roller-compacted concrete is therefore only suited to low-speed roads or industrial applications.

3.7.1.3 Asphalt

The point made above in relation to roller-compacted concrete also applies to asphalt, which means that the uppermost layer of an asphalt road has to be of relatively low thickness in order to achieve tolerances suited to high-speed usage; 50 mm is just about the upper limit and 30–40 mm is more common. Even with a suitably thin surfacing, it will only be possible to achieve the specified tolerances (for high speed) if the surface of the underlying layer is also reasonably even – and this principle applies right the way through the pavement. The evenness of the surface of each layer can be constructed slightly better than that of the one below, but only slightly; the logic, therefore, is that thick and not particularly accurately laid materials can be permitted

Table 3.2 UK HA tolerances

Level	Tolerance
Pavement surface	±6 mm
Binder course	±6 mm
Base	±15 mm
Sub-base	+10–30 mm

low down in the structure, with ever thinner and more accurately finished layers as the final running surface is approached. This is the reason why it is common practice to use a so-called 'binder course' between the base and the surface course. The current UK Highways Agency tolerances at each level are given in Table 3.2.

However, as with concrete, surface evenness is not the only factor contributing to ride quality. A number of different surface course materials are in common use; Table 3.3 summarises the impact of each surface type on likely ride quality.

The table is only intended as a crude summary. In reality there is a vast spectrum of alternative mixtures from asphalt concrete, through stone mastic asphalt to porous asphalt. However, the key points seem to be that a negative texture (holes rather than protrusions) minimises disturbance to the tyre tread and therefore gives low vibration,[60] while low material stiffness leads to high energy absorption and therefore vibration damping. From the point of view of ride quality, porous asphalt is the perfect surface.

3.7.1.4 Block paving

Block paving is not of course designed to give a particularly good ride quality. It would out-score surface dressing or concrete as a material with particularly poor vibration-generating properties and is therefore

Table 3.3 Asphalt surface ride quality

Surface type	Vibration generation	Energy absorption	Ride quality ranking
Asphalt concrete	Medium	Medium	3
Rolled asphalt + chippings	Medium	Low	4
Stone mastic asphalt	Low	High	2
Porous asphalt	Low	Very high	1
Surface dressing	High	Low	5

not suited to high-speed applications. Surface evenness on the other hand is often of high quality, although this is driven more by aesthetics and a desire to avoid any ponding of surface water than out of consideration for ride quality.

3.7.2 Material strength and contribution to pavement strength

The word 'strength' is used here in a very general sense as the structural properties of the surface material and the surface's contribution to the load-bearing capacity of the pavement as a whole.

There is no need to deal separately with concrete options here. Surface concrete is of exactly the same strength as the rest of the concrete slab and so there are no specific surface strength properties to consider. However, this is not true of other surface options.

3.7.2.1 Unbound surfaces

The problem with fully unbound pavements is that the stress conditions at the surface are particularly hard to withstand. Right at the edge of the wheel load patch, the horizontal stress near the surface must: (1) be sufficiently large to withstand the high vertical stress from the tyre without significant permanent strain; but (2) not be so large that failure occurs outside the loaded area due to the zero overburden stress applying there. In an almost entirely frictional material such as a crushed rock, these twin requirements are virtually impossible to fulfil; the material needs a degree of *cohesion*. Where unbound pavements are to receive significant traffic loads, as is the case over much of the world, it is therefore common to include clay fines (usually naturally occurring, for example in lateritic gravels).

However, clay brings its own problems. At exactly the right clay content, the beneficial properties (cohesion, very low permeability) are combined with the benefits of an aggregate skeleton, resulting in an excellent, stable and dust-free surface. The protruding aggregate particles can even give a reasonable level of skid resistance. On the other hand, if the clay content is too high, the result during wet weather will be a low-strength material with a dangerous low-friction surface. It is a difficult balance to achieve – but crucial to economic design. As a rough guideline, there should be between 25 and 45% retained on the 425 µm sieve and the optimum Plasticity Index of material passing 425 µm would usually be between 4 and 9%.[61]

3.7.2.2 Asphalt surfaces

Base quality asphalt is designed to give an optimum combination of stiffness, deformation resistance and fatigue strength in the most cost-effective way possible, and this commonly means a low-to-medium bitumen content and relatively large stone size (compared to the surface). The surface course on the other hand has to have relatively small stone size due to its low layer thickness (required in order to achieve level tolerances) and, consequently, a relatively high bitumen content. This leads to a less stiff material, although deformation resistance and fatigue strength can be as high or higher than those of the base. Table 3.4 lists the likely properties relative to those of an asphalt concrete base.

Table 3.4 is a rough guide to a very large range of possible materials. However, the fact is that the stiffness of the surface course is often no more than about 60% that of the base (assuming the same binder grade), while the binder course is often considered to be of the same stiffness as the base. This reduced stiffness can be taken into account directly in multi-layer linear elastic pavement analysis or, if an estimate is needed, it can be assumed that a proportional difference in stiffness is approximately equivalent to the inverse square of a corresponding difference in thickness. Thus a factor of 2 difference in stiffness is equivalent to a factor of around 1.4 difference in thickness. In simple terms, a 40 mm surfacing is structurally equivalent to about 30 mm of conventional asphalt base – nearer 25 mm if porous asphalt is used. Where an asphalt surface is used over PQC, the stiffness ratio is often around 20, giving a ratio of 4–5 in equivalent thickness; i.e. a 40 mm surfacing becomes structurally equivalent to about 10 mm of PQC.

Turning to the other measures of quality, surface course materials (with the possible exception of porous asphalt) should generally have

Table 3.4 Asphalt surface structural properties

Surface type	Stiffness	Deformation resistance	Fatigue strength
Asphalt concrete	Medium	High	Medium
Rolled asphalt + chippings	Medium	Low	High
Stone mastic asphalt	Medium-low	High	Medium-high
Porous asphalt	Low	Medium-high	Medium-low
BASE	HIGH	HIGH	MEDIUM

at least as good fatigue properties as an asphalt base. However, it is not uncommon for both surface course and binder course to have relatively poorer deformation resistance; the designer should be aware that there is a higher risk of deformation problems with some surface types, particularly rolled asphalt, which relies heavily on the quality of the sand-size fraction within the mixture. Note that deformation problems often stem from the binder course, largely because the binder course generally experiences the most damaging combination of stresses.

3.7.2.3 Block paving

Blocks themselves are high-stiffness components. However, the effective layer stiffness is a function of the permissible rotation and shear at joints, which in turn depends on how well the joints are filled. Using the computational routine presented in Part 2 for a discontinuous layer, the effective stiffness generally comes out at 500–1000 MPa, and this range of stiffness has also been obtained both by field testing and by laboratory investigation. In fact, it is common practice to assume a stiffness of 500 MPa for a combined block-bedding sand layer, as stated in Section 3.6.5.1. Using the rule of thumb introduced above for asphalt surfacing, this means that blocks placed over PQC would only be structurally equivalent to 10–15 mm of concrete and, bearing in mind the rather uncertain nature of these assumptions, it is usual to ignore their contribution entirely. In an analytical computation, the 500 MPa value can, of course, be used directly.

3.7.2.4 Performance under high tyre contact stress

All surfaces are sensitive to applied pressure, even though whole-pavement analysis may not be. Calculation of stress or strain at the bottom of a structural layer is primarily a function of total wheel load, with little effect from contact stress, whereas stress level near the surface is almost independent of total load and entirely dependent on contact stress. If a sophisticated analysis of crack propagation is carried out, including top-down crack propagation, then these facts will properly affect the result; in most design analyses however they will not.

The usual approach therefore is to rely on experience – which is that PQC is more than adequate for the highest contact stresses likely (around 3 MPa from some military aircraft) even taking into account the weakening effect of texturing the surface. Since the tensile strength of PQC is typically at least 4 MPa, this is hardly surprising. However, asphalt is much more susceptible to damage, particularly if subject to slow-moving loads. The chief danger is deformation, to combat which asphalt relies heavily on aggregate interlock, a difficult property to assess. A common approach for those using the Marshall method of mixture design (see Part 2, Section 2.3.7.2) is to insist on a very high Marshall stability value for the surface course in high stress applications, sometimes as high as 20 kN. For those relying on the repeated load axial test, a strain of under 1% is required after 3600 load applications at 100 kPa if pressures of 1.5 MPa or more are to be accommodated. An extreme solution to the problem is to use grouted macadam, which is in effect a fully deformation-resistant asphalt.

When properly proportioned, block paving is fully capable of withstanding the highest tyre pressures. However, design is important since there is the potential for very high bending stresses within a block (see Section 3.6.5.3), particularly when the possibility of non-uniform support is taken into account.

3.7.3 Achieving skidding resistance

Part 1 has outlined the influence which skidding resistance requirements have on choice of pavement type. This section will explore the technical details of skidding resistance further.

3.7.3.1 Microtexture

Microtexture is the term usually applied to describe the intrinsic frictional properties of the surface. In an asphalt, the microtexture in question relates to the aggregate particles at the surface; in a wet-formed concrete it relates to the cementitious mortar; in block paving it relates to the surface of the block. The term 'microtexture' is used because the surface features which give rise to friction are invisibly small. A stone may appear rough to the eye, but that is little indication of the level of friction achievable between tyre rubber and the stone surface.

Microtexture can be measured in the form of a coefficient of friction, or a number related to it. A common technique is the 'pendulum test',[62] illustrated in Fig. 3.34. A typical coefficient of friction would be between 0.5 and 0.7. It is the microtexture which represents the ultimate skid resistance potential of a surface, the level applying in dry conditions and without any intervening dirt, bitumen or ice lens. In theory, a friction coefficient of 0.5 would allow a vehicle travelling at 25 m/s (around

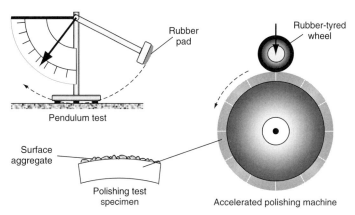

Rubber pad

Rubber-tyred wheel

Pendulum test

Surface aggregate

Polishing test specimen

Accelerated polishing machine

Fig. 3.34 Microtexture evaluation

60 mph) to come to a halt in 64 m; at a friction coefficient of 0.7, the distance becomes just 46 m. It is logical therefore to insist on improved microtexture at sensitive locations such as approaches to pedestrian crossings and roundabouts, and this approach is adopted by highway authorities all over the world. Certain aggregate types such as 'grit-stones' therefore take on a premium value because of their excellent microtexture.

3.7.3.2 Polishing

It is an observed fact that the frictional properties of a surface tend to change under the action of traffic. In dry weather they are 'polished' by the relative motion of tyre and surface, activated partly by tyre vibra-tion. The effect is a reduction in microtexture and a reduction in the coefficient of friction. It is standard practice in many countries including the UK to assess the so-called 'Polished Stone Value' (PSV)[63] of an aggregate by first subjecting it to an accelerated polishing regime (see Fig. 3.34) before measuring the frictional properties using the pendulum test. In the case of concrete, a 'Polished Mortar Value' applies; in the case of block paving, a 'Polished Paver Value'. And the result of such tests is that many stone types are found to be inadequate for applica-tions where high skid resistance is required; concretes on the other hand are generally found to be satisfactory for all but the most onerous locations.

This approach is realistic and acknowledges the reduced friction generated by tyre action. However, there is some evidence that it may be unfairly penalising certain surface types. The point seems to

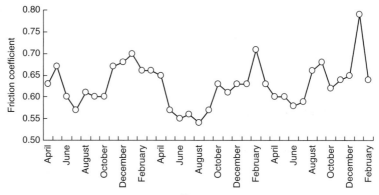

Fig. 3.35 Example skid resistance data[65]

be that polishing is strongly linked to the energy dissipated by the tyre during contact with the pavement surface and that this is inversely related to the amount of energy absorbed by the pavement. Thus, an energy-absorbing surface such as porous asphalt or stone mastic asphalt, which induces much less tyre vibration, also suffers much less polishing. Initially, this may not be a good thing since bitumen remaining on the surface of the stone may take a while to rub off, causing an initial period of low friction, but once this has occurred the lack of polishing of the aggregate particles themselves is likely to preserve a relatively high skid resistance. Anecdotal evidence is that this deduction is supported by accident statistics, although further study is required before the case can be considered proven.[64]

Microtexture is seasonal – see example in Fig. 3.35. Polishing occurs mainly in dry weather, whereas wet weather actually restores frictional properties to some extent due to the abrading effect of small particles of grit which are present in surface water. For this reason, skid resistance should preferably be assessed in summer or during the dry season.

3.7.3.3 Macrotexture

If it never rained it would not be necessary to introduce any visible texture to a pavement surface nor for tyres to include tread depth. Neither tread nor visible surface texture make the smallest contribution to basic skid resistance; they are only present to ensure that surface water has somewhere to go. The point is that direct contact is needed between tyre and surface in order for friction to be activated; if a water film remains in between, the vehicle will 'aquaplane' as soon as brakes are applied. It's not a precise science, but the principle

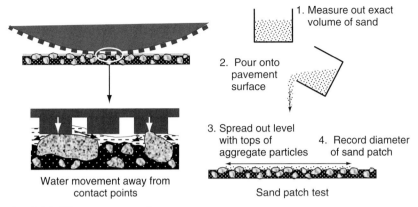

1. Measure out exact volume of sand

2. Pour onto pavement surface

3. Spread out level with tops of aggregate particles

4. Record diameter of sand patch

Water movement away from contact points

Sand patch test

Fig. 3.36 The importance of macrotexture

is clear enough – see Fig. 3.36. The faster the vehicle, the less time is available for the water to be forced away from the contact point. An optimised macrotexture therefore ensures that there is only a short distance between individual contact points and regions where water can be accommodated without danger. It also ensures that there is enough storage volume in these regions to cope with the envisaged quantity of surface water. It is the macrotexture requirement which gives rise to the wide variety of surface finishes already introduced, all of which in one way or another have to ensure that a pavement surface includes high points, where tyre contact takes place, and low points, where water can lie. Experience suggests that water should not be asked to travel more than a very short distance (i.e. millimetres only) during the few milliseconds of contact time, thus giving a further reason to restrict the aggregate size in surface course mixtures and also restricting the choice of technique used to texture wet concrete for high-speed applications.

Macrotexture is generally expressed as a 'texture depth' in milli-metres. The basic measure comes from a procedure known as the 'sand patch test' (Fig. 3.36), although there are numerous laser-based pieces of equipment on the market for rapid, sometimes traffic-speed, measurement.

Unfortunately macrotexture can deteriorate under traffic loading. The useful wet-season abrasion which restores microtexture also reduces the height by which individual aggregate particles protrude, eventually reducing the texture depth excessively. For this reason, it is usual to specify abrasion resistance by one of several available techniques, such as the Los Angeles Abrasion value.[66]

311

3.7.4 Reducing spray

Spray from surface water is a serious safety hazard. The traditional UK highway surfacing known as 'hot-rolled asphalt' (HRA), with rolled-in chippings, has developed a particularly bad reputation for spray, which was one of the driving forces toward use of stone mastic asphalt (SMA) or alternative thin surfacings. Basically, if water cannot easily flow across the surface of a pavement then it will be available to form spray. The issue is not that of texture depth but of barriers to lateral flow. The problem with HRA + chippings is that each individual chipping sits in its own small indentation into the asphalt surface, allowing a small 'pond' of water to remain around it until it either evaporates or is dispersed in the form of spray. Most other surfaces consist of protrusions from a more general surface level and water can flow around these protrusions and make its way tortuously sideways. Asphalt concrete and SMA therefore generate much less spray than HRA. Grooved concrete is also generally satisfactory. However, for real excellence, porous asphalt is undoubtedly the premier material. Porous asphalt allows water to drain straight into the pavement itself and then to pass laterally through it, below the level of the tyre-surface contact. The result: virtually no spray at all. Of course, the pavement has to be able to cope with the presence of water within the porous asphalt. Except in the specific case of a drainage pavement (Section 3.6.4), it is vital to make sure that the porous asphalt surface course overlies a dense, impermeable binder course; otherwise pavement durability problems are likely.

3.7.5 Low-noise pavements

Another powerful political driver in some countries is reducing tyre noise, either to ease the discomfort of the motorist or to protect the interests of nearby residents. This is a highly complex field and it is not necessary for the pavement engineer to appreciate the exact acoustic mechanisms involved – which is just as well since these are not wholly understood. What is clear however is the experience of users. Figure 3.37 presents a series of measurements taken in the immediate proximity of a tyre.

As expected, noise level generally depends on texture depth, i.e. roughness. However, the picture is clearly more complicated than this, with a 10 dB(A) difference – a factor of about 3 in actual sound pressure magnitude – between block paving and porous asphalt for the same texture depth. Furthermore, surface dressing seems to buck

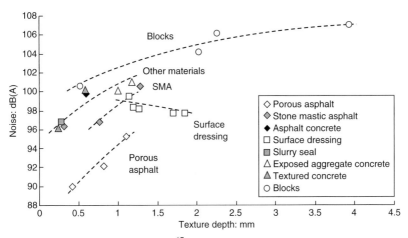

Fig. 3.37 Noise measurement data[67]

the trend, giving a relatively steady noise level whatever the texture depth. Of the more common asphalt surfaces, SMA is evidently the quietest at normal texture depths (around 1 mm).

Conceptually it is not hard to understand why this ranking order should be. Noise is caused by vibration, principally of the tyre tread elements. The pavement surface elements will vibrate as well, but mainly at frequencies well outside the audible range. However, the surface type affects both the amplitude and, to a much lesser extent, the frequency of tyre tread vibration. Basically, a rough surface will induce a high amplitude of tyre vibration and therefore high noise. Some of this noise will then be absorbed by the surface, and this will depend principally on the hardness of the surface material. Concrete has poor ability to absorb any sort of vibration energy including noise and this means that it is intrinsically difficult to produce a low-noise concrete surface, however brilliantly designed the surface texture may be. In contrast, porous asphalt has very low stiffness and therefore causes little excitation to the tyre tread elements; it also has excellent noise absorption properties.

3.7.6 Summary

The surface layer of a pavement is almost always the most expensive. This is no surprise considering the variety of roles which it has to fulfil, but it does mean that the choice and design of that layer carries a high economic weighting. This is amplified further in that it commonly lasts for a shorter time than lower layers, being either replaced or overlaid within about 10–15 years on most major highways.

Efficient pavement engineering will therefore demand that the requirements in a given case are clearly understood. Low noise is unlikely to be an issue for an industrial pavement; likewise skid resistance. However, high strength probably is. Airfield runways demand good skid resistance – but not taxiways or aprons. On high-speed roads spray may be a serious issue, leading to the consideration of porous asphalt, but this is much less important on low-speed roads. Ride quality is always a compromise between what is desirable and what is achievable, but there is no point over-specifying in situations for which excellent ride quality is not really required.

All of this means that it is economically worthwhile devoting a little thought to surface layer policy.

3.8

Design reliability

A pavement is quite unlike many other engineering constructions. The level of uncertainty is always high, even for the best-controlled projects, purely due to variations in material properties and layer thickness, quite apart from the fact that design traffic loading is never known with any great precision. There is therefore a distribution of pavement quality right from the outset, a distribution which will increase in breadth during the life of the pavement.

3.8.1 Selecting the appropriate reliability level

This is an economic issue. If pavement failure was associated with route closure or with multiple fatalities, then engineers would strive to get as close to 100% reliability as possible – and society would pay accordingly. However, pavements simply do not fail like that; pavement failure is a gradual process. It is unfortunate if certain areas of pavement deteriorate more quickly than expected, but it certainly isn't the end of the world. It simply isn't cost-effective to aim too high.

But just how high should one aim? The nominal standard for major UK highways has been to design for a 15th percentile condition, giving an 85% design reliability. This means that 15% of the pavement will actually have a life less than that for which it was designed; 85% will exceed it. Although not explicit in current standards, this was the basis upon which the evidence of past performance was interpreted when designs were being developed.[68] In the US, reliability is an explicit item in the current AASHTO method, as it has been for many years,[69] with the advice that reliability should depend on the type of highway. A 90% reliability would be the norm for major roads. A similar level of reliability should logically be adopted for major airfield pavements. On the other hand, minor roads, industrial pavements, many airfield taxiways, car parks, footways etc., pavements which can be maintained without serious knock-on effects (e.g. disruption to business), these should logically be built to a lower standard of reliability, perhaps 75% or even 50%. There are no absolute rules, only principles. No one can know the full economic equation, certainly not with regard to the future, but the key point that really should be understood by pavement owners is that they are always designing such that a certain percentage of the pavement will fail early.

3.8.2 A statistical view of design inputs

Having selected a design reliability, say 85%, the next issue is just how this affects the individual inputs used in pavement analysis. The problem is that a combination of the 15th percentiles of asphalt stiffness, asphalt thickness and foundation stiffness (taking the example of an asphalt pavement) would be equivalent to something like a 5th percentile overall (giving a 95% design reliability), since it is unlikely that poor values of all three will occur at the same location. This approach would therefore give an ultra-conservative prediction of pavement life. The issue is clearly one for which practical guidance is required rather than precise theoretical analysis.

3.8.2.1 Asphalt pavements

The first task is to estimate the relative influence of each design input parameter on the different modes of pavement deterioration, and Calculation Sheet 3.19 presents an approach which is based on a *beam on elastic foundation* analysis. This is a two-dimensional analysis and so can only be considered approximate, but it is a simple, practical way of judging how important each parameter is. And the result, assuming typical relationships between key strain values and pavement life, is that asphalt modulus E is found to be relatively influential in its effect on fatigue life (with an exponent of 3) but much less so on deformation life (exponent 1). Conversely, subgrade stiffness k has much greater influence on deformation than fatigue. Asphalt thickness h is highly significant for both, particularly fatigue.

The next important matter to be established is the likely degree of variability in each of the design parameters. This is expressed in Table 3.5 as coefficient of variance (standard deviation divided by mean; note that ± 1 standard deviation $\approx$ 15th and 85th percentile conditions). The values in Table 3.5 are based purely on the author's

---

Calculation Sheet 3.19 Relative influences of pavement parameters

Parameters considered: asphalt modulus E, asphalt thickness h, foundation modulus – characterised by modulus of subgrade reaction k.

Treat as beam on elastic foundation:

$$y = (P\lambda/2k)\, e^{-\lambda x} (\sin \lambda x + \cos \lambda x)$$
$$\text{where } \lambda = (k/4EI)^{0.25}$$

Double differentiate: $d^2y/dx^2 = (P\lambda^3/k)\, e^{-\lambda x} (\sin \lambda x - \cos \lambda x)$

But $d^2y/dx^2 = $ curvature $=$ moment/EI; and moment $= \sigma_t h^2/6$

Therefore, at $x = 0$: $\sigma_t = 6EIP\lambda^3/kh^2 = 6E^{0.25}I^{0.25}P/[(2\sqrt{2})k^{0.25}h^2]$
$$= 1.14E^{0.25}P/(k^{0.25}h^{1.25})$$

And strain $\varepsilon_t = \sigma_t/E = 1.14P/(E^{0.75}k^{0.25}h^{1.25})$

Assume **fatigue life** $\propto \varepsilon_t^{-4} \propto E^3kh^5$

Similarly, say ε_z in subgrade is approximately related to y_{max}
Therefore: $\varepsilon_z \propto P\lambda/2k = 0.35P/(E^{0.25}k^{0.25}I^{0.25}) = 0.19P/(E^{0.25}k^{0.75}h^{0.75})$

Assume **deformation life** $\propto \varepsilon_z^{-4} \propto Ek^3h^3$

---

subjective experience; the reader should feel free to substitute alternative values where evidence exists.

Now there is a practical problem; some of the coefficients of variance shown in Table 3.5 are quite large and, when the effect of an exponent of 3 or even 5 is considered, as in the relationships in Calculation Sheet 3.19, there is no way that pavement life can be considered as 'normally' distributed. A sensible move, therefore, is to replace the coefficients of variance with the multipliers (or dividers for lower limit values), shown in parentheses in the table and to assume a log-normal distribution.[70] These can now be used in a full statistical analysis of the design issue, as illustrated in Calculation Sheet 3.20.

The analysis in Calculation Sheet 3.20 can be repeated to derive equivalent percentiles other than the 15th. A more complete set of recommendations would therefore be as follows:

Table 3.5 Suggested coefficients of variance for different design parameters

Pavement type	Coefficient of variance			
	Asphalt stiffness	Asphalt thickness	Hydraulically-bound base thickness	Foundation stiffness
1. Major highways etc.	20% (×1.2)	10% (×1.1)	10% (×1.1)	40% (×1.4)
2. Minor highways etc.	25% (×1.25)	20% (×1.2)	20% (×1.2)	60% (×1.6)

Calculation Sheet 3.20 Statistical analysis of pavement life

Replace relationships from Calculation Sheet 3.19 with logarithms

Fatigue life: $\quad N_f = aE^3kh^5 \rightarrow \ln(N_f) = \ln(a) + 3\ln(E) + \ln(k) + 5\ln(h)$

Deformation life: $N_d = bEk^3h^3 \rightarrow \ln(N_d) = \ln(b) + \ln(E) + 3\ln(k) + 3\ln(h)$

A: Apply multipliers/dividers from Table 3.5 to each parameter for each case, and sum the effects. This is equivalent to using the 15th percentile of each parameter.

$\ln$(divider on N_f) 1. $\rightarrow 3\ln(1.2) + \ln(1.4) + 5\ln(1.1) = 1.36 \quad \rightarrow N_f \div 3.90$

$\qquad\qquad\qquad$ 2. $\rightarrow 3\ln(1.25) + \ln(1.6) + 5\ln(1.2) = 2.05 \rightarrow N_f \div 7.78$

$\ln$(divider on N_z) 1. $\rightarrow \ln(1.2) + 3\ln(1.4) + 3\ln(1.1) = 1.48 \quad \rightarrow N_f \div 4.38$

$\qquad\qquad\qquad$ 2. $\rightarrow \ln(1.25) + 3\ln(1.6) + 3\ln(1.2) = 2.18 \rightarrow N_f \div 8.85$

B: Combine by squaring, summing and taking a square root. This assumes the parameters are independent and will give a realistic equivalent 15th percentile of pavement life.

$\ln$(divider on N_f)

$\qquad$ 1. $\rightarrow \sqrt{\{[3\ln(1.2)]^2 + [\ln(1.4)]^2 + [5\ln(1.1)]^2\}} = 0.80 \quad \rightarrow N_f \div 2.22$

$\qquad$ 2. $\rightarrow \sqrt{\{[3\ln(1.25)]^2 + [\ln(1.6)]^2 + [5\ln(1.2)]^2\}} = 1.22 \rightarrow N_f \div 3.40$

$\ln$(divider on N_z)

$\qquad$ 1. $\rightarrow \sqrt{\{[\ln(1.2)]^2 + [3\ln(1.4)]^2 + [3\ln(1.1)]^2\}} = 1.06 \quad \rightarrow N_f \div 2.90$

$\qquad$ 2. $\rightarrow \sqrt{\{[\ln(1.25)]^2 + [3\ln(1.6)]^2 + [3\ln(1.2)]^2\}} = 1.53 \rightarrow N_f \div 4.61$

Take ratios of (dividers) by methods B and A: 0.59, 0.60, 0.72, 0.69; average 0.65

$\therefore$ Use 0.65 × (multipliers/dividers) in Table 3.5 for each design parameter to calculate equivalent 15th percentile pavement life (85% design reliability):

$\qquad\qquad\qquad\qquad\qquad\qquad\qquad\qquad\qquad\qquad$ ≈ <u>25th percentiles</u>

- 50% design reliability; use 50th percentiles of individual parameters
- 75% design reliability; use 33rd percentiles of individual parameters
- 85% design reliability; use 25th percentiles of individual parameters
- 95% design reliability; use 14th percentiles of individual parameters
- 99% design reliability; use 6th percentiles of individual parameters.

In no way can these figures be considered exact (other than that for 50% reliability); however, they open the way to rational design, based on a fundamentally sound understanding of pavement performance. They allow the life of a pavement to be calculated in a reasonable way and sensible confidence limits to be placed on that calculation.

Note that the above figures assume that the same percentile is to be applied to each design parameter, but this does not have to be the case. If necessary, the relationships for the two aspects of pavement life given in Calculation Sheet 3.19 can be used to explore the option of using an increased percentile for one parameter and a decreased percentile in another – to achieve the same overall design reliability.

Note also that the advice in this section applies to pavements which may be considered 'fully flexible'. There may be a weak hydraulically-bound base or sub-base present, but if so it should be considered as part of the foundation.

3.8.2.2 Pavements with strong hydraulically-bound bases

In the case of fatigue of a strong hydraulically-bound base, a stress ratio has to be computed at the bottom of the base layer, as opposed to the strain used to characterise asphalt fatigue. Referring to Calculation Sheet 3.19, the relationship for ε_t therefore has to be replaced by one for σ_t/σ_f, namely:

$$\sigma_t/\sigma_f = 1.14PE^{0.25}/(k^{0.25}h^{1.25}\sigma_f)$$

Also, the slope of the fatigue characteristic is quite different from that for asphalt – an exponent of 12 is suggested – which means that fatigue life is now proportional to $k^3h^{15}\sigma_f^{12}/E^3$. Notice that modulus E now appears on the bottom of the equation, not the top; i.e. life is *inversely* proportional to the cube of modulus. Conceptually, this shouldn't be a surprise; it simply reflects the fact that a stiff material will tend to attract stress. But the consequence is that the appropriate percentiles for the modulus of a strong hydraulically-bound layer, when considering fatigue, are the opposite of those used for asphalt. Thus, a 33rd percentile would be replaced by a 67th percentile etc. Please note that this *only* applies when considering fatigue of the hydraulically-bound material, *not* when dealing with any other failure mode; neither does it apply to any other parameter, including the asphalt.

Following the calculation through for fatigue of hydraulically-bound base, the recommended percentiles are:

- 50% design reliability; use 50th percentiles of individual parameters
- 75% design reliability; use 35th percentiles of individual parameters
- 85% design reliability; use 28th percentiles of individual parameters
- 95% design reliability; use 18th percentiles of individual parameters
- 99% design reliability; use 10th percentiles of individual parameters.

Note that the thicknesses of asphalt and hydraulically-bound base should not be considered as independent variables.[71] This means that the percentile used should be applied to the *combined* thickness of the two layers, individual layer thicknesses being given according to the ratio of the two design thicknesses.

Also note that the calculation is only for fatigue failure of the base; other modes of failure should be treated as for asphalt pavements.

3.8.2.3 Concrete pavements

Exactly the same principles apply to concrete pavements as to strong hydraulically-bound bases. The form of the relationship between fatigue life and the individual material and thickness parameters is the same, as are the recommended percentiles. Remember that the percentile for concrete modulus is an exception, and should be the opposite of those shown (65th instead of 35th, etc.), for the reasons given above in relation to strong hydraulically-bound bases.

3.8.3 Design assurance

The next difficulty is just how to ensure that the required value of the appropriate percentile for each parameter is achieved. Taking, for example, the case of a 95% reliability design of a concrete pavement, as in the previous section, the design should, in theory, be based on 18th percentiles of individual parameters (or a 82nd percentile in the case of concrete modulus). Now, supposing the design were to demand that the 18th percentile flexural strength of the concrete was 4.5 MPa, this would therefore mean that the average strength would have to be higher. A reasonable estimate for the actual coefficient of variance of concrete flexural strength might be around 15%,[72] from which it can be calculated that the required average flexural strength would be about 5.1 MPa. This is quite straightforward and easy to incorporate into a material specification, whether of a material property or a thickness; the only real engineering judgement needed is the coefficient of variance. However, the picture can become much more confusing, as the following subsections explain.

3.8.3.1 Measurement variability

Measured variability is always likely to be considerably greater than real variability. In the case of laboratory testing, this is an unavoidable consequence of testing small samples of material containing relatively large aggregate particles. If reliance is placed on field tests, the level of test control tends to be poorer and test variability consequently greater. Figure 3.38 illustrates the problem. It is therefore dangerous to specify material properties other than in terms of a mean. The

320

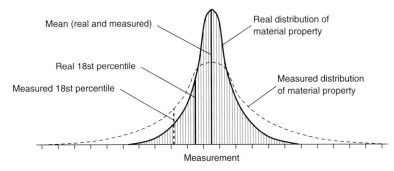

Fig. 3.38 The concept of real and measured variability

design may call for a certain absolute minimum value for concrete flexural strength, but one would have to allow a lower value for the measured strength, and this can only be judged if a good estimate of inherent test variability can be made. Needless to say, each test will carry its own inherent variability, and this will probably depend partly on the material being tested, particularly the aggregate gradation.

3.8.3.2 Other sources of error

It isn't too hard to find reasons to increase the uncertainty in any prediction of pavement performance. Pavement analysis is hardly a precise science and, whichever form of distress is being predicted, there are plenty of questionable assumptions. Here are some:

- an assumed relationship between compressive and flexural strength of a hydraulically-bound material
- an assumed temperature and/or loading rate correction for asphalt
- an assumed fatigue relationship for both asphalt and hydraulically-bound material
- an assumed long-term stiffness modulus for unbound materials.

Depending on the type of pavement and the vehicle load type, there may be others, for example concerning dynamic load effects, joint load transfer, drainage function etc.; the list goes on. Each uncertainty effectively adds an additional term to the variance in each parameter. For example, the first mentioned, the relationship between compressive and flexural strength, probably adds a coefficient of variance of around 30% to the strength parameter, dwarfing the 15% which is suggested for the real coefficient of variance of strength, and probably also significantly exceeding that due to measurement uncertainty. A similarly large effect should probably be assigned to the fatigue characteristic of asphalt.

These are very important matters. The modest 15% coefficient of variance for strength becomes around 35% (equivalent to a factor of 1.35) once uncertainty in the compressive–flexural strength relationship is included, treating the two effects as independent (as in part B on Calculation Sheet 3.20). Thus, if 4.5 MPa is the design requirement for flexural strength and quality control is to be by means of compressive strength testing, and if the appropriate percentile is the 18th (suggested above for 95% reliability of concrete pavements), then the target mean value, converted from compressive strength tests, becomes 5.9 MPa.

3.8.3.3 Recommendations

As one can see, when all the various causes of uncertainty are factored in, the picture can look rather complicated. However, the key is always to assign a value for the coefficient of variance for each cause of uncertainty, and to combine assuming that all causes of uncertainty are *independent*.

With regard to specification of properties which require testing, it is always preferable to specify the mean or 50th percentile value (from a suitably large number of tests) rather than a different percentile, since this avoids most of the problems of scatter in test data.

3.8.4 Summary

Statistics is a subject too often ignored by pavement engineers. Yet, almost more than any other civil engineering structure, pavements demand to be treated statistically. They are inherently variable and have no clearly defined failure point, just a gradual decline in serviceability. It makes no sense at all to claim that the life of a pavement is some fixed number of years, or passes of a certain design wheel load, however attractive such a simplistic view may seem. To make such a claim is to deny the pavement authority the tools it needs to predict maintenance and to manage budgets. While pavement engineers refuse to view their designs in a probabilistic way, it is no surprise to find that pavement maintenance is often a very hit-and-miss affair.

3.9

Conclusion to Part 3

Pavement design is a complex subject, involving a proper understanding of materials, their properties and their modes of deterioration, but also the myriad interactions which make up the whole pavement structure. For instance, it is no good being an expert at predicting the rate of growth of cracking, without also appreciating whether such cracking is likely to lead to pavement failure or not. In some cases (e.g. sandy soil, arid climate), post-cracking deterioration may be very slow; in others, ingress of water may lead to severe softening of unbound layers, not to mention debonding between asphalt layers or break-up of a cement-bound base. The point is that the pavement is a whole, not just the sum of its parts.

One of the key messages from this part of the book is that the engineer should never be afraid to approximate. Precise computations mean very little because of the numerous uncertainties involved, particularly in pavements which are still on the drawing board. However, it is absolutely vital that the fundamental understanding is correct. Computations must be well founded and related to the actual modes of deterioration expected. So long as this is the case, then the results will be meaningful.

The key skill in pavement design is to balance scientific knowledge of materials and of analysis methods with what one might describe as 'common sense', although the term 'engineering judgement' tends to be preferred. Since no computation can be believed 100%, it is extremely important to be able to sift through the evidence, appreciating where the uncertainties lie, in order to come up with the best possible design. And if this is the case for design of new pavements, it is more applicable still when considering maintenance and rehabilitation, the subject of Part 4.

Notes

1. See Stripple (2001).
2. See CEN (2002) for test specification. Peploe and Dawson (2006) give an overview of the subject.
3. See Highway Research Board (1961).
4. See Transport Research Laboratory (1993).
5. See De Beer *et al.* (1997).
6. German and Finnish national design standards are among those that include a lateral wander factor.
7. For example, Defence Estates (2006) include what is effectively a wander factor of 1.6.
8. See Highways Agency (2006a).
9. The FAA design method (FAA, 1995) is now computerised in the form of the LEDFAA program.
10. See Defence Estates (2006).
11. The ACN–PCN (Aircraft Classification Number–Pavement Classification Number) system was devised by the International Civil Aviation Organisation (ICAO, 2004) as a convenient means of describing the damaging power of an aircraft and the strength of a pavement respectively. Each aircraft has an ACN value (actually several depending on subgrade category and pavement type) and will only be permitted to use pavements with a PCN at least as great as the aircraft ACN.
12. The equation is: N_f [in millions] $= 3.09 \times 10^{10} \, \varepsilon_z^{-3.95}$ [ε_z in *micro*strain]. See Powell *et al.* (1984).
13. The equation is: N_f [in millions] $= 8.511 \times 10^{-3} \, \varepsilon_z^{-7.14}$ [ε_z in *milli*strain]. See NAASRA (1987).
14. The equation is: N_f [in millions] $= 7.6 \times 10^8 \, \varepsilon_z^{-3.7}$ [in *micro*strain]. See British Airports Authority (1993), following Brown *et al.* (1985).

324

15. Evaluation of road performance over sandy soils in the Middle East led researchers at the University of Nottingham to suggest a factor of 10 increase in life (at a given calculated strain level) compared to pavements on UK clay soils.

16. These values are taken from measurements carried out at the University of Nottingham.

17. See relationships in notes 12–14 and the comment in note 15.

18. See Hansen (1961) and Meyerhof (1963) for derivation of this equation.

19. See Terzaghi and Peck (1967).

20. The tangent of the 'dilation angle' is given by the ratio of volumetric to shear strain. In the case of a compacted aggregate, any shear will tend to cause significant dilation, and the angle suggested, 15°, is therefore at the upper end of the normally expected range.

21. This figure is simply based on deductions from laboratory test data and should be treated as no more than a rough approximation.

22. Melan (1936) is one of those credited with formulating the 'shake-down' concept. Yu (2006) presents an up-to-date explanation, while Raad *et al.* (1989) demonstrate its application to pavement rutting.

23. This is, of course, a highly approximate figure – but fit for the purpose for which it is used here. Pure bitumens would tend to have a rather higher change in viscosity (around × 4–5 per 10°C), but the influence of the aggregate reduces this for mixtures.

24. The measurements were taken approximately 20 mm beneath the surface of a car park pavement at the University of Nottingham.

25. A factor of 50 on viscosity represents a drop in penetration from 100 to 10 or slightly less.

26. Although it is the purpose of this book to give a good understanding of the fundamental behaviour of pavements, it has to be admitted that there are a number of good empirical pavement design procedures that guard against cracking of concrete pavements. These include Mayhew and Harding (1987) for highways, the Federal Aviation Administration (1995) and Defence Estates (2006) airfield design guides, and Knapton and Meletiou (1996) for industrial pavements.

27. See Westergaard (1926).

28. See Griffiths and Thom (2007).

29. This type of analysis was pioneered by Meyerhof (1962). An example of a current design manual based on this type of calculation is Concrete Society report TR34 (Concrete Society, 2003).

30. See Packard and Tayabji (1985).

31. See Bradbury (1938).
32. See Thompson (2001).
33. See AASHTO (1993; 2007b).
34. Mayhew and Harding (1987), adopted by the UK Highways Agency in design standard HD26 (Highways Agency, 2006b).
35. This technique was pioneered in France (Bonnot, 1988) during the 1980s and is now widely accepted.
36. The alternative to pre-cracking is post-cracking, carried out within a few days of construction. This can be achieved by use of a heavy guillotine, or by controlled rolling of the layer. Both techniques have proved successful. Rolling is particularly applicable where close-spaced cracks are required, usually where the asphalt is thin.
37. UK Highways Agency design standard IAN73 (Highways Agency, 2006c) assigns 20% for cement-bound materials and 10% for slower-setting hydraulically-bound materials.
38. Each individual element of the tyre tread will compress on loading, giving a Poisson's ratio effect horizontally. This is restrained by shear from the surface, generating a theoretical strain high enough for early crack formation – but only extending to a depth of a few millimetres. See de Beer *et al.* (1997) and de Beer (2006) for measurement of the complex stress pattern under a tyre.
39. If the AASHTO (2007b) fatigue assumption is applied to a typical asphalt pavement on a major road, it still turns out that the most rapid cracking is predicted to occur at the highest temperatures, something which is not borne out by observation.
40. See Shell (1978), Asphalt Institute (1999) and Powell *et al.* (1984).
41. See AASHTO (2007b).
42. The AASHTO (2007b) pavement design method is an exception in that a thickness (h) dependent constant (k_1') is included: $k_1' = 1/[0.000398 + 0.003602/(1 + e^{(11.02-3.49h)})]$ for bottom-up cracking. This constant is actually an empirical means of addressing the 'thin asphalt' problem.
43. See Paris and Erdogan (1963).
44. See Odemark (1949).
45. See Boussinesq (1883).
46. See Thom (2000) for details.
47. The author has implemented this approach successfully, although a full description has not yet been published.
48. The experience referred to here comes from field tests using the falling weight deflectometer – see Part 4.

49. The basis of this approach is contained in Thom (2000).
50. For example, see CEN (2003a).
51. Croney and Jacobs (1967) describe the UK test; ASTM (2007) gives the US version.
52. The author has experienced 'wading' through a stabilised material that, a few weeks previously, had been as hard as concrete.
53. In Scandinavia, so-called 'oil gravels' have traditionally been used in these situations. These mixtures use a very soft bitumen emulsion as the binder, extremely resistant to low-temperature cracking, though less resistant to conventional fatigue and rutting.
54. See Oliveira (2006).
55. See South African standard TRH4 (Committee of Land Transportation Officials, 1996).
56. In the UK, CIRIA has brought out a series of useful documents on the subject of SUDS. Report C697 (Woods Ballard *et al.*, 2007a) and C698 (Woods Ballard *et al.*, 2007b) give general advice; report C582 (Pratt *et al.*, 2002) relates specifically to pavement design. CERTU (1999) is an excellent French document on the subject.
57. The most appropriate fatigue characteristic for porous asphalt is not agreed. The equivalent material used on airfields, known as Friction Course, has been found to have an almost indefinite life when traffic frequency is low, presumably because of self-healing properties. The implication is that the fatigue characteristic may be strongly dependent on the intensity of traffic expected.
58. The principal justification for this figure comes from in situ tests using a falling weight deflectometer (see Part 4), although similar stiffness values had already been proposed based on laboratory tests, and the prediction for the stiffness of a discontinuous layer presented in Part 2 also gives similar results.
59. See Sandberg and Ejsmont (2002).
60. 'Negative texture' refers to the 'skew' or 'asymmetry' of the surface profile around a mean level. Negatively textured surfaces have much of their profile a little above the mean, with deeply penetrating cavities at intervals; in positively textured pavements, much of the surface is below the mean level, with protruding asperities at intervals. See Sandberg and Ejsmont (2002) for a full discussion.
61. This advice follows the US Corps of Engineers recommendations for roads in wet climates (United Facilities Guide Specifications, 2006.
62. See CEN (2003c).
63. See BSI (1989).

64. This point should not be treated as anything more than speculative at this stage. Real evidence is yet to be presented.
65. These data were measured by a 'Griptester'.
66. See AASHTO (2002a); ASTM (2003; 2006a); CEN (1998a).
67. This information is derived from Sandberg and Ejsmont (2002). For an investigation into low-noise surfacings see FEHRL (2006).
68. See Powell *et al.* (1984).
69. Both the 1993 and 2007 AASHTO design guides (AASHTO, 1993; 2007b) incorporate reliability as a key input to design.
70. This assumes that the logarithm of pavement life is normally distributed.
71. The point here is that any low region on the surface of a hydraulically-bound base will be corrected by additional asphalt since the finished level of the asphalt does not depend on base levels.
72. This suggestion is not based on any scientific evaluation of evidence and should be treated as no more than an estimate.

Part 4
Maintenance

4.1

Regular treatments and repairs

The word 'maintenance' in the title for this part is intended to cover all types of treatment as well as the associated investigation, decision-making and management process. It therefore includes both minor repairs, for which little advanced decision-making is required, and also major rehabilitation treatments, for which proper pavement evaluation is needed. This section, however, is restricted to those treatments which many would classify as 'maintenance', as distinct from 'rehabilitation', 'renewal' or 'improvement', i.e. regular and generally comparatively minor treatments designed to keep the pavement in a fully serviceable condition.

4.1.1 Sealing

Sealant technology is a complex field and one in which significant advances have been made over the years. For the pavement engineer, sealing is an important if not particularly exciting activity. With the exception of drainage pavements and those incorporating porous asphalt surface course to avoid spray and reduce noise, water is the enemy of the pavement engineer. Water will potentially degrade asphalt, seriously weaken hydraulically-bound materials and reduce the strength and stiffness of unbound layers; it will corrode reinforcement and accelerate debonding between layers. Often most damaging of all, it expands on freezing, breaking materials apart, destroying soil structure and even causing the whole pavement to 'heave' upwards. There is no doubt about it; water genuinely is the enemy and every effort should be made to limit how much of it is present in a pavement – which means that sealing is important.

4.1.1.1 Joints in concrete pavements

The main problem with water ingress through a joint in a concrete pavement is that the foundation is almost certain to suffer. Concrete is 'rigid', which in pavement terminology means that it is fully elastic and so will return to its original position after a load is removed. Deflection will take place under load, compressing the underlying foundation materials, but the deflection will then return to zero. However, the foundation materials themselves are far from rigid; they can deform plastically and so a proportion of the deflection of the foundation will never be recovered. The result is that a gap will begin to appear beneath a concrete slab either side of a joint, only a very small gap, but nevertheless a large enough one to affect the efficiency of load transfer across the joint. If the foundation consists of relatively strong materials, this build-up of plastic deformation will be slow and will not progress beyond an acceptably low level; if the materials are weak, the gap may grow to the extent that, even under full load, the slab only just makes contact with its supporting foundation. If a hydraulically-bound sub-base is present, this will either be so strong that it moves with the overlying slab or, more likely, it will have broken such that it deflects with the foundation beneath, as shown in Fig. 4.1. Either way there will be a gap somewhere in the system.

The point is that water will weaken the foundation and accelerate gap formation, with consequent reduction in slab support and load transfer efficiency. Thus, resealing of concrete joints is strongly recommended as soon as they begin to show signs of deterioration and leakage; delay really can prove fatal to the pavement.

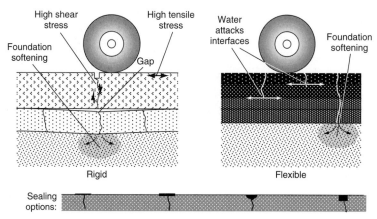

Fig. 4.1 Joint and crack sealing

However, it has to be acknowledged that delay isn't always fatal. The world is full of concrete pavements with poor or non-existent joint seals which remain in perfectly serviceable condition. It may be the case that slab support has disappeared either side of each joint and that load transfer is negligible, but if the concrete itself is strong enough then it still will not break. So, while it is good practice to reseal defective joints it is worth assessing the structural capacity of the concrete before panicking. After all, joint sealing of an in-service road or airfield is a highly disruptive activity and one should therefore be sure that it needs doing before committing to it.

4.1.1.2 Crack sealing

Whether in concrete or asphalt, cracks happen. In asphalt, this means that water has access to interfaces between asphalt layers, to regions of higher void at the base of layers, and, once the crack is full depth, to the foundation. Crack sealing therefore has the potential to greatly extend the service life of a pavement. Figure 4.1 illustrates the potential damage if pavements are left unsealed; it also illustrates conceptually the different possible approaches taken to crack sealing. In simple terms, 'you get what you pay for'. The quickest and cheapest solution is to paint or pour on a thin film of bitumen or bituminous mastic (bitumen + filler) without preparing the crack in any way other than general cleaning of the surface. The problem is that there will be very little penetration of bitumen into the crack, which means that it will be relatively easy for the film of sealant to refracture under combinations of thermal and traffic-induced stress and strain. This solution can only be considered as short term therefore, with no lasting reduction in the ability of the crack to transmit water.

A more time-consuming treatment consists of first scabbling the surface around each crack, thereby presenting a suitably rough material onto which the sealant mortar can bond. It also allows a slightly greater thickness of sealant, presenting a much increased resistance to refracturing. There will still be little penetration of bitumen into the crack however.

More time-consuming still are treatments which consist of routing out a channel along the crack and then filling it with a sealant material, generally a high-durability bitumen–fines mixture. These treatments give real depth to the seal, making it much harder for the crack to repropagate through it. The weak point becomes the bond between the sealant and the routed faces.

Among the most effective treatments of all is 'saw cut and seal'. A square cut is made in the same way as is common for joints in concrete pavements and this is then sealed using a similar sealant to those used for concrete joints. The sides of the saw-cut will bond well to the sealant, making it very hard for water to penetrate or for general debonding to occur.

It is impossible to give general rules here as to the most appropriate technique to use. It depends on the type of crack (transverse thermally-induced; wheel-path traffic-induced), whether it is likely to have penetrated full depth, how water-sensitive the foundations are, what the long-term strategy for a particular pavement may be, etc. Two key points must be borne in mind: first, active cracks (i.e. cracks with large relative movement between the faces) are difficult to seal effectively; second, crack sealing is most important where underlying layers are water-susceptible. The rate of deterioration of a pavement can often be slowed significantly by judicious application of crack sealing and, when whole-life costing is considered, the price is probably worth paying.

4.1.1.3 Slurry sealing

Individual crack sealing is a sensible option when crack numbers are few. It also has the advantage that the overall surface properties (particularly skid resistance) are only affected very locally. However, in cases where there are large numbers of cracks or where skid resistance is not particularly important, a more cost-effective solution may be to 'slurry seal', that is to apply a coat of bituminous slurry over the whole pavement surface. This is well suited to footways, cycleways, car parks, low-speed city roads and airfield taxiways.

A slurry seal generally consists of a mixture of bitumen emulsion with filler and fine aggregate and it is commonly spread to a thickness of between 3 and 8 mm. Specialist spreading machines are available, with paving screeds as in conventional asphalt paving. As well as speed of operation and certainty of coverage, this technique has the advantage that a degree of surface regulating can be achieved, i.e. minor improvement to the profile of the surface. The natural surface texture will be relatively smooth, but can be roughened by means of brushing. Slurry seal surfaces are suited to the requirements of low-speed pavements.

Since the slurry seal material will have a high binder content, a consequence of the lack of coarse aggregate, it will form a relatively crack-resistant layer and may therefore provide several years of additional life to the pavement before the cracks start to reoccur.

4.1.2 Reprofiling

This type of maintenance is generally associated with unbound roads. Whereas concrete pavements are commonly designed to last 40 years or more without significant maintenance, and asphalt surfaces are typically expected to last 10–20 years, unbound pavements are designed in the full knowledge that they will need regular upkeep. Deformation, either in the form of ruts, potholes or corrugations (see Section 4.3.3.3) is expected, but the beauty of unbound materials is that they lose none of their integrity when they deform. They can be regraded back to their proper surface shape and recompacted, and should still retain as much strength as they had originally. This may not be quite true in the case of a specially mixed surface course containing a proportion of clay binder, but the loss of properties will be slight over several such maintenance cycles.

It is also possible to plane off excess material from an asphalt road surface in order to restore surface profile. Where rutting has occurred within the surface course, giving rise to very sharp shoulders, it is a perfectly feasible measure to plane the shoulders off, reducing the nuisance to road users and increasing safety. It can only be seen as a means of postponing the need for more extensive treatment since the cause of the deformation is not being tackled but, for certain categories of road, this may nevertheless prove an economic strategy.

4.1.3 Local repairs

None of the treatments listed under 'sealing' can do anything significant for the structural condition of a pavement; they merely serve to reduce the deterioration rate. However, the nature of pavement construction is that there will always be certain areas which, due to material defects, lack of thickness, concentrated load (e.g. due to cornering), drainage problems or some other reason, begin to fail much earlier than the rest of the pavement. These local failures may start as individual cracks which can be sealed, but they will progress to multiple cracking (known as 'crazing'), surface spalling, potholes, edge defects etc. As local phenomena, it clearly makes sense to carry out local repairs.

4.1.3.1 Concrete spall repairs

Concrete spalling can occur due to frost or mechanical damage (e.g. from accidents), but is most commonly found adjacent to joints or

335

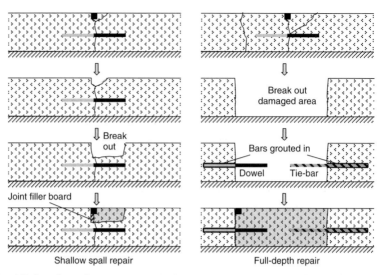

Fig. 4.2 Local patch repairs in concrete pavements

developed cracks, occurring as the concrete flexes under load, cracks and joints tending to act as hinges. This induces high horizontal compressive forces in the surface adjacent to cracks and joints, forces which can lead to fracturing. So long as fracturing and spalling are only shallow, specifically so long as damage is restricted to material above the level of dowels and tie-bars, a shallow repair is suitable. The repair must make use of suitably strong material, be well bonded to the existing pavement quality concrete (PQC), and joints have to be reformed and sealed (see Fig. 4.2). Nowadays, rapid-setting compounds allow trafficking as little as one hour after placement (depending on ambient temperature[1]), although the cost of such materials is of course considerably greater than that of standard PQC. Nevertheless, on busy highways speed is vital and, when user delay costs are factored in, it becomes worthwhile.

It is also quite possible to patch concrete pavements with asphalt. Inevitably, the asphalt will deform under load and so such a repair is not suitable for the long term; however, it may be cost-effective to carry out rapid emergency repairs in asphalt before completing a planned cementitious repair at a later date.

Repairs to concrete pavements are not without cost in terms of ride quality. Concrete is much more sensitive to minor surface imperfections than asphalt – as witnessed by the fact that even transverse joints are easily noticeable to the motorist – and a patch repair cannot possibly be finished to the same standard of evenness as is achieved by a concrete paving machine. This lack of repair-friendliness certainly counts against concrete in high-speed applications.

4.1.3.2 Full-depth concrete repairs

A shallow repair is useless if the defect penetrates as far as a dowel bar. In this case (termed 'deep spalling') or in the case of full-depth cracking, the whole PQC slab thickness needs to be replaced, as shown in Fig. 4.2. This is obviously a much more time-consuming procedure, even when rapid-setting repair material is used. Joints have to be re-formed; other interfaces require that a tie-bar is inserted to avoid a crack forming easily between old and new materials. Both tie-bar and dowel installation mean that holes have to be drilled into the faces of the existing concrete and bars grouted in. This is clearly not an operation which can be undertaken lightly.

In many cases individual concrete bays, i.e. lengths between joints, suffer cracking while adjacent bays remain intact. This occurs as minor differences such as joint defects lead to minor cracking, and the consequent lack of concrete continuity then places ever greater stress on remaining materials, leading to a more general fragmentation of the bay. The enclosing joints form barriers to progression of cracking beyond the individual bay, although it must be appreciated that these barriers will eventually be breached. In such a case, it is logical to carry out a 'whole bay repair', following exactly the principles shown in Fig. 4.2 for full-depth repairs. Care must be taken to ensure that joints are replaced and, where they are displaced longitudinally (as shown in Fig. 4.2), the mismatch at adjacent longitudinal joints must not be allowed to inhibit transverse joint performance. The length of 'stagger' at longitudinal joints between new and old transverse joints should therefore be treated to allow slip (using bituminous primer or similar).

One further point is that the possibility of thickening a replaced bay should be considered. If the local deterioration was due to factors which are likely to continue, e.g. foundation weakness or high loads from cornering, then it makes sense to increase the pavement strength.

4.1.3.3 Concrete crack stitching

An alternative to expensive and time-consuming full-depth repairs is the technique known as crack stitching.[2] It does not represent as complete or long-lasting a treatment, but it can be effective at slowing

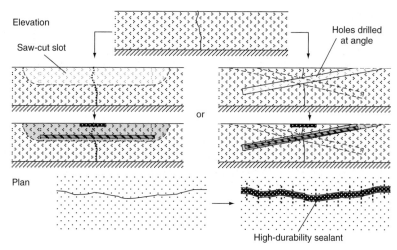

Fig. 4.3 Crack stitching techniques

down the rate of deterioration. The idea is to tie the two sides of a crack together. Thus, although the crack is not repaired it is at least prevented from widening further, preserving load transfer and making crack sealing more likely to be effective. Figure 4.3 illustrates two different crack stitching options.

In both cases, tie-bars are grouted (into slots or holes) such that they prevent further crack movement. The sealant layer will usually be recessed into a shallow channel milled into the surface and should preferably consist of a high-deformation-resistant asphaltic material; a cementitious product would be too brittle to withstand the expected flexure at the crack.

4.1.3.4 Asphalt patching

Local defects in an asphalt pavement can be repaired locally, just as in concrete. The key is to determine the depth of patch required. It is of course easiest simply to plane out the surface course and replace it but, if problems extend deeper, this will only be a short-term measure.

Patching materials can be either hot or cold. Hot-mix asphalt can be stored in a 'hot box' housed on the back of a vehicle; cold-mix is more user-friendly in that it needs no special storage and has a much longer 'shelf life'. On the other hand, as was made clear in Part 3, cold-mix is unlikely to produce such a stiff, durable material, all other things being equal. But, of course, all other things are never equal. Compaction of a patch is always difficult, relying on small manually-controlled rollers or

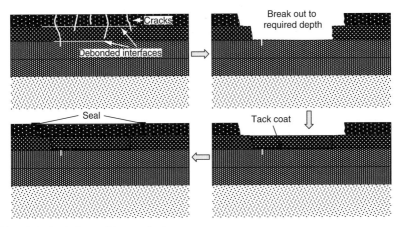

Fig. 4.4 Asphalt patching method

vibrating plates, and a thin layer of hot-mix does not give much time for compaction to be carried out. The result is that low density is almost inevitable. Cold-mix imposes no such time constraints, allowing compaction to be continued longer if necessary, particularly in awkward corners. Whichever material is used, it is virtually impossible to produce a layer of equivalent properties to a machine-laid hot-mix, which means that a patch always represents a point of weakness. Figure 4.4 illustrates the process.

In addition to compaction, three further features contribute significantly to the life of a patch. The first is the 'stepping' shown between layers, making it more difficult for water to penetrate; the second is the use of a tack coat (i.e. bitumen film) on the bottom and sides; the third is the surface seal at the joint between old and new material.

4.1.3.5 Asphalt edge repairs

An edge repair is simply a patch at the side of the pavement. The edge is always a vulnerable location, particularly on narrow roads subject to heavy goods vehicle traffic. The result is that edge deterioration is a common feature of such roads. The repair is known as a 'haunch'.

The key to successful haunching is the understanding that it is possible to actually improve the situation by local thickening (or some other form of strengthening). As shown using the Westergaard analysis introduced in Part 3 (Section 3.4.1.1) for concrete pavements, the tensile stress induced at the bottom of a bound layer in an edge situation is typically around 80% higher than the equivalent stress remote from an edge. A useful rule of thumb here, too approximate for normal pavement design but ideal for the rather indeterminate case of pavement edge strengthening, is that tensile stress or strain is approximately related to the square of layer thickness. This means that the bound layer thickness at a trafficked edge should be about 35% greater than elsewhere in the pavement in order to give comparable life. This is an appallingly crude analysis of course, but the problem is a highly complex one and also subject to plenty of unknowns (wheel location, variation in foundation quality etc.). It is also, frankly, not worth spending a long time over the design of individual edge failures; thus a general recommendation for a 35% bound layer thickness increase compared to the rest of the pavement is not unreasonable. One could argue for a greater thickening still if local softening of the foundation has occurred and drainage is either non-existent or malfunctioning.[3]

4.1.4 Surface treatments

Slurry sealing has already been introduced and, technically, it could have been included here. However, slurry sealing is not primarily intended to improve surface properties but simply to seal the pavement. This section presents those techniques which actually restore the surface, notably in terms of its skid resistance.

4.1.4.1 Gritting

There are two circumstances where gritting (i.e. application of a spread of approximately 3 mm size particles) might be required. The first is during the early life of certain surface courses in which the individual surface particles have been well coated with bitumen, sometimes tough, modified bitumen, and this bitumen takes some time to wear away and expose the microtexture of the aggregate itself. It is therefore a practical short-term safety measure.

The second circumstance is where excess bitumen has worked its way to the surface of the pavement (the phenomenon known as *'bleeding'* or *'fatting up'*), usually during hot weather, and the surface becomes a smooth textureless plane, ideal for skidding in the wet. Gritting represents a short-term emergency response to this dangerous situation.

4.1.4.2 Bush-hammering etc.

As described in Part 3 (Section 3.7.3.2), the microtexture of surface aggregate, the property which gives basic frictional grip, tends to reduce during the life of a surface due to the polishing action of tyre tread. Although there is a natural tendency for microtexture to recover during the winter months due to the action of grit within surface water abrading the aggregate, this may not always be sufficient. 'Bush-hammering' represents a way of abrading the surface aggregate sufficiently to restore its original microtexture. It is carried out by an automated machine and consists of controlled impacts delivered to the surface, impacts of relatively high velocity but low inertial mass, inducing local fracturing of the surface of the aggregate rather than any deeper breakage. Alternatives are shot-blasting (firing steel balls at the surface which are automatically recovered and reused) or impacting by means of rotating discs.

There is no doubt that the technique works and that it can sometimes extend the safe working life of a surface by several years. There is also no doubt that it can significantly reduce the texture depth present, which may impact on the wet weather skid resistance because of lack of water drainage. It is therefore a technique for particular circumstances rather than being suited to all situations. The engineer has to weigh up the advantages and disadvantages carefully.

4.1.4.3 Jet-blasting

This is the counterpart to bush-hammering. Whereas bush-hammering is designed to chip small fragments off the aggregate, jet-blasting, using a high-pressure water jet, is designed to remove some of the bituminous mortar material from between the aggregate pieces. The aim is to increase the macrotexture, i.e. the texture depth of the surface. As with bush-hammering, there is no doubt that the technique works; as with bush-hammering, there are accompanying dangers. Depending on the type of surface, it may well be that some of the aggregate pieces become dislodged as their surrounding mortar is partially removed. Thus, here too, the engineer has to weigh up the pros and cons carefully before deciding to go ahead.

4.1.4.4 Grooving

Grooving has already been introduced as a technique for finishing the surface of a concrete road, and which can also be applied to asphalt if necessary. It is achieved by saw-cutting of hardened material and so is not cheap. However, it is an effective method for improving the macrotexture. It is unlikely to be the most cost-effective technique for an asphalt, but it may be for a concrete.

341

4.1.4.5 Surface dressing

If none of the above techniques proves suitable, then the obvious alternative is to apply a brand new thin surface layer, one with excellent texture depth and, depending on aggregate, excellent microtexture. It also has the bonus that it achieves a similar sealing effect to slurry seal. This technique is usually known as *surface dressing* but also as *chip seal*.

In its simplest manifestation, surface dressing means the spraying of a layer of bitumen over the surface followed by the spreading of a single layer of aggregate particles, usually 10–15 mm in size. Both bitumen spraying and aggregate spreading are normally carried out by automated pieces of equipment designed to give an even coverage of both; hand-controlled spraying and spreading is possible of course but the finished product will never be as well controlled.

Aggregate selection depends primarily on the level of microtexture required for the site in question. Size then depends on the degree of embedment likely into the existing surface. For example, surface dressing of an old concrete pavement demands a relatively small aggregate size whereas if the surface is asphalt and is already rich in bitumen, perhaps from earlier surface dressing applications, a larger size is called for. The rate of spread of particles is generally designed to give just about 100% coverage. As shown in Fig. 4.5, it is possible to design for additional durability by including more than one aggregate spread operation. A 'racked-in' surface dressing includes a second application, of much smaller aggregate size, designed to fill the gaps between larger particles. One can go further and introduce a second binder spray operation and yet more aggregate, increasing quality – but at the same time increasing cost. In effect, multi-stage surface dressings resemble thin asphalt layers.

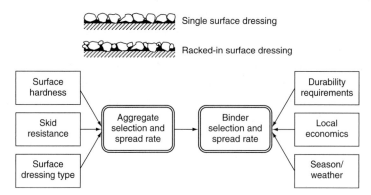

Fig. 4.5 Surface dressing design

Bitumen selection depends on several issues, not least local economics. It is possible to use pure hot bitumen of low viscosity; more usually an emulsion will be used, allowing a harder grade of binder but ensuring that it can still be sprayed over the surface. The use of cut-back bitumen (bitumen dissolved in lighter oils) is reducing these days due to health and safety concerns. In all cases, polymer additives may be used. This will depend on the site and whether it is a high-stress location, for example at a roundabout or junction, or not. Bitumen selection will also depend on ambient temperature since this will affect the rate and degree to which the aggregate particles will develop adhesion to the bitumen. Finally, bitumen spread rate depends primarily on the aggregate size and spread rate to be used. Figure 4.5 describes the decision-making process. Various documents from all over the world detail specific design advice.[4]

In temperate northern climates, surface dressing is carried out during a limited season (e.g. March–October) in order to ensure that the adhesive bond between aggregate and bitumen is fully developed.

Surface dressing can give a long-life surfacing. As noted in Part 3 (Section 3.7), it does not provide the best ride quality for users, particularly with respect to noise and vibration, and so is best not used for high-speed, intensively trafficked locations. However, it gives a high skid resistance and therefore a safe surface and it has the very considerable advantage that it seals the pavement. It is therefore ideally suited as a maintenance measure in locations where the structural strength of the pavement is not too badly compromised.

It is also a logical choice for the first stage in the transition from unbound pavement (gravel road) to surfaced road. A high-quality surface dressing has sufficient flexibility and toughness to survive perfectly well when placed directly onto a granular base, something that a genuine asphalt course may struggle to achieve because of its reduced flexibility under load. The point is that the curvature of the surface under wheel load will still be largely controlled by the base and, for a given curvature, a thicker layer will develop a higher tensile strain. It is also likely (though hard to prove) that the fatigue characteristic of a surface dressing layer is better than that of most asphalts because of its proportionally higher bitumen content.

4.1.5 Summary

For most local highway authorities, the treatments described in this section form a large part of annual maintenance expenditure, which is reason enough in itself to take the subject seriously. Crack sealing may not be a glamorous activity, but the benefits to be derived from it can be large; on the other hand, sealing cracks which do not really need sealing is equivalent to pouring money down a drain. There is therefore genuine scope for engineering input. Anyone can follow a routine prescription of measures; only an engineer who understands what is really going on in the pavement can tailor that prescription to maximise service life.

However, there comes a stage when no amount of engineering understanding is enough on its own. The cost of local repairs and surface treatments is by no means negligible, but that of major treatments such as structural overlays or partial reconstructions is an order of magnitude greater. Before such major treatments are even considered, it is essential to obtain a sound factual measure of the health of the pavement, i.e. to carry out a pavement evaluation.

4.2

Pavement evaluation

The previous section dealt largely with treatments for which little specialist design input is required in order to decide whether to go ahead or not. Admittedly that's not quite true of surface dressing, but the other treatments have not called for any real design, just experience. However, when such treatments have run their course, when simple patching and surface treatment is incapable of maintaining the pavement in a proper state of serviceability, that is the time when a deeper engineering appreciation is needed in order to enable the right decision to be taken. And, in order to achieve that engineering appreciation, it is necessary to gather condition data in a scientific way. It is a little like diagnosing an illness in a human patient. If insufficient tests are carried out, then even the best medical professional is relying on intuition rather than genuine knowledge – and that can be decidedly dangerous. The same is true of a pavement. Inspired guesswork is unlikely to prove an effective decision-making strategy. In this section, the different methods of gathering data will be presented and, at the end, the issue of planning a pavement evaluation will also be tackled.

4.2.1 Visual condition surveys

The treatments outlined in Section 4.1 in effect relied on a visual survey having been carried out although that was not explicitly stated. A visual survey is the most basic and yet often the most useful survey type of all. Put simply, not all cracks are the same; nor are all ruts or surface defects. An experienced engineer can deduce a great deal about the internal health or otherwise of a pavement just by inspecting the surface.

It is not the intention here to describe directly any of the many dozens of methodologies, procedures, condition indexes etc. which have been devised by highway and airport authorities all over the world.[5] Effective pavement management demands that visual condition data are treated in a statistical way and that scores are awarded according to overall condition, perhaps divided into certain key categories. However, this section will concentrate on identifying the detailed engineering knowledge that can be obtained. The reader will then be in a position to judge the relevance or effectiveness of any given system or indeed to devise his/her own if necessary.

Diagnosis Guide 4.1   Cracking of asphalt

Q. *Is there more cracking in the wheel path than elsewhere?*
Very obviously, if wheel path cracking predominates, then it is the traffic which is responsible, whatever that cracking may look like. Similarly, if cracking extends more or less equally over all areas of the pavement, then the traffic is irrelevant and the cause is environmental or due to a general material defect.

Q. *Are there transverse cracks right across the pavement?*
These are thermally generated. Either the climate is severe enough to cause low-temperature cracks in asphalt or the asphalt surface overlies a cracked (or jointed) hydraulically-bound base and reflective cracking has occurred. If there are irregular connecting longitudinal cracks then low-temperature cracking is most likely. If the cracks are regular, then an underlying hydraulically-bound layer, possibly a pre-existing jointed PQC pavement, is present.

Q. *Are there more transverse cracks in the wheel paths and in the most heavily trafficked locations (e.g. lane 1 of a multi-lane highway)?*
This may still represent reflective cracking from an underlying hydraulically-bound layer, but the traffic is the dominant cause. This indicates poor load transfer across underlying cracks or joints. However, if the cracks are short, frequent and restricted to the area immediately around the wheel-path then they may represent defects built in during construction (roller cracks, poor-quality asphalt) which have been developed by subsequent trafficking.

Q. *Is there a single well-developed longitudinal crack in the wheel path?*
This indicates traffic-induced fatigue of a thick asphalt pavement with no significant layer debonding. Crack direction is almost certainly top-down and crack depth is often no more than 50 mm or so.

Q. *Is there multiple cracking (crazing) in the wheel-path?*
This implies a shallow failure. Either the asphalt is thin or the upper layer or two have become debonded and are cracking independently of the rest, possibly due to deterioration at one of the layer interfaces.

Q. *Is slurry pumping up to the surface through cracks?*
Water has become trapped within the pavement, either within the bound materials, for example at an interface, or else in the upper part of a granular foundation. Damage is expected to accelerate rapidly.

Q. *Are there localised wheel-path depressions where more than one crack is present?*
These are typical of pavements with hydraulically-bound base. Localised damage to the base, usually at a transverse crack location, has led to water ingress, loss

---

4.2.1.1 Crack patterns – asphalt surfaces

Cracks can be longitudinal or transverse, close or widely spaced, wide or narrow, short or long – and every crack has a meaning. Diagnosis Guide 4.1 presents a checklist.

The list can only be an overview of the diagnosis possible. In reality every crack pattern is different. There will often be a combination of transverse and longitudinal cracks present because, unsurprisingly, more than one mode of damage may be taking place at the same time. Deterioration of the base may be masked by top-down cracking for example. In old pavements which have already been subject to previous strengthening treatments these issues become ever more complicated. Cracks may simply be reflective cracking from an older pavement construction. Crack patterns can tell the engineer a lot – but not everything.

4.2.1.2 Crack patterns – concrete surfaces

It is probably fair to say that the range of options is a little more limited with concrete. The questions in Diagnosis Guide 4.2 are some of those worth asking.

Diagnosis Guide 4.2   Cracking of concrete

Q. *Is cracking (of a jointed pavement) largely restricted to transverse cracks?*
This is a very common scenario. Transverse cracks, often at mid-distance between joints, indicate thermally-induced stress, assisted by traffic loading. The pavement is making up for an excessive joint spacing. These cracks will often stop at an adjacent longitudinal joint and go no further.

Q. *Are significant longitudinal cracks present in or around the wheel-path?*
This almost certainly indicates traffic-induced damage. Cracks may not be exactly in the wheel-path and may wander around either side. The likelihood is that they will jump across transverse joints and so may propagate rapidly along the pavement. This is a severe form of distress and the prognosis is not good.

Q. *Are longitudinal cracks narrow, relatively close-spaced and straight?*
The likelihood is that the pavement is reinforced and that these cracks have formed due to minor defects at the time of construction as the concrete 'slumped' around each reinforcement bar. They may not be full depth and probably do not represent a real threat to the pavement.

Q. *Are there corner cracks at joint intersections?*
This implies a lack of slab support close to joints. In itself the damage is limited and will extend no further, although cracks may widen and spall.

Q. *Are there regular transverse cracks at 1–2 m spacing but no joints?*
The pavement is continuously reinforced. If cracks are hairline or narrow then the pavement is performing well. If they have become wide and are spalling, then there is a serious lack of pavement strength somewhere (low PQC strength? poor foundation?) and a serious maintenance problem.

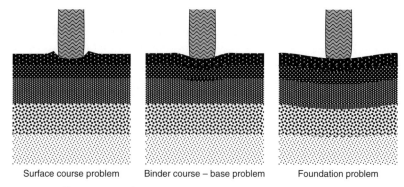

| Surface course problem | Binder course – base problem | Foundation problem |

Fig. 4.6 Different types of rutting

One should never panic at the sight of a crack, however wide. Pavements are designed to crack. In many cases, such as transverse cracking of jointed concrete or top-down cracking of asphalt, they barely affect pavement serviceability at all and are unlikely to lead rapidly to any more serious form of distress. They may need sealing, but nothing more. In other cases, the engineer has some serious worrying to do.

4.2.1.3 Rutting

As with cracks, not all ruts are the same. A rut is a function of deformation taking place in all the various layers of a pavement and, depending on which layer or layers are dominant, the shape will be different. For example, if it is the surface course which is primarily to blame, the rut will typically be narrow with marked shoulders either side. It is possible to judge from the width of a rut, taking into account the likely lateral distribution of wheel locations, as well as the overall shape, approximately where the problem lies. Figure 4.6 illustrates.

The distinction between the first two cases shown in Fig. 4.6 is particularly important but often not easy to discern from visual appearance. It is common for the assumption to be made that any narrow rut must be due to surface course problems, whereas this is frequently not the case, and merely replacing the surface course will not solve the long-term problem if it is a function of binder course or base; ruts will reoccur.

4.2.1.4 Surface defects

Besides cracks and ruts, several other surface features can be observed visually and may be important in diagnosing pavement problems.

Chipping loss
Individual aggregate particles may be lost from the surface for two principal reasons. The first is a loss of adhesive properties in the binder, an indication that the bitumen has aged significantly. The second reason is that cracks are beginning to develop, although they may as yet be invisible. A developing crack is associated with a concentration of curvature in the pavement under load, with associated high surface strain, and it is this high strain which leads to an eventual loosening of surface aggregate. Either way, chipping loss gives an early indicator of developing problems.

Ravelling
When loss of aggregate particles is more widespread, the term 'ravelling' is commonly used. This is an indication of an aged binder at the surface. Ravelling is eventually likely to lead to the development of potholes.

Bleeding
Otherwise known as 'fatting up', this is the phenomenon whereby excess bitumen in the pavement works its way up to the surface. It is seen as a smooth black sheen on the surface and is a significant safety hazard.

4.2.1.5 Other visual survey data
A visual survey will also be able to pick up the following:

- edge distress
- condition of construction joints
- road ironwork problems
- marking defects
- drainage defects.

All of these are important to the decision-maker who has to balance the various needs of the pavement and come up with the most cost-effective treatment or set of treatments. However, there is a limit to how far a visual survey can reach. Where large sums of money are at stake, the engineer needs more quantitative information.

4.2.2 Profile surveys
The two primary input parameters used in the discipline known as 'Pavement management' (see Section 4.6) are visual survey data and

profile data. Visual surveys can be cheap and they rely on no specialist technology, but they are not particularly quick and they cannot be carried out on heavily trafficked highways without a lane closure (other than a coarse survey from a vehicle). For rapid objective assessment of condition, an automated profile survey is the obvious answer.

4.2.2.1 International Roughness Index (IRI)

IRI[6] is one of the few measures of pavement condition with genuine international acceptance. It is primarily a measure used on highways rather than other sorts of pavement. It is defined by the amplitude of motion of a standard vehicle suspension system as it travels along the road, measured in cumulative metres of suspension system movement per kilometre of travel (m/km or mm/m). However, there are a large number of vehicles on the market (commonly known as *bump integrators*) which purport to measure IRI, and they vary significantly in their details (wheels, axle, suspension system and vehicle mass); calibration is therefore absolutely vital. Most bump integrators are car or van size, and speed of travel can be that of normal highway traffic. Figure 4.7 illustrates the idea.

Bump integrator surveys have many advantages: the equipment is not particularly expensive and it is therefore suited to use in developing countries; the measurement (IRI) is a direct indication of ride quality and is therefore directly related to 'serviceability' as felt by both vehicle and driver; data can be rapidly obtained. These qualities mean that IRI

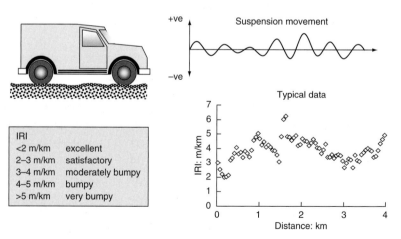

Fig. 4.7 Bump integrators and IRI

has become the primary indicator of pavement condition in many highway pavement management systems, usually supplemented by a visual condition index (VCI) of some sort – a combined score for visual condition from all different distress modes. IRI is a 'blunt instrument'; a high IRI may be due to many different actual distress types, including rutting, ravelling, potholing, surface texture issues and cracking. However, it is ideal for monitoring the change in condition over the years. The trend can be observed and, when IRI reaches a certain level, a more detailed survey can then be carried out to determine the actual deterioration mode and therefore the most appropriate maintenance strategy. It will only be at this detailed investigation stage that it becomes apparent just how much money needs to be spent, which means that, until then, the management system will simply have to assume average spend quantities based on experience. However, for network-level budgeting purposes, this is quite sufficient.

4.2.2.2 Laser profile surveys

At the high technology end of profile measurement there are a string of laser-based systems.[7] Lasers are used throughout the engineering world as accurate and remote distance sensors, and they can be used for profile measurement by aiming them down at the road from a vehicle-mounted frame and monitoring the reflection from the surface. Over distances of a few centimetres, the variation gives a measure of texture depth; over distances of metres, the data can be interpreted in terms of longitudinal profile (averaging out the texture depth element). Most commonly, a series of at least three sensors is mounted longitudinally and the measurements from each are compared. Sensors can also be mounted transversely, giving a measure of rut depth. These types of survey can be carried out at normal traffic speed.

It is possible to derive an approximate equivalent IRI value from the data, but this under-utilises the information available. Therefore, in many European countries, including the UK, the data are interpreted scientifically as a measure of variance (or standard deviation) of surface profile from a moving mean. The number is less directly related to ride quality than IRI, but it is more readily understandable in terms of pavement distress.

As well as measuring longitudinal profile, transverse profile and texture depth, it is common to mount a video camera (or cameras), giving both inventory data and also information on surface condition;

it makes sense to maximise the benefit to be derived from every survey vehicle kilometre.

4.2.3 Skid resistance surveys

Together with visual condition and profile surveys, skid resistance surveys also form a logical ingredient into a pavement management system. While visual condition and profile give general data relating to all aspects of condition, skid resistance is a single property. However, it is a property which is directly related to the safety of users (except in the case of slow-speed applications), applying to both highways and airfield runways. In the case of airfields, there are international standards and it is necessary for airport authorities to check skid resistance regularly, particularly under adverse weather conditions (rain or snow). Highways are governed by standards set by individual countries, regions and cities, but in many parts of the world skid resistance is specified both as an initial requirement and to be checked at intervals. It is also sometimes necessary to carry out measurements at particular locations where accidents have occurred or where safety is under review.

The Sideways Force Coefficient Routine Investigation Machine (SCRIM) is a standard device for skid resistance measurement on highways and is used in many parts of the world.[8] The principle of operation is shown in Fig. 4.8. An extra wheel is set at an angle to the direction of travel and dragged forwards (while being allowed to rotate). The result is a sideways force which, when divided by the applied vertical force,

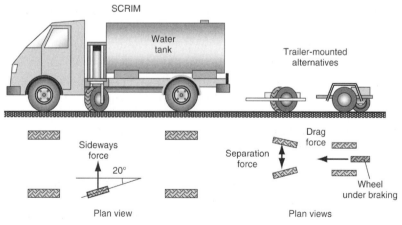

Fig. 4.8 Skid resistance measurement devices

gives a SCRIM coefficient. A water tank on the back of the vehicle supplies water continuously to the measurement wheel since wet conditions are always the most severe.

Also shown in Fig. 4.8 are two examples of light-weight trailer-mounted friction testing devices.[9] These are typical of the machines used at airfields and by many highway authorities for the purpose of localised investigations into particular problems. For wet skid resistance, a water tank has to be mounted in the towing vehicle. In these cases too, a friction coefficient results, although it may differ from the SCRIM coefficient because of differences in vertical force, tyre type and mode of drag. On UK highways, for example, a calibration to SCRIM is needed.

The point was made in relation to surface design in Part 3 (Section 3.7.3.2) that surface friction is a season- and weather-dependent quantity and that summer conditions are normally worst (other than if ice is present) because of the effect of polishing on surface aggregate. This must of course be borne in mind when measuring skid resistance whatever the device used; absolute judgements about inherent surface properties should really only be made after at least three measurements, preferably during the summer (or dry) season.

4.2.4 Cores and trial pits

In the end, there is no substitute for digging down and taking a look beneath the surface. Coring, using cutters which need be no more than 100 mm in diameter, is a relatively non-destructive method of sampling a pavement providing the hole is properly back-filled afterwards. Coring is also not too time-consuming or disruptive. However, it does require a coring machine.

Trial pits represent an alternative, labour-intensive method of sampling. They are suitable (1) where bound layer thickness is low; (2) where samples of unbound foundation material are required; or (3) where specific information is needed which demands a larger view (or a larger test specimen) than can be afforded by a core. However, modern coring machines are quite capable of obtaining cores of 300 mm diameter or more if necessary, and techniques now exist for retrieving samples of unbound material from holes as little as 150 mm in diameter, so serious thought should be given to avoiding trial pits on heavily trafficked roads if at all possible.

The following subsections detail the information which can be obtained from cores and trial pits.

4.2.4.1 Construction information

The first and most immediate benefit to be derived is that cores and trial pits reveal what is actually there. Layers can be identified and their thicknesses measured; a visual assessment of quality (void content, bitumen appearance, friability of hydraulically-bound materials, reinforcement, aggregate type) can be made; any lack of bond is evident (sometimes caused by coring – but indicative of weak bond nevertheless). In many cases something of the history of the pavement can be deduced, as buried surface courses or additional binder courses are frequently found. If an overlay has been carried out in the past, then one can generally assume that this was done for a reason – although the nature of that reason is unlikely to be deducible from a core alone.

However, a core is unlikely to reveal anything to do with water, since water is usually added to cool the core cutter. Only if a layer is thoroughly saturated, or in cases where water continues to weep out from an interface long after coring has been completed, can it be deduced that this was almost certainly not coring water. Coring also only allows a very small sample of underlying unbound material to be retrieved. Trial pits on the other hand readily allow water problems to be identified and also allow excavation deep into the foundation if necessary.

If an *unbound material sampler*[10] is used, a device which is driven into the foundation layers, usually through a core hole, then an excellent picture of foundation materials and underlying soil can readily be obtained. The operation adds considerably to the time taken at a single core location, but may under certain circumstances be worthwhile. It does however preclude carrying out the in situ testing described below.

4.2.4.2 In situ tests

The relatively small size of most core holes means that there is a limit to the types of test that can be carried out. In fact, there is only one in situ test device that is commonly used and that is the *dynamic cone penetrometer* (DCP) – see Fig. 4.9. It is a conceptually simple tool, consisting of a cone on the end of a rod, which is driven into the ground under impulse forces from a dropped weight. The rate of penetration (in mm/blow) is recorded, and usually converted to an equivalent California Bearing Ratio (CBR – see Part 2, Section 2.1.1.9). It isn't really CBR, but it is at least a measure of the quality of the material, and it means that a profile of material quality with

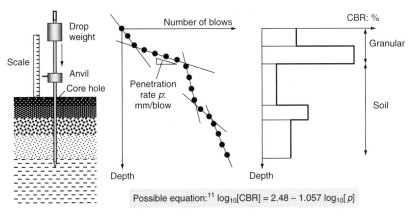

Fig. 4.9 The dynamic cone penetrometer (DCP)

depth can be generated, often revealing the thickness of granular sub-base as well as the strength of the underlying soil. The test is a relatively rapid one and the information generated is extremely useful.

It is important to appreciate the difference between the resistance to a cone and properties such as stiffness and shear strength. Two points are particularly noteworthy. The first is that if individual aggregate particles are of comparable size to the cone (20 mm diameter), then the precise arrangement of particles can dramatically affect the penetration rate; an individual particle can temporarily block progress. The second point is that saturation of a granular material will only slightly lower resistance to cone penetration whereas it will greatly reduce shear strength and stiffness of the aggregate under traffic loading.

While cores permit only the DCP, trial pits open up the possibility of plate tests. The traditional *plate loading test* has already been described in Part 2 (Section 2.1.1.10), where the point was made that the measure is a combination of stiffness and shear strength, depending on the material type being loaded. However, of more likely use, the portable *dynamic plate test* (DPT) is a pure stiffness test; it takes just a few seconds to carry out and is ideally suited to use within a trial pit. The equipment and its interpretation have also been described in Part 2 (Section 2.1.2.5). The interpretation given was in terms of an elastic stiffness modulus, assuming the whole foundation to be a single uniform material of infinite extent. In reality, of course, it has to be remembered that there will be contributions from all the different layers down to a depth of 1–2 m.

Finally, it should be noted that some DPT devices allow measurement of surface deflection at locations adjacent to the plate. This potentially gives additional useful information; the interpretation principle is the same as that of the falling weight deflectometer and will be covered in Section 4.2.6.3.

4.2.4.3 Information on damage mechanisms

Both cracking and rutting can be investigated by means of cores or trial pits. Most obviously, a core through a surface crack will reveal how deeply it penetrates. However, it can also reveal much more. A comparison of cores at cracked and non-cracked locations frequently reveals that water-related damage has occurred in asphalt or hydraulically-bound layers at the crack location. In some cases the comparison is between a fully intact specimen and a pile of fragments. Similarly, there is often a correlation between the occurrence of layer debonding and crack locations, suggesting water influence. The point here is not that any such finding is unexpected, but that it gives a direct indication of the sensitivity of the bound layers to water and therefore the importance or otherwise of sealing the surface.

Rutting is less easy to investigate. However, a well-placed trial pit or a transverse line of cores can give an indication of which layers are reducing in thickness at a rut location.

Figure 4.10 gives examples of both cracking and layer disintegration and the potential usefulness of cores in identifying damage mechanisms.

Surface course

Binder/base course debonding

HBM base

Crack; reflected from HBM base through asphalt surfacing

Crack; top-down, penetrating through about 50% of the asphalt

Bottom-up reflective crack beginning to grow

Crack in HBM base possibly reflected from sub-base

Serious crack in disintegrating HBM sub-base

Fig. 4.10 Damage mechanisms revealed[12]

4.2.4.4 *Laboratory test specimens*

The various tests which can be conducted on different pavement materials have been described in appropriate sections of Part 2, and many of them can be used on specimens taken from a pavement. In fact, many laboratory tests are designed to be carried out on 100 mm or 150 mm diameter cylinders, which means that cores are an ideal source of such specimens. These tests include:

- compressive strength of hydraulically-bound material (note that a height to diameter ratio of at least 1.0 is required)
- uniaxial stiffness modulus of hydraulically-bound material
- indirect tensile strength (ITS), of either hydraulically-bound material or asphalt
- indirect tensile stiffness modulus (ITSM) of asphalt
- indirect tensile fatigue test (ITFT) for asphalt
- repeated load axial test (RLAT) for asphalt deformation
- inter-layer bond strength tests – see next section.

If test specimens are required of a different shape then matters become rather more complicated – and therefore expensive. Beam tests, very popular among researchers and widely used in specification of concrete, require a specimen of 300 mm or more in length, obtainable from a trial pit or by sawing from a core of over 300 mm diameter.

Density and void content can be obtained on a specimen of any convenient shape. Asphalt specimens can also be broken down into their constituents, by means of a centrifuge, with solvents used to extract the bitumen. Aggregate gradation can be checked, as can binder content. Binder quality can also be measured using a dynamic shear rheometer (DSR – see Part 2, Section 2.3.1.3), although it should always be borne in mind that the properties may have been affected by the method of binder extraction.

Unbound material can be sampled by means of an unbound material sampler, but the quantity of material retrieved is small. Pocket cone penetrometer tests, giving a measure of shear strength, are sometimes possible; determination of water content, liquid and plastic limits can also be carried out. However, if gradation of a granular layer is required, then a larger sample has to be obtained, in which case a trial pit or a very large-diameter core are the only options.

Clearly it will not be appropriate to carry out all tests on all occasions. Testing has to be carefully targeted in order to provide information relevant to each particular investigation. Section 4.2.7 will discuss the planning of a pavement evaluation.

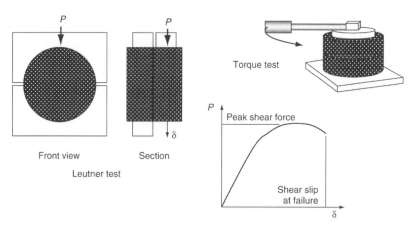

Fig. 4.11 Inter-layer bond strength tests

4.2.4.5 Bond tests

Bond can be measured at any stage in the life of a pavement, and is some-times specified at initial construction. There are two principal methods of measurement, both of which are described in Fig. 4.11.[13] Neither should be seen as giving a pure measure of the shear strength of an inter-layer bond because of the non-uniformity of stress conditions applying; one should also expect different results from the two different tests. Never-theless both enable the quality of the bond to be assessed and either may be used in a specification.[14] Where the Leutner test is specified, the bond strength called for is typically around 1.5 MPa at the surface course–binder course interface, and 1.0 MPa at lower interfaces.

4.2.5 Ground-penetrating radar (GPR)

GPR introduces the subject of truly non-destructive testing. Cores may be thought of as being minimally destructive, but they are certainly intrusive, as well as being time-consuming and also restricted to providing information at discrete and usually widely-spaced points. GPR on the other hand has the capability of providing a continuous picture of the pavement structure, and nowadays it is not even particu-larly expensive. It sounds too good to be true!

4.2.5.1 Principle of operation

GPR is a very powerful technique. The concept is that radio waves are transmitted from a point while a receiver at an adjacent point 'listens'

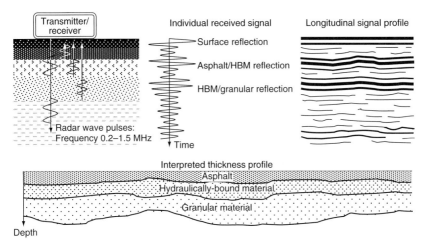

Fig. 4.12 Ground-penetrating radar (GPR)

for reflected waves. Reflections will take place when a wave encounters a change of material; this may be air–surface; it may equally well be asphalt–granular. Thus, if radar is pointed down into the ground, the receiver will pick up a reflected signal corresponding to each change in material properties. The time elapsed between transmission and reception is then directly related to the distance travelled down to an interface between two materials and then back up to the surface. Furthermore, since only a proportion of the wave strength is reflected while the remainder continues down into the pavement, there will be a series of reflections as each interface is encountered. Figure 4.12 describes the equipment and the way in which results are typically interpreted.

On the individual received signal trace illustrated in Fig. 4.12, the strong contributions from layer interfaces (and from the surface) are clear. The profile shown on the right is generated by a processor which assigns 'black' where the received signal is above a certain amplitude only. This profile can then be interpreted, partly by image recognition software but with human assistance also, converting from 'time' to 'depth', for which an estimate of wave speed in each medium is required. This is usually achieved by calibrating the GPR data against core records.

4.2.5.2 Information obtained

Thickness determination is the primary reason for carrying out a radar survey on a pavement and it is usual to obtain thoroughly excellent data, accurate to around 1 cm.[15] One has to be slightly wary of material identification, and it is not uncommon for a radar analyst to conclude that a certain material is present, for example asphalt, when in fact it is something different, for example hydraulically-bound material. When the full range of possible material types within each generic class is considered, this is hardly surprising.

However, radar can also give data on the presence of moisture (since water molecules become excited at radar frequencies), on voids (because of the strength of a solid–air interface), and on steel reinforcement (steel interferes with wave propagation). Basically, the more information is required the more expensive the survey becomes as additional frequencies need to be used and, for accuracy, slow travel speed is required. A normal travel speed for thickness determination is around 20 mph (30 km/h). Information from thickness determination is often extremely useful and minor errors in material identification are usually unimportant, although information on moisture, voids and reinforcement is, in the author's experience, less frequently of value. In some cases this is because the radar interpretation appears suspect; in most cases it is because the radar information adds little to what is known already.

4.2.6 Deflection surveys

Radar can help the engineer to 'see' beneath the surface, but it cannot give much in the way of direct information on the structural condition of the materials. For this there is no alternative but to assess performance under load, which means measuring the deflection of the pavement surface under the action of an applied wheel load (or similar alternative). The stiffness of response will then give direct information which might logically correlate to the ability of the pavement to carry multiple load applications.

4.2.6.1 The Benkelman Beam[16]

This is the oldest and simplest form of deflection test device and it has been successfully used throughout the world for many decades. Figure 4.13 illustrates the principle of operation and the interpretation procedure commonly used.

As shown in the figure, the Benkelman Beam itself is a simple frame with an arm on a hinge, the rotation of which is read from a dial gauge. The equipment is placed on the ground immediately behind the twin

360

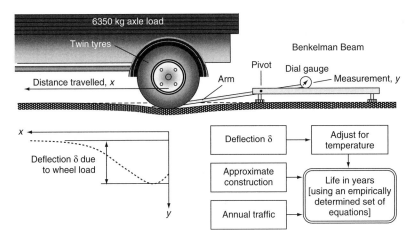

Fig. 4.13 The Benkelman Beam

rear tyres on one side of a goods vehicle loaded to a standard weight, the arm resting on the pavement surface between the twin tyres. When the operator is ready, the goods vehicle is slowly driven forward and a maximum reading is taken as the tyres pass the end of the arm; when it has driven forward some metres, a minimum reading is also taken. The difference relates to the deflection caused by the loaded wheel.

This is a practical, low-technology tool. Like the bump integrator, it is therefore well suited to developing countries. One could criticise the slow vehicle travel speed, which means that any asphalt layers will appear to have a lower stiffness than would be the case under more normal traffic speed. One could also draw attention to the fact that the reference frame feet are close enough to the wheels to be affected; the measurement is therefore not an absolute one. Nevertheless, since the usual method of interpretation is with reference to equations based on empirical experience, these criticisms have little validity. And even without any accepted method of absolute interpretation of the readings, the measure of relative performance between one point and the next is always useful.

4.2.6.2 The Lacroix Deflectograph

The Deflectograph is an extension of the Benkelman Beam idea, initially developed in France, and the UK has been one of the countries to make most intensive use of it. The problem with the Benkelman Beam is that productivity is low; it takes a minute or two to set up, take measurements, and move forward to the next point. The Deflectograph

361

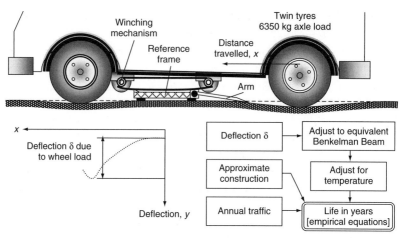

Fig. 4.14 The Lacroix Deflectograph

uses exactly the same principle, i.e. the recording of deflection between the twin tyres of a rear axle, but with a quite different reference frame, one that allows the vehicle to travel continuously along the road. Figure 4.14 indicates conceptually how this is achieved. The reference frame is now in front of the measurement axle, and it is repeatedly dragged forward relative to the body of the vehicle and then released. As soon as the rear tyres of the vehicle have drawn level with the tip of the measurement arm, the frame is winched forward toward the front of the vehicle ready for the next reading. The result is that a measurement is taken every 3–4 m and that the vehicle can travel continuously at a speed of 2–3 km/h. Readings are taken in both wheel paths.

This is clearly a massive improvement on the Benkelman Beam from the point of view of productivity, allowing a near-continuous profile of pavement stiffness to be determined. However, it is not any more accurate; in fact it is less so. The reference frame is even more greatly affected by adjacent wheels, both front and back, and the arm is shorter. However, since the method of interpretation is still according to empirically determined equations, this is not a serious criticism.

In the UK method of usage, for example, worked out by the Transport Research Laboratory over a period of many years' study, a series of charts was produced for pavements of various types and thicknesses, giving relationships between deflection and the passage of traffic.[17] Thus, if the past traffic is known then a measured deflection can be translated straight to a remaining life, by simply reading off the chart. Similar charts were produced for overlay designs, again based on monitoring the gradual deterioration (and change in Deflectograph deflection) of a large number of pavements. These charts have, of course, been digitised into equations which are built into the data-processing systems currently used.

Note the temperature adjustment required when interpreting both the Benkelman Beam and the Deflectograph – and indeed any deflection test on an asphalt pavement. The usual procedure is to drill a small hole into the pavement, pour glycerine or oil into the bottom, and to record the glycerine/oil temperature once it has reached an equilibrium. Infrared sensors now provide an alternative method of sensing surface temperature. Temperature adjustment is, like everything else in this analysis, based on empirical evidence.

There is no doubting the usefulness of Benkelman Beam and Deflectograph data, both in pavement management and also for project-level design of maintenance or rehabilitation. However, the information provided will always be crude, no matter how much empirical evidence is used. There is absolutely no way of knowing the relative contributions of the different layers to deflection. A high reading may indicate poor asphalt; it may equally indicate a soft subgrade. A standard processing package will give the same remaining life in the two cases – and the same overlay thickness – but the actual performance will not be the same at all. This is a serious drawback. It means that the Benkelman Beam and Deflectograph can be used to give a first estimate of structural condition, an estimate that may be appropriate for network-level management but which certainly is not sufficient on its own for project-level design. For this, a more sophisticated deflection test is needed.

4.2.6.3 *The falling weight deflectometer (FWD)*
The FWD has taken the world of pavement structural evaluation by storm since it was first used commercially in the early 1980s.[18] As far as productivity is concerned, at a test per minute it is only slightly quicker than the Benkelman Beam; but where the FWD scores is that it gives a very precise value of absolute deflection (accuracies of $\pm 2\,\mu m$ commonly quoted), and that opens the door to a much more sophisticated method of interpretation. Figure 4.15 illustrates the equipment and the data analysis methodolgy.

The machine is usually trailer-mounted. Tests are performed with the equipment stationary and with the loading plate and deflection sensors lowered onto the surface. The load pulse is then generated by the action of a falling weight onto a set of rubber buffers. However, despite the

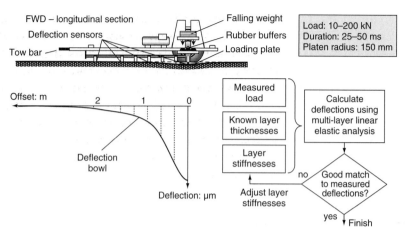

Fig. 4.15 The falling weight deflectometer (FWD)

stop–start nature of the testing procedure, the FWD actually has several desirable features. First, the load magnitude can be selected to match a typical wheel load; second, the pulse duration is similar to that from a moving vehicle; third, the deflections are absolute and highly accurate (generally achieved by use of velocity transducers); and fourth, measurements are taken not only at the load location (through a hole in the centre of the loading plate) but also at selected distances from it.

This last point is particularly important. The full set of readings describes what is termed a *deflection bowl* (or basin) – whose interpretation is presented conceptually in Fig. 4.16. This means that, whereas neither the Benkelman Beam nor the Deflectograph are able to distinguish between two pavements with the same deflection under load but with quite different individual layer stiffnesses, the FWD can; each particular combination of layer stiffnesses gives a near-unique deflection bowl. So, with a knowledge of the full deflection bowl, it should in theory be possible to deduce just which combination of layer stiffnesses was responsible. This procedure is termed *back-analysis* (or back-calculation).

There are numerous back-analysis computer programs on the market, almost all making the following assumptions:

- all layers are of uniform thickness and of infinite lateral extent
- all materials are linear elastic and homogeneous
- the load consists of uniform stress on a circular area
- dynamic effects due to inertia are negligible.

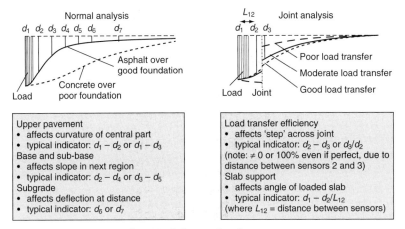

Fig. 4.16 Interpretation of FWD deflection bowls

None of these are true of course. And that means that even the best back-analysis procedure will struggle to achieve a perfect match between the measured deflections and those calculated, and that the resulting stiffnesses must be treated with a healthy degree of scepticism. It also means that it is asking for trouble to try to subdivide the pavement into more than four layers – less if possible. Where materials differ significantly in stiffness, for example asphalt, granular sub-base and soft soil, back-analysis should be able to arrive at a reasonable esti-mate for the stiffness modulus of each, so long as no layer is too thin (and therefore too insignificant in its effect on deflection). Where layers have similar stiffness, for example asphalt and cement-bound base, there is always a danger that back-analysis will greatly exaggerate the stiffness of one while the other is underestimated. An appreciation of the real degree of confidence (or otherwise) can only come with experience, but a general rule would be that simple, intact pavement structures can be analysed with reasonable certainty; more complex and variable cases will still generate valuable answers, but these should always be considered alongside other evidence.

One argument with considerable validity is that whatever incorrect assumptions are made when back-analysing FWD data, the same incorrect assumptions will usually be made when evaluating remaining pavement life under design wheel loading. The calculated strain in the pavement under wheel load should therefore still be approximately correct.[19]

A final advantage over the Benkelman Beam and Deflectograph is that the FWD is equally at home on concrete or asphalt, whereas the other devices have been used almost exclusively on asphalt and would give only very small deflections on concrete because of the non-absolute nature of the measurements. The FWD is particularly well suited to measuring load transfer efficiency across a joint. The loading plate is positioned one side of the joint and deflections are measured either side. As well as summarising the meaning of different components of a 'normal' deflection bowl, Fig. 4.16 also illustrates the information which can be obtained from a joint test.

4.2.6.4 Rolling wheel deflectometers

The ultimate deflection test device would be one that measured a full deflection bowl like the FWD, but which travelled at traffic speed along a highway, thus combining both quality and quantity of information. Such a device is the rolling wheel deflectometer, and several versions have been developed over the years, achieving their goal to varying degrees. There is an inevitable trade-off between measurement accuracy and travel speed. Several companies and research organisations have used lasers to measure distance from a datum, averaging data over a certain length to give a reasonable approximation to the correct deflection bowl. Surface texture and vehicle oscillation are two of the larger problems which have to be overcome, together with the fact that it is not easy to reach the area of surface immediately adjacent to the tyre (and certainly not the area which is actually loaded).

At the time of writing (2007) it is fair to say that some of the laser-based systems appear very promising but that no device has yet made it to the stage where it has been adopted by any pavement management authority.

4.2.7 Pavement evaluation planning

Resources are always limited, so it is clearly imperative that pavement evaluation is sensibly targeted; there is no point spending vast amounts on understanding exactly what problems there might be on a particular pavement if there is then no money left to carry out the necessary maintenance. However, this is easy to say but much harder to put into practice, not least because it is quite impossible for anyone to see the whole economic picture. All that will be attempted here, therefore, is to set out a few guiding principles, accepting that the real economic equation will vary from circumstance to circumstance. The larger question of pavement management will be discussed in Section 4.6.

4.2.7.1 Network level

A pavement authority needs to monitor performance regularly so as to plan budget allocation well in advance, and this is true whatever the political difficulties involved in securing that budget. In fact, the greater the political constraints, the more important it is for that authority to be equipped with up-to-date information on pavement condition in order to argue the spending case from a position of strength. Some sort of regular condition evaluation is therefore essential. Table 4.1 lists the alternatives.

Traffic counts have not been mentioned under 'pavement evaluation' previously since they are not directly connected with pavement condition; however, they are essential to highway network management. Counting can be automatic, using piezo-electric strips buried in the road surface, or it can be manual. The advantage of automatic counts is that they can continue day and night for long periods with little expenditure. The advantage of manual counts is that traffic can be classified accurately into different vehicle types (cars, buses, light goods, heavy goods – different axle configurations). Both are extremely useful in assigning the relative value of different spend proposals.

Axle weight surveys have also not been mentioned so far. They can be carried out either by stopping and weighing wagons on a fixed weighbridge or by installing a weigh-in-motion (WIM) device into the pavement, many designs for which now exist.[20] Results from a fixed weighbridge can be considered accurate; those from a WIM device are less reliable and depend on regular calibration of the installation. Such surveys would normally only be carried out at state or country level, in order to monitor trends in goods traffic development through

Table 4.1 Network-level monitoring options

Survey type	Information	Usefulness
Traffic count	Trends; design traffic	High
Axle weight	Vehicle damage factors	Low–medium
Visual condition	Roughness (approx.)	Very high
	Structural condition (very approx.)	
	Skid resistance (possibly)	
Profile	Roughness	High
	Structural condition (very approx.)	
Deflectograph	Structural condition (approx.)	Medium
SCRIM	Skid resistance	Medium

Table 4.2 Possible construction of condition indicators

Distress type	Ride quality indicator	Structural condition indicator	Skid resistance indicator
Cracking		60%	
Rutting	10%	30%	
Edge distress		10%	
Patching	20%		10%
Ravelling	40%		
Potholes	30%		
Visible texture			90%

the years, enabling 'damage factors' (see Part 3, Section 3.2.2) to be updated as necessary.

The only absolutely essential ingredient as far as pavement condition assessment is concerned is visual survey data. The information which results is certainly approximate, but it relates to *ride quality*, *structural condition* and also safety-related features such as *skid resistance*. It can be processed to give single numbers related to each, numbers which can be used to assign likely remaining life and future maintenance costs – albeit very approximately. Table 4.2 suggests a way in which indicators of ride quality, structural condition and skid resistance can be built up with contributions from different visual survey condition parameters. Note: the table is conceptual; details will depend on the way in which each condition parameter is measured.

Visual survey data allow relatively minor maintenance of the type described in Section 4.1 to be programmed; they also give an excellent basis for estimating future costs as an average across a network, although predictions may be wildly inaccurate in any individual case.

However, visual surveys of very heavily trafficked multi-lane roads are not easy to carry out safely. For these reasons, profile surveys, Deflectograph measurements and SCRIM surveys should all be considered. Each will give a more accurate evaluation of individual aspects of condition, namely *ride quality*, *structural condition* and *skid resistance* respectively. However, the high productivity achievable from a profile survey, together with the fact that structural condition tends to correlate very roughly with profile, propels profile surveys to the top of the list. They are second only to visual condition surveys in terms of usefulness and it is worth considering employing them at least on major highways at reasonably frequent intervals (e.g. annually or biannually).

368

It may also be possible to justify Deflectograph and SCRIM (or similar alternatives) as network-level survey tools but, if so, their usage would logically be much less frequent. At this level one is moving away from the overall aim of obtaining an average network condition and a whole-network budget towards the more specific aim of being able to decide when to carry out a more detailed survey of individual parts of the network. A combination of visual condition and profile is probably sufficient for budgeting purposes.

4.2.7.2 Programming a project-level survey

A good pavement management system, whether entirely manual or incorporating purpose-designed software, will include 'triggers' to indicate when detailed evaluation at project level is needed. These triggers may be based on individual indicators (visual, profile etc.) or a combination of them all, but the key point is that detailed evaluation should be triggered in time for cost-effective maintenance (of a more major nature than those activities described in Section 4.1). Figure 4.17 illustrates the challenge.

The question as to what constitutes cost-effectiveness is not easily answered. Clearly it is not worth spending too early or the pavement is brought into an unnecessarily strong condition, with the possibility that future unforeseeable changes in use, changes in traffic load etc. will mean that the potential life of the pavement is never fully utilised. On the other hand, spending too late means that materials which might

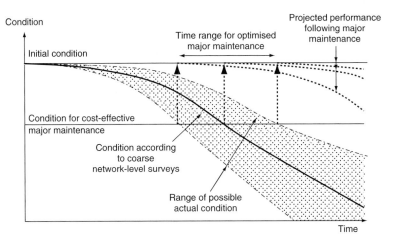

Fig. 4.17 Pavement condition uncertainty

have been structurally sound as a base layer no longer are, requiring increased expenditure, and this is on top of the nuisance to users of allowing continuing usage at a poor standard of ride quality. The actual optimum will definitely depend on the type of pavement (earlier for major highways and airfield runways; later for minor roads and industrial areas), but there will be an approximate optimum somewhere.

However, network-level surveys inevitably include a large degree of uncertainty, as illustrated in Fig. 4.17. It is therefore sensible to carry out a detailed evaluation well before the optimum intervention level is reached – according to network-level survey data. For example, if optimum intervention level is assumed to occur when the network-level 'condition indicator' falls to 60% of its original value, it would be worth programming a detailed evaluation when the survey data indicate 70–75%; the real level may already be at 60%.

Unfortunately, it is only possible to describe the principle here because of the quite different requirements of different classes of pavement and the large number of possible condition indicators in use. To summarise:

- Decide on one or more network-level condition indicators.
- Estimate what condition (according to the condition indicators) represents the optimum time for major maintenance.
- Set triggers for project-level surveys at condition indicator values significantly higher than those for optimum major maintenance.

4.2.7.3 Designing a project-level survey

Having established that a particular section of the network is ready for its detailed (project-level) pavement evaluation, the question arises as to what types of survey are most appropriate. There are basically two aims to this exercise, namely:

1. to establish the deterioration mechanism(s)
2. to provide parameters for analysis and rehabilitation design.

To satisfy the first aim it is necessary to understand the root cause of any cracking, rutting or surface distress which is taking place, and the prime tools are likely to be cores and/or trial pits, combined with a detailed visual survey. Cores through cracks and cores or pits across rutted sections are obvious tasks, with control cores/pits in areas with no distress. The immediate visual evidence (surface + cores/pits) is often enough for near-certainty of distress mechanism; laboratory

Table 4.3 *Project-level evaluation tools*

Survey type	Information	Frequency
Cores; trial pits; laboratory tests	Layer thickness Bound material stiffness modulus Fatigue strength Deformation resistance Foundation strength	Occasional
Radar (GPR)	Layer thickness High moisture locations	Continuous
Detailed visual survey	Crack density Rutting locations/severity	Continuous
Falling weight deflectometer	Layer stiffness modulus Joint condition	@1–100 m
Drainage survey	Drainage efficiency	Targeted

tests, for example establishing binder hardness, may be required to prove the point.

However, to obtain the quantitative data required for pavement analysis and rehabilitation design, a much more thorough job is needed. The key design parameters are *layer thickness, stiffness modulus, fatigue strength* and, for asphalt or unbound materials, *deformation resistance*, and it is necessary to build up a near-continuous picture throughout the site. Table 4.3 lists the tools available and suggests their likely use.

The most logical approach is to consider the parameters needed for design and then to decide how best to obtain them.

Layer thickness
Cores/pits and GPR are the methods listed in Table 4.3; however, construction records form another source of information. There are therefore three options:

1. rely on construction records
2. use construction records supplemented by cores/pits
3. use GPR, together with cores/pits and construction records.

For a pavement of relatively recent construction, records may be sufficient; however in older pavements, particularly those which have undergone maintenance in the past, cores or pits are often essential. GPR is more of a luxury and should therefore only be used where the economic importance of the pavement warrants the expenditure,

371

although the information obtainable from GPR is of excellent quality and allows treatment lengths to be specified with much improved confidence.

In practice, it is rare to have to rely on construction records alone because there are usually other reasons besides thickness determination for taking cores or digging trial pits.

Stiffness modulus

This is an essential ingredient in analytical pavement design, but may be replaced in empirical methods by a 'condition factor' of some sort. If no quantitative assessment is needed, then it is probably unnecessary to carry out measurements of FWD accuracy; sufficient reliance can be placed on the combined evidence of visual condition and cores/pits, preferably supplemented by relatively coarse deflection measurements such as those from the Benkelman Beam or Deflectograph. However, where quantitative analysis is to be carried out, the FWD (or similarly accurate rolling wheel devices as they become available) is required. The intensity of usage will depend on the likely variability of the pavement structure and the economic importance of the pavement. Typical patterns of usage might be:

- @ 20 m in near-side wheel path + occasional tests in lane centre
- @ 50 m in less trafficked lanes on a multi-lane highway
- @ 100 m in near-side wheel path for long, overview-type surveys
- @ 20 m at ±2–5 m offsets from runway or taxiway centreline
- @ 50 m in less trafficked parts of airfield pavements
- in a grid pattern, 20–50 m spacing, on large areas such as airfield aprons, parking areas and industrial sites
- @ 1 m over short lengths to establish an underlying crack pattern.

Due thought has to be given to the practical time demands. Traffic management will almost certainly be necessary in order to enable coring or pitting to be carried out and the same time window should logically be used for FWD testing.

Tests in the most heavily trafficked areas (the wheel paths) are obviously necessary. However, it is often very informative to be able to make a comparison with other much less heavily trafficked regions; hence the suggested occasional tests in lane centres, in less heavily trafficked lanes and on outer parts of airfield pavements. The tests at 1 m centres are only suggested in cases where it is suspected that a hydraulically-bound base underlies an asphalt surface. The pattern of deflections can reveal the approximate spacing of underlying cracks or joints.

The reader may be surprised that the recommendations related to stiffness modulus so far only concern in situ tests rather than laboratory measurements. In fact, laboratory measurements are extremely useful as the following sections will explain but, as tests on discrete elements, they are not necessarily representative of the effective in situ behaviour of the pavement as a whole. Laboratory stiffness measurements on asphalt specimens are strongly advised but they should preferably not be used on their own to derive stiffness moduli for pavement design.

This is also where the possibility of a drainage survey comes in. The FWD may allow derivation of an in situ modulus at the time of test but, if a drainage survey reveals problems, then subsequent drainage improvement may allow a higher long-term modulus to be assumed in pavement rehabilitation design. Drainage is such a vital ingredient in ensuring long pavement life that a drainage survey should be considered anywhere where problems are suspected. Since no traffic control is usually required, it may be carried out in targeted locations after completion of other tests.

Fatigue strength

Quantitative information on fatigue strength is only needed where analytical design is used. For asphalt, two approaches present themselves, namely:

1. rely on published data for typical materials
2. carry out indirect tensile fatigue tests (at least five).

In many cases it is impractical to carry out fatigue tests because of the number of different bituminous materials present on different pavement sections and in different layers. However, particularly where visual appearance suggests a reduced fatigue strength compared with normal expectations (friable, dry-looking materials), testing can be very useful. The indirect tensile test mode is suggested since core specimens are already cut to the right size; at least five tests (and preferably ten) are required because of the need to establish a fatigue characteristic (see Part 2, Section 2.3.4.4). Evaluation of fatigue data will normally be comparative, i.e. by comparison with the performance expected for typical new materials.

In the case of hydraulically-bound materials, it is reasonable to assume that a standard fatigue relationship between stress/strength ratio and life applies (as presented in Part 2, Section 2.2.2), in which case the missing item of knowledge is strength. This can most readily be obtained by carrying out compressive strength tests (at least five advised) on core specimens, although indirect tensile strength testing is also possible where the appropriate equipment is available. In either case, a judgement has to be made as to the appropriate design flexural strength. This should logically be a value a little less than that derived from an average of the test data, following the reliability principles in Part 3 (Section 3.8). This recognises the likely real variability in material properties, whereas the test data will often exaggerate this variability because of the small sample size being tested.

Deformation resistance

The appropriate measurement for asphalt is a repeated load axial test, carried out on a core specimen. These tests should logically be carried out where rutting has occurred and each layer of asphalt construction should be tested. In this way, it will become apparent which layer is the source of the rutting and data will be available to predict future behaviour, including behaviour after one or more layers have been replaced. If no rutting is present, this sort of test is usually unnecessary.

For unbound materials, three levels of evaluation are possible:

1. Use a stiffness modulus derived from FWD data and then rely on an assumed relationship between vertical strain in the subgrade (under a design wheel load) and number of load applications to failure – see Part 3 (Section 3.3.1.4).
2. Supplement this by carrying out DCP tests in core holes or trial pits.
3. Extract samples for shear strength testing.

It is undeniably common practice to rely on calculation of vertical subgrade strain, taking stiffness moduli from FWD back-analysis; however, this is a very approximate approach. Use of the DCP is strongly recommended in any project-level investigation (buried services permitting) since it does at least provide an independent measure of quality of unbound foundation materials. It is likely to provide supporting evidence as to whether reliance should be placed on subgrade strain or not.

The final option, carrying out shear strength tests, is an extreme one and would rarely be adopted. However, situations arise where subgrade strength is absolutely critical to performance so, if the economic value of the pavement is high (major highway, international airport) and subgrade deformation is a real or potential problem, then shear strength tests should be considered. Samples would have to be obtained from trial pits or large-diameter cores.

4.2.8 Summary

Pavement evaluation plays a key role in pavement management. There are plenty of different types of survey available, each with its particular advantages and limitations, and the trick is to use each in the most appropriate way. The choice of network-level evaluation tool (or tools) is clearly important, although it is at least as important to develop an effective system for processing the data and then for planning project-level investigations.

It is worth repeating that project-level surveys need 'designing' rather than reliance being placed on following a set procedure. Cores or trial pits are seen as almost essential for every investigation, together with a detailed visual inspection of the pavement. Other surveys depend on situation. However, if analytical design procedures are to be used then the FWD (or rolling wheel deflectometer) is a key tool, supported by appropriate laboratory tests and by use of the DCP in core holes or trial pits. Radar is less essential and its use should depend on the likely variability in construction. Drainage surveys are important where water-related problems are suspected.

4.3

Diagnosis

Once a detailed project-level survey has been carried out, it has to be properly interpreted. If the correct treatment is to be prescribed then it is absolutely essential that a correct diagnosis is made of pavement condition. The process can sensibly be compared to making a medical diagnosis – or to solving a crime. The evidence has to be assembled and then processed in a logical manner, weeding out all possible explanations for the observed symptoms other than the correct one; that at least is the theory. And that is what the following sections will attempt, addressing a number of likely questions and charting a path through the data to arrive at probable answers.

4.3.1 Pavements with an asphalt surface

4.3.1.1 Why is the pavement rutting?
Check the visual condition. If ruts are narrow with shoulders, the problem is near the surface (surface course or binder course probably); the wider the rut, the deeper the problem. Remember that it is possible to check directly on site by digging a trial pit or taking a series of cores right across a rutted wheel path; however, this is an expensive option and would only be carried out where an understanding of the rutting problem is seen as the key to future maintenance. The advice in Diagnosis Guides 4.3–4.5 applies to the majority of cases, where this is not carried out.

4.3.1.2 Why are there transverse cracks?
The first question is: what do the cracks look like? The major distinction is between large cracks extending across much or all of the

376

Diagnosis Guide 4.3   Rutting — asphalt layers suspected

- Inspect the cores carefully. If one or more asphalt layer appears rich in binder, especially if that binder is soft (check with a pointed instrument), that is likely to be the cause of the problem.

- Consider carrying out repeated load axial tests to check whether materials are deformation-susceptible.

- Also consider testing specimens of recovered binder to evaluate viscosity (or recovered penetration).

Diagnosis Guide 4.4   Rutting — granular layers suspected

- Inspect any available samples, even if they only comprise handfuls of stones from the bottom of core holes. Check for visible quality, i.e. whether crushed rock or similarly angular aggregate, or whether natural gravel or similar more rounded material. Rounded materials, whether sand-size or larger, tend to deform much more easily than angular materials.

- Look at DCP data if they exist. These should relate closely to intrinsic material quality, i.e. angularity. However, do not trust high equivalent CBRs if very large particles are present.

- Also check stiffness from FWD if available. Be prepared to discount it; FWD stiffnesses for granular layers are frequently unreliable. However, it is still evidence.

- Consider whether the granular layers may be near saturation. If trial pits have been carried out this may be readily known, but a low stiffness from the FWD raises suspicions. Lack of obvious functioning drainage, together with a clearly permeable (e.g. cracked) asphalt surface, are also important indicators.

Diagnosis Guide 4.5   Rutting — subgrade suspected

- Check any data on the type of material present, either from construction records, trial pits or unbound material samples. In general, clayey material can rut; sandy materials do not.

- Inspect the DCP records if available. CBRs of 2% or less are always rut-susceptible, but stronger materials can rut if the pavement is thin enough or the load is high enough.

- Check FWD data if available. A stiffness of 50 MPa or less indicates potentially deformable material. Higher stiffness indicates a material that is unlikely to rut (either because the intrinsic properties are good enough or the level of confinement is high).

Diagnosis Guide 4.6   Transverse cracking in asphalt — individual large cracks

- Look at the detailed crack shapes. If they are straight and regularly spaced, they represent reflective cracks from joints in an underlying concrete pavement. If the asphalt cover is thin, these may appear as pairs of close parallel cracks, originating from either side of a short debonded zone around each joint.

- If the shape is less regular, the cause is either reflection of thermally-induced cracks in a hydraulically-bound base or else low-temperature cracking of the asphalt. A core will prove which one is occurring (if records are insufficient). Also note that low-temperature cracking of asphalt is only likely in continental or desert climates.

- If reflective cracking is suspected, check the crack distribution. If there is a concentration in more heavily trafficked lanes or in wheel-paths, then traffic is clearly playing an important part; if not, then the effect is almost entirely thermally driven.

- Inspect cores through reflective cracks. If cracks are surface-originating and have not penetrated the full thickness of the asphalt, this gives information on the rate at which the process is occurring.

---

pavement width (see Diagnosis Guide 4.6) and shorter cracks (see Diagnosis Guide 4.7), usually in the wheel-paths.

In many cases transverse cracks do not occur on their own, but are found together with longitudinal cracks. If the appearance is that the transverse cracks are the more dominant while the longitudinal cracks simply connect between transverse cracks in places, then the points made in Diagnosis Guides 4.6 and 4.7 apply. If not, read on.

Diagnosis Guide 4.7   Transverse cracking in asphalt — multiple short cracks

- If confined to wheel-path areas then these are clearly traffic driven, although they may have originated as construction defects and they may be progressing partly due to binder embrittlement. Cores through such cracks will reveal whether they are near-surface phenomena or whether they are more serious.

- Crack spacing also provides a clue as to the nature of the cracking. If close spaced (e.g. <150 mm) then this is a shallow feature, affecting no more than the surface course; if wider spaced, the problem may extend deeper.

- If FWD data are available, check the magnitude of any loss of effective asphalt layer stiffness in the wheel-paths. This will provide further evidence of the severity or otherwise of the damage.

- If cracks are more generally distributed across the pavement then the effect is clearly thermally driven. This is quite possible where starter cracks in the form of construction defects (e.g. due to rolling while too cold) are present. These will be surface-originating cracks, the extent of which can be checked by coring.

4.3.1.3 Why is there longitudinal cracking in the wheel-path?

The fact that this cracking is in the wheel-path proves that it is the traffic which is doing the damage. The principal issue which has to be resolved is the depth affected; however, it is also very important to understand why the cracking is occurring and whether it is symptomatic of anything more serious. Diagnosis Guide 4.8 offers advice.

Having established the physical nature of the cracks, whether superficial or deep, full or partial depth, and having identified contributing factors within the asphalt such as debonding, it is necessary to consider whether, based on that information, the cracking is occurring at the expected rate, faster or slower – and why. These issues are covered in Diagnosis Guide 4.9.

Fundamentally, longitudinal wheel-path cracking occurs due to repeated straining of the asphalt. The investigation has to determine

---

Diagnosis Guide 4.8   Longitudinal cracking in asphalt — why?

- Check the visual appearance. If there are several parallel cracks within the zone of the wheel-path then the effect is almost certainly shallow, possibly associated with debonding between asphalt layers. In such cases, linking transverse cracks are usual. If, on the other hand, the cracking is largely confined to a single crack, then little can be deduced directly.

- Cores through cracks are strongly advised here. In many cases, crack depth is shallow. Top-down cracking is expected in pavements with thick asphalt layers and crack propagation is often slow. On the other hand, the cores may reveal full-depth cracks. They will also indicate where debonding between layers has occurred and whether cracking is restricted to layers above the debonded interface, quite a common phenomenon. In other cases, an underlying asphalt layer is shown to have substantially disintegrated. Cores through uncracked locations will indicate whether the layer in question is generally weak, or whether water ingress has caused local deterioration.

- If an FWD survey has been carried out, check the asphalt layer stiffness. If it is low or variable then this implies significant damage. In debonded cases, or where an asphalt layer appears to be disintegrating, care must be taken to interpret the data sensibly, assigning appropriate stiffnesses to the different layers within the asphalt. A disintegrating layer may sometimes be considered together with the underlying layer(s) in FWD analysis.

- Compare FWD-derived stiffnesses with those from laboratory testing of recovered samples, being careful to adjust to a common temperature and loading rate (see Part 2). If the two measures agree then the asphalt layers are likely to be intact and well bonded. If the FWD-derived value is lower, this indicates damage which is not represented in core (or trial pit) samples, i.e. either cracking or debonding.

- If no FWD tests have been conducted, the Benkelman Beam or Deflectograph will give an idea of relative condition from point to point; a high level of variability is almost always associated with significant cracking damage.

379

Diagnosis Guide 4.9   Longitudinal cracking in asphalt — how quickly?

- Carry out a review of the pavement condition by comparing the past traffic with the traffic which such a pavement might have been expected to carry, according to design guidance.

- Check evidence for binder hardening. This can be seen in unusually high stiffness of laboratory specimens or from direct tests on samples of recovered binder. Binder hardening is often associated with increased susceptibility to fatigue.

- Also check evidence for poor binder adhesion. This will show up as unusually low stiffness, even of undamaged material (e.g. from a lane centre location). A likely visual sign on the surface is the presence of multiple fine cracks rather than a single large crack.

- Consider carrying out indirect tensile fatigue tests (ITFTs) on cored specimens (at least five specimens needed) to compare the fatigue characteristic to standard data. This should only be done for a layer which is of high importance for a significant length of pavement.

- In the case of pavements with a significant hydraulically-bound layer beneath the asphalt, measure the compressive strength of the hydraulically-bound material using core specimens.

- Also evaluate the in situ stiffness of any hydraulically-bound layer from FWD evidence. The degree to which the in situ stiffness is less than the expected stiffness for intact material is evidence of the degree of cracking present.

- Also check the condition of supporting pavement layers. The FWD will supply realistic foundation stiffnesses; the DCP reveals strengths, and these often correlate approximately with stiffness. However, the DCP will be less affected by high water content values than will stiffness under dynamic (i.e. traffic or FWD) load. Trial pits allow direct investigation of water contents as well as revealing exactly what materials are present.

- Using the best available evidence for the stiffness of each layer and for the fatigue of both asphalt and hydraulically-bound layers, carry out a multi-layer linear elastic pavement analysis and associated computation of pavement life. Compare the theoretical life from this approach with past traffic numbers — and with current general pavement condition.

---

whether the asphalt itself is less resistant to such strain than it should be – and why. It also has to determine whether the pavement is straining more than it should be – and why.

4.3.1.4 Why is the surface ravelling?

Ravelling (and associated potholes) can only occur if the adhesion between binder and aggregate is breaking down for some reason. The tests suggested in Diagnosis Guide 4.10 may assist in unearthing that reason.

Diagnosis Guide 4.10   Ravelling in asphalt

- Check by direct testing of recovered surface course binder, whether it has hardened appreciably. If so, this may be a contributory factor.

- Also measure the surface course stiffness; the ITSM test is suitable. This should have increased in line with binder hardening. If not, this implies that more general lack of adhesion is present.

- Check gradation and binder content from analysis of recovered specimens. Both low binder content and high filler content can contribute to lack of adhesion to the larger aggregate particles.

If a general lack of adhesion is deduced and neither the binder content nor the filler content appears suspect, the implication is either that the particular binder–filler–aggregate combination is a poor one, probably due to chemical incompatibility, or that asphalt manufacture was deficient. If the problem regularly occurs with a particular aggregate, filler or binder source, the former is likely; if not, then operation of the asphalt plant may be suspect, possibly related to incomplete drying of aggregate prior to mixing. Either way, the ravelling observed on the surface will also be reflected in poor resistance to cracking throughout the mixture. This type of problem is therefore a serious one and implies a much reduced structural life for the pavement.

4.3.1.5 Why is bitumen bleeding from the surface?

The simple answer to this question is trivial: there is too much bitumen present. However, it is instructive to find out why this should be, in which case the approach given in Diagnosis Guide 4.11 may help.

Bleeding is not a deep-seated distress type. Once it is established whether the source of the binder is the surface course itself or additional surface dressing layers, a decision can be taken as to what depth of material should be planed out and replaced.

Diagnosis Guide 4.11   Bleeding in asphalt

- Inspect the cores. Multiple layers of surface dressing are one obvious source of excess binder.

- If surface dressing is not the prime cause, carry out determination of void content of the surface course. Bleeding should only occur at void contents of 2% or less; this implies close to saturated conditions such that traffic loads will squeeze binder from the surface.

- Also check the visual condition for rutting within the surface course. Rutting of this type is often (but not always) symptomatic of low void content.

4.3.2 Pavements with a concrete surface

4.3.2.1 Why are there transverse cracks?

There is unlikely to be any real mystery here. In a jointed concrete pavement, transverse cracking, either at mid-bay or a metre or so from joints, is common; it simply implies that the joint spacing was too large for the thermally-induced stresses and strains which have occurred. Diagnosis Guide 4.12 suggests the appropriate questions to consider.

Diagnosis Guide 4.12   Transverse cracking in jointed concrete

- Was the cracking present soon after construction? If so, the cause is likely to have been inadequate protection to the PQC during curing, resulting in shrinkage cracking.

- Is the joint spacing greater than about 20 times the slab thickness? This, very approximately, marks the maximum spacing at which joints in unreinforced concrete can be expected to function properly.

In the case of a continuously reinforced concrete (CRC) pavement, transverse cracks are expected. They should form at a spacing of 1–2 m but, in a properly functioning pavement, they will remain narrow and there should be no spalling. If there are more than this or if many are no longer narrow, then this implies that the pavement is not functioning as designed and that it will almost certainly continue to deteriorate steadily. The reasons why this has occurred can be investigated; see Diagnosis Guide 4.13.

Diagnosis Guide 4.13   Transverse cracking in CRC

- Check concrete strength by carrying out compressive strength tests on core specimens.

- Check slab thickness from cores and/or radar.

- Check foundation stiffness from FWD data.

- The combination of these three parameters should be enough to check whether the pavement as it was constructed should have lasted longer than it has — or not. This may involve reference to a design manual or else analytical computation of the shear stress across cracks and the horizontal stress in the underside of the slab; preferably both.

4.3.2.2 Why is there longitudinal cracking?

Longitudinal cracking is a sure sign of overloading and a very serious mode of distress in concrete pavements; significant pavement rehabilitation is likely to be required. However, the cause demands a knowledge

---

Diagnosis Guide 4.14   Longitudinal cracking in concrete

- Check concrete strength by carrying out compressive strength tests on core specimens.

- Check slab thickness from cores and/or radar.

- Check foundation stiffness from FWD data.

- If the computed life is less than the current condition suggests, then the inference is that one of the input parameters was more favourable in the past, and the most likely possibility is that the foundation used to be stiffer and has deteriorated over the years. Check for evidence for voiding under the slab, notably poor slab support as deduced from FWD deflections. Also check evidence for subgrade softening, from DCP, unbound material samples or the results of a drainage survey.

- If the computed life is greater than the current condition suggests, then something has occurred which the computation doesn't take into account. This could be the occurrence of shrinkage cracks during initial concrete curing. Investigate the distribution of longitudinal cracking. If it is localised then this indicates particular circumstances in certain areas, e.g. defective concrete or inadequate curing; the rest of the pavement should have much longer life.

---

of concrete strength, slab thickness and foundation stiffness. Calculations using these three parameters can be compared with the current state of the pavement. Diagnosis Guide 4.14 details the necessary steps.

4.3.2.3 Why is there faulting across joints?

This is a particularly damaging form of distress from the point of view of ride quality. It most certainly implies joint deterioration, and strongly suggests defective design or construction. Diagnosis Guide 4.15 gives a brief check-list of points to consider.

Diagnosis Guide 4.15   Faulting in jointed concrete

- If dowels or tie-bars are present, there should be no faulting. If faulting is present, this can only mean serious corrosion of the bars and disintegration of the surrounding concrete, implying water ingress and very poor load transfer characteristics.

- Even without dowels or tie-bars, faulting implies poor load transfer. This could be due to excessive joint spacing, giving little aggregate interlock across joints. It could also be that the aggregate was insufficiently durable and that it has degraded at the joints; or that the concrete strength was low (in which case more general cracking is also likely).

- Faulting also implies a deformable foundation, such that one side of the joint has been able to settle more than the other. This suggests a low-quality granular sub-base, quite possibly at a high moisture content.

383

4.3.2.4 *Why is the surface deteriorating?*

Concrete is a hard and durable material, but it relies on the presence of a balanced combination of cement mortar and aggregate throughout. At the surface, it is not uncommon to find an excess of cement mortar, particularly if the mixture was slightly wetter than optimum, and this results in a relatively weak surface layer, a few millimetres thick. Trafficking will eventually remove this excess mortar, but the result can be a decrease in ride quality. The appearance will be one of exposed aggregate rather than smooth mortar (between grooves or other textured indentations). Once this loss of surface mortar has occurred, there should be no further deterioration.

The other possibility is 'scaling', which means the loss of discrete areas of surface, often 30 cm or so in dimension. This is caused by frost action and implies that whatever precautions were taken against frost attack in the design (strong concrete; air entrainment) were insufficient for that location.

4.3.3 Other pavement types

4.3.3.1 *Grouted macadam*

Grouted macadams are basically special asphalts, and many of the points made already with regard to diagnosis of asphalt pavement problems also apply to grouted macadam. Grouted macadam is rightly portrayed as a jointless product – but it can certainly crack in much the same way as asphalt. However, a particular issue is the occurrence of localised distress, often around the edge of an area of grouted macadam, suggesting less than 100% grout penetration. This shows itself as localised cracking, sometimes also with minor depressions.

4.3.3.2 *Block paving*

The strength of block paving depends very much on the supporting layers. Any rutting or other deformation of the surface implies lack of foundation strength, and this can be investigated in just the same way as for an asphalt-surfaced pavement. Diagnosis Guide 4.16 gives only those points relating to distress types which are peculiar to block paving.

Diagnosis Guide 4.16   Block paving

- If individual blocks have fractured, then the original block specification may have been at fault. Industrial applications commonly demand a thickness of 80 mm or more and a length of no more than 200 mm. Longer or thinner blocks are susceptible to fracture under normally applied tyre pressures. If block specification was satisfactory, then overloading (for example by trailer feet) has to be suspected. A further possible cause, for blocks bedded on cement mortar, is local loss of adhesion between block and mortar. This can lead to very high stresses within the block.

- Uneven block settlement implies a sand bedding rather than mortar. It is likely that the sand was not laid to an even thickness, probably due to lack of base level control. Excess sand thickness (>50 mm) can lead to localised settlement, followed by localised ponding of water, which makes the situation worse.

- In very warm weather, restrained thermal expansion induces high compressive stresses. If these become too high then a whole line of blocks can be raised up at an angle; in effect, this is a buckling failure. The design has made insufficient allowance for expansion.

4.3.3.3 *Unsurfaced pavements*

Rutting can of course occur in an unsurfaced pavement, and the points made in relation to asphalt-surfaced pavements therefore also apply. To some extent, the surface distress possible in an asphalt is mirrored in an unbound surface also, except that internal 'cohesion' is the binder rather than bitumen. Stone loss and potholing are both likely.

However, there is one type of distress which is not found in bound pavements. *Corrugations* are regular undulations along a road, which occur due to a resonance being set up between a vehicle's suspension system and longitudinal defects in the road surface. This results in slightly higher dynamic load being applied in depressed areas, and the depressions are then magnified by the resulting permanent deformation. This is an expected occurrence on unsurfaced roads and does not necessarily imply any particular defect in design, material provision or construction. It does however imply a need for ongoing maintenance.

4.3.4 Summary

This has not been an easy subject. There are a surprisingly large number of ways in which a pavement can deteriorate, and it really is quite important to understand which ones are applying in a given case. There is no way that a correct prognosis can be given if the diagnosis is incorrect – and the chances of coming up with a sensible maintenance strategy would be slim.

4.4

Prognosis

Despite this being a relatively short section, it represents an important phase in the decision-making process. To make a diagnosis is clearly vital, but the question now arises as to just what the future holds. For example, it would be useful to know that observed longitudinal cracking of an asphalt pavement can be traced to a debonded interface 100 mm below the surface, but it would be even more useful to know just how quickly the pavement will continue to deteriorate, including any possible deterioration to layers deeper than 100 mm. Only by knowing this – or at least being able to estimate it – can sensible decisions be made about the timing and nature of any future rehabilitation treatment.

Unfortunately, this is far from easy. A pavement is a complex beast, each element depending on those above and below for its own survival. Predicting the life of a new pavement, as detailed in Part 3, is quite possible because one has the luxury of being able to ignore little practical details such as construction defects, drainage failures or sub-standard materials. While a project is simply a theoretical entity, the real world need only intrude as far as forcing the designer to select a suitable design reliability. Once it has been built, the annoying realities can no longer be ignored. This section must therefore address those realities – commencing at the easy end of the spectrum.

4.4.1 Substantially intact asphalt pavements
Following diagnosis, a decision has to be taken as to whether the pavement under consideration has substantially retained the properties of each component material which it had at the start of its life. Cracks may be present, but they should only be shallow; or else very infrequent.

Moderate rutting may have occurred, but not enough to have actually caused loss of material integrity. Localised distress may be present, but only localised; it should not have reached the stage where it becomes typical of large sections of the pavement. Only if these conditions are satisfied can the pavement be treated as 'intact' – and the following paragraphs applied.

4.4.1.1 *Statistical treatment of data*

Since the pavement is basically intact, it can be analysed in the same manner as a new pavement, and a remaining life predicted following the guidance in Part 3. For this, due account must be taken of the measured properties of each layer and a statistical view should be adopted. Predictions might sensibly be made for both an average (50th percentile) condition and a conservative (e.g. 15th percentile) condition. This is a difficult area to get right; however, the principle is exactly the same as explained in Part 3 (Section 3.8). The relative influence of each input parameter (e.g. asphalt stiffness, asphalt thickness, foundation stiffness) must first be estimated and, adopting the simplifications suggested in Part 3, the following equations may be used:

- Fatigue life: $\propto \varepsilon_t^{-4} \propto E^3 k h^5$
- Deformation life: $\propto \varepsilon_z^{-4} \propto E k^3 h^3$

where E is asphalt stiffness, k is foundation stiffness and h is asphalt thickness, and these three may be considered as independent of each other.

Next, the degree of variability in each of the input parameters has to be established. This might be based on measurements, but care should be taken to subtract the variability due to the measurement itself from real variability. Thickness variability can often be estimated quite accurately from cores or GPR data. Failing measurements, the estimates suggested in Part 3 (Section 3.8.2.1) may be used. As to which percentiles should be used in remaining life calculations, the following advice was given in Part 3.

- 50th percentile of pavement condition; use 50th percentiles of individual parameters
- 25th percentile of pavement condition; use 33rd percentiles of individual parameters
- 15th percentile of pavement condition; use 25th percentiles of individual parameters

- 5th percentile of pavement condition; use 14th percentiles of individual parameters
- 1st percentile of pavement condition; use 6th percentiles of individual parameters.

4.4.1.2 Pavement life prediction

The method of choice here is certainly an analytical computation, making direct use of the percentiles from the previous subsection. However, if no analytical prediction can be made, then creative use of design manuals is always possible; the key point is that this must include consideration of the real properties of materials. Some design approaches, for example the 1993 AASHTO Manual,[21] are flexible enough for this to be carried out without difficulty; others, particularly those presenting a catalogue of designs, are less easy to use.

Whichever predictive approach is used, the result is a set of pavement lives for the various possible deterioration modes. The next step is to take account of the damage which, though it may not show up in terms of loss of stiffness, has actually taken place already. For *fatigue*, whether of asphalt or hydraulically-bound material, the assumption is commonly made that pavement materials follow what is known as *Miner's law.*[22] This law states that relative damage is cumulative. Thus, if the predicted fatigue life is, say, 30×10^6 axle loads, and the past traffic is 12×10^6, then the relative damage stands at 40% and the remaining life is predicted to be just 18×10^6. The concept of relative damage becomes important for strengthening designs since, whatever the predicted life of the strengthened pavement, up to 40% of it may have to be discounted straight away due to past damage.

In the case of *rutting*, whether of asphalt or foundation materials, it is suggested that sensible account should be taken of what has actually occurred; the current rut depth divided by the number of years since the road was last resurfaced gives a measure of rut development rate, and past trends are likely to continue into the future. It can even be used to calibrate predictions based on vertical strain in the subgrade under a standard axle load, or on repeated load axial test data from asphalt specimens, something which may prove useful when designing strengthening.

The result of all this is that a set of predicted pavement lives is determined, which can then be compared with future traffic estimates, allowing informed decision-making as to the need for and optimal timing of any future maintenance. It would be foolish to pretend that such predictions are actually accurate, particularly when factors such as continuing ageing of asphalt and increasing danger of drainage failure are considered, but they will be the best possible under the circumstances, and the experienced engineer should even try to factor in the effects of continuing future change in material properties. It may be an uncomfortable truth for those who believe rigid procedures are required to achieve a mythical 'quality assurance' level, but the fact is that there is absolutely no substitute for engineering judgement here. Calculations should *never* be believed without question, especially when so many assumptions are being made.

4.4.1.3 Pavements with strong hydraulically-bound bases

If the pavement is considered as substantially intact, this means that evaluation of the fatigue susceptibility of the hydraulically-bound base is required which, following the guidance in Part 3, means that a stress ratio has to be computed at the base of the layer. The approximate equation suggested in Part 3 (Section 3.8.2.2) was:

- Fatigue life $\propto k^3 h^{15} \sigma_f^{12} / E^3$

Use of this equation resulted in the following recommendations for cracking of the hydraulically-bound layer:

- 50th percentile of pavement condition; use 50th percentiles of individual parameters
- 25th percentile of pavement condition; use 35th percentiles of individual parameters
- 15th percentile of pavement condition; use 28th percentiles of individual parameters
- 5th percentile of pavement condition; use 18th percentiles of individual parameters
- 1st percentile of pavement condition; use 10th percentiles of individual parameters.

Remember that because stiffness modulus E appears on the bottom of the equation, the appropriate percentiles for the modulus of a strong hydraulically-bound layer are the opposite of those used for other parameters, e.g. a 35th percentile is replaced by a 65th etc. There is also a new parameter to consider, namely stress at failure σ_f. The appropriate percentile of strength has to be determined, either by estimation or from laboratory strength tests on cores. Failing other information, it is suggested that a value 80% of the expected average strength should be assigned. Note that the thicknesses of asphalt and hydraulically-bound base should not be considered as independent variables here and the percentile used should therefore be for the combined layer.

4.4.2 Substantially intact concrete pavements

The same equation and percentiles apply here as for hydraulically-bound base pavements. As in the case of asphalt pavements, Miner's law can in theory be applied to fatigue life, leading to the determination of a proportion of life already 'used up'. However, in the case of concrete, this is a slightly questionable move. The problem is the slow increase in concrete strength which occurs over time, and it raises the question as to what value of strength should be used in any calculation of pavement life. If the current value is used, based on tests on core specimens, then it may be argued that the calculation will overestimate the life of the pavement since greater damage would have been occurring during the earlier years while the concrete was weaker. On the other hand, if an adjustment is made to bring the strength back to what it might have been at 28 days (for example by taking around 80% of the current value), then this will overestimate the damage which has been occurring more recently. There is no simple answer to this dilemma; however, it seems most logical to adopt the current value (using the appropriate percentile), accepting that past damage may be underestimated but in the knowledge that future damage will be overestimated.

On a practical level, if few cracks have occurred in the past, while the concrete was weaker, this gives considerable confidence that fewer still will occur in the future.

With regard to deterioration other than traffic-induced fatigue cracking, thermally-induced cracking may be a maintenance nuisance but it does not represent structural failure. Faulting at joints is considered to be just too hard to predict; if it is occurring then, as in the case of rutting of asphalt pavements, a calculation may be made regarding the rate of development in the past and the same rate may be taken as likely to continue into the future.

4.4.3 Failing asphalt pavements

The key question to pose here is whether there is any layer (or part-layer) in the pavement which is substantially damaged, i.e. cracked or partially disintegrated. This layer could be either asphalt or hydraulically-bound. The evidence for this may come directly from the visual condition of cores or trial pits – or indeed from surface appearance; it may also come from the determination of a lower than expected modulus value for a layer based on FWD data. However, care has to be exercised in interpreting the FWD. It must be remembered that debonding between bound layers (to be discussed in Section 4.4.5) can lead to very considerable loss of apparent stiffness. Core data should be able to confirm whether such debonding is present. The influence of debonding must be taken into account when evaluating material modulus. However, once this is done, any bound layer which is found to have a genuine in situ modulus half what would have been expected or less, has to be considered as 'failed' – in the sense that it is meaningless to compute a life *before* cracking since cracking has already occurred. In fact, such a layer is almost certainly still in the process of failing and its long-term modulus would therefore be lower than that recorded currently.

4.4.3.1 Full-depth crazing

Asphalt pavements can fail in many ways – and at greatly differing rates. However, in the case of full-depth crazing the prognosis is usually not good. Figure 4.18 illustrates the situation.

In theory it may be possible to compute a life to rutting failure considering the likely rate of deformation of the unbound layers (as outlined in Part 3, Sections 3.3.1 and 3.3.2). In practice, this sort of prediction is so sensitive to the strength parameters assumed that it is unlikely to be at all reliable. There are many such 'failed' pavements which continue to take heavy traffic loads without any dramatic problems, so it would be premature simply to assume that the pavement's life has come to an end. Even

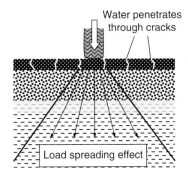

Water penetrates through cracks

Asphalt acts in a similar way to block paving

Low-strength granular material due to high water content

Low-strength upper subgrade

Higher strength material at depth

Load spreading effect

Fig. 4.18 Asphalt pavement with full-depth crazing

391

wet layers of high-quality crushed rock sub-base have considerable load-bearing capacity, particularly under the overburden pressure provided by asphalt and hydraulically-bound layers.

The point at which ride quality becomes unacceptable depends on the type of pavement and traffic speed. If the foundation is not sufficiently strong to prevent deformation, then ultimate failure of the pavement comes when differential settlement between damaged and undamaged locations becomes excessive, which probably means when settlement in damaged locations reaches 40 mm or so. On the other hand, if the foundation is strong enough to resist deformation, failure is more likely to be defined by the degree of surface break-up of the asphalt, something which will accelerate markedly if freeze–thaw conditions are encountered. Either way, prediction definitely cannot be based simply on computations but must include a large dose of engineering judgement, based on empirical experience.

4.4.3.2 Lower asphalt layer disintegration

This is actually not uncommon, despite not correlating with any of the failure modes normally considered at the design stage. The cause of the failure is usually durability related, perhaps because the void content in a road base layer was too high and/or water has managed to find its way in. Layer debonding is commonly followed by progressive failure of an overlying material as water seeps along the debonded interface.

An approximately similar situation is found when a failing pavement has been overlaid; or when the surface course has been planed out and replaced with fresh material, leaving broken lower layers in place.

Evidence from cores or trial pits should be sufficient to reveal whether an underlying layer is disintegrating or not, although it has to be remembered that coring is a hit-and-miss affair. If FWD testing has taken place, then the overall stiffness of the asphalt will be low, contrasting with the results of laboratory tests on core specimens from the upper layer or two.

The difficult task, if an analytical assessment is to be attempted, is to assign stiffness moduli to the intact and disintegrated layers respectively. It may be possible to deduce something about the intact material from FWD testing or from laboratory stiffness testing; otherwise typical values would have to be assigned. For the disintegrated materials, it is advised that they are treated as being no better than a granular layer in the long term, with a modulus of 150 or 200 MPa at best. The computation of remaining life then considers only the upper, intact asphalt as being a bound material; the computed life should also be reduced to take account of fatigue damage using Miner's law as described in Section 4.4.1.2.

4.4.3.3 *Intermediate asphalt layer disintegration*

It is not unusual to find that an intermediate layer is disintegrating, quite often the binder course, while the base remains more or less intact. In such a case, it is practically impossible to compute a meaningful life for the overlying surface course using traditional analytical design methodology because the layer is too thin. However, it is still possible to predict the life of the base. It is simply necessary to include a suitable long-term modulus for the disintegrating binder course in the calculation. When checking against a design manual prediction, it is suggested that the thickness of the disintegrated layer is reduced to an effective contribution of only 15–20% of its actual thickness – reflecting its lack of contribution to reducing flexure of the base. Miner's law should also be used to take account of past damage to the base.

4.4.3.4 *Surface layer(s) disintegration*

It is not uncommon where shallow debonding has taken place, either beneath the surface course or beneath the binder course, to find that the overlying materials then craze and fail. The mechanism may be aided by water or ice, but it will be traffic that actually does the damage. The key here is to realise that the apparently disastrous appearance of the pavement surface only relates to the upper layer or two. This should be deducible from the relatively close-spaced nature of the cracks compared to the overall thickness of the asphalt; also from the appearance of debonding in cores, and from the fact that the layer modulus as determined from the FWD is greater than would be the case if full-depth crazing were present.

Clearly no meaningful computation of surfacing life can be made – it has already failed. However, the life of the remaining base can still be assessed, again taking a 15–20% thickness contribution from the failing layers when checking against design manual predictions.

4.4.3.5 *Failure of a strong hydraulically-bound base*

In most pavements with hydraulically-bound bases, a degree of failure is expected. As explained in Part 3 (Section 3.4.1.10), thermal stresses

393

will always induce transverse cracking and, to control this, it is common practice nowadays to deliberately introduce cracks, often at a spacing of around 3 m. However, it is always possible that break-up of a hydraulically-bound layer goes much further than this. It may have been underdesigned; it may have been of substandard construction; it may just be that the durability of the material was inadequate, something which is hard to predict in advance with confidence. The long-term presence of water is another common reason for premature loss of strength, water that may have come either from the underlying unbound foundation or from above. Local degradation is often found beneath cracks in overlying asphalt.

If the asphalt is still intact, then the difficulty lies in assigning an appropriate stiffness modulus for the hydraulically-bound material – and values obtained from the FWD should, in general, *not* be used. As noted already in Part 3 (Section 3.4.2.10), it is common to assign an artificially low stiffness, often 500 MPa, to the material when designing the asphalt against reflective cracking, and there is no reason to increase this once the hydraulically-bound layer starts to break up. Although the stress concentration at cracks that causes reflective cracking will reduce as cracks become more numerous, this is hardly a well-controlled process. Only if the FWD back-calculated stiffness modulus is 1000 MPa or less should direct use of this number be contemplated and, even then, allowance should be made for future loss of stiffness; engineering judgment again! Existing damage to the apparently intact asphalt can be taken into account using Miner's law.

4.4.4 Failing concrete pavements

It is important to understand the deterioration mode(s) applying, which relate to the type of concrete pavement present. In general terms, transverse cracks are not unexpected; in the case of a CRC pavement they will always be present. This means that, if damage is restricted to transverse cracking, then the pavement can probably be considered substantially intact. Calculations of stress in the PQC should take into account the likelihood of poor load transfer across some of the cracks as well as loss of slab support due to the softening effects of ingressing water, but the procedure can nevertheless follow that for intact pavements described in Section 4.4.2.

However, as soon as longitudinal cracking occurs then the prognosis takes a serious turn for the worse. A transverse crack can only propagate across the width of a carriageway and no further; a longitudinal crack knows no limit. Once it starts, it will tend to propagate rapidly along a wheel-path, and to generate further transverse cracks as it does so. In such a case, it is fairly meaningless to try to calculate a remaining life since the life before cracking is effectively zero. The rate of subsequent deterioration will be governed by the durability of the foundation under the influence of significant water ingress. A judgement has to be made as to whether the condition of the foundation layers is likely to reduce to the extent that localised settlement occurs, the effect of which at the surface will be 'faulting', the occurrence of steps between individual intact concrete slab elements. The best clue always comes from careful observation of past performance; i.e. if faulting has already commenced then it will generally accelerate.

4.4.5 The effect of debonding
This issue is one of the hardest of all to resolve. It is common to find that one or more layer interfaces are debonded, at least to the extent that they separate under the action of coring, yet it is relatively uncommon to hear of debonding being blamed for pavement failure. This section explores the factors to be borne in mind.

4.4.5.1 The theoretical effect of debonding
One effect which is much more than theoretical is the fact that debonding between bound pavement layers significantly decreases the overall apparent stiffness of the bound layers. Calculation Sheet 4.1 presents a mathematical assessment of this effect, which is really a reduction in the second moment of area I. It also derives a formula for the strain in the bottom of the asphalt, the parameter most

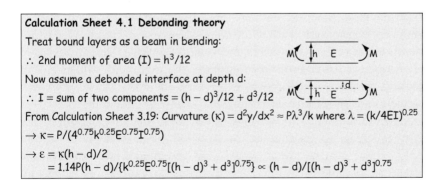

Calculation Sheet 4.1 Debonding theory

Treat bound layers as a beam in bending:

$\therefore$ 2nd moment of area $(I) = h^3/12$

Now assume a debonded interface at depth d:

$\therefore I = $ sum of two components $= (h-d)^3/12 + d^3/12$

From Calculation Sheet 3.19: Curvature $(\kappa) = d^2y/dx^2 \approx P\lambda^3/k$ where $\lambda = (k/4EI)^{0.25}$

$\rightarrow \kappa = P/(4^{0.75}k^{0.25}E^{0.75}I^{0.75})$

$\rightarrow \varepsilon = \kappa(h-d)/2$
$= 1.14P(h-d)/\{k^{0.25}E^{0.75}[(h-d)^3 + d^3]^{0.75}\} \propto (h-d)/[(h-d)^3 + d^3]^{0.75}$

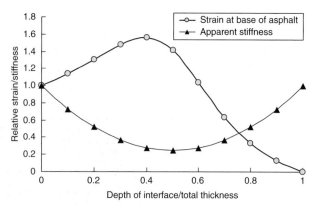

Fig. 4.19 The theoretical effect of debonding (zero interface friction)

commonly used in fatigue crack prediction. Both the apparent stiffness and the strain resulting from this prediction are plotted in Fig. 4.19 in relative terms.

The loss of apparent layer stiffness is very clear in the figure, although it has to be remembered that the debonded interface is assumed to transfer no shear stress at all, which is an extreme case. However, it is common to find that the apparent stiffness of the bound pavement layers is no more than half that expected, with no clear cause other than debonding; thus the effect is real enough. But the most interesting finding is definitely that relating to the tensile strain at the bottom of the asphalt. According to Fig. 4.19, it can be almost 60% higher than it would have been in a non-debonded pavement if the debonding occurs at just the wrong level in the pavement, about 40% of the full layer thickness, which would imply a noticeable reduction in life. Even allowing for some friction at the debonded interface, the increase in asphalt tensile strain might be expected to be at least 30% (reducing fatigue life by a factor of 3 if a 'fourth power law' is used).

In the layer of bound material above the interface, the strain mirrors that of the lower part, with a maximum value when the interface is at a depth about 60% of the full bound layer thickness. Thus, while either the upper or lower part may fail early, the other part will not – at least in theory – which means it is hard to be certain just how much reduction in overall pavement life debonding actually brings.

One thing is certain, however, and that is that it is definitely *not* correct simply to assume that an apparent layer stiffness (e.g. from FWD data) for an asphalt with a debonded interface represents a single uniform layer. In the extreme case shown in Fig. 4.19, with an interface at mid-depth, the apparent stiffness would be one quarter of what it would have been if fully bonded, and this would lead to the calculation of a strain around 2.8 times that of the fully-bonded case (following the approximate relationship in Calculation Sheet 4.1). This compares to a strain of 1.4 times that of the fully-bonded case shown in Fig. 4.19. The message is therefore: be very careful. The real effect on fatigue life may be much less than it initially appears.

However, there is no doubt that the loss of effective stiffness from the bound layers due to debonding leads to an increased stress and strain in the foundation, and this can be calculated in the usual way (e.g. multi-layer linear elastic computations) using the apparent asphalt stiffness, allowing prediction of pavement life against rutting failure in the foundation.

4.4.5.2 The real effect of debonding

Clearly, theory does not hold all the answers. While it does indeed appear to be true that debonding has much less direct negative effect on the asphalt than is often thought, it is frequently accompanied by indirect effects. The first question to ask is: why did debonding occur in the first place? And the answer is most likely to be, at least in part, that the binder is either embrittled or else at a low content. This immediately warns of the likelihood that asphalt durability is low. One then has to realise that a debonded interface provides an ideal channel along which water can flow, thereby compounding the danger. If the surface is perfectly sealed then this danger may be avoided – but as soon as water enters it will begin to attack the materials above and below the debonded interface, materials which are likely to be susceptible to water damage. Thus, it is strongly recommended that a predicted life for a debonded pavement should be treated with a healthy degree of scepticism, particularly if there is already evidence of water damage having occurred.

4.4.6 Summary

The principles and techniques described in this section lie at the heart of the decision-making process in relation to pavement maintenance. They give the possibility of predicting future performance. However, the importance of a correct statistical treatment of the data is worth highlighting. There is no fundamental meaning in a claim that a pavement has *x* number of years of remaining life; it is always the case that there is an average condition and a spread above and below this state. It is therefore critical, if proper decision making is to be carried out, that the spread of possible future lives is understood. It would be criminal not to make the fullest possible use of the data.

4.5

Rehabilitation design

This is where pavement engineering really does begin to look much more like an art than a science. A diagnosis may often be made with reasonable confidence; after all one is still dealing with the past, with things that have already happened. A prognosis is rather trickier since it requires extrapolation from the present into the future, sometimes the distant future. Nevertheless, in making a prognosis one is still dealing with the same materials and layers that have been in position for many years, and so experience from the past has a high degree of relevance. But on entering the realm of rehabilitation design the level of confidence inevitably drops still further. The problem is not only that new materials are being introduced but also the fact that the conditions (stress, moisture state) applying in those materials being left in place are being altered. Calculations can still be carried out – but a lower level of assurance is commonly present compared to new pavement design.

The basic tools of the trade remain unchanged. The design approaches described in Part 3 are no less valid; the material properties detailed in Part 2 still apply. There are certainly issues regarding the properties which should be assumed for existing materials, issues which require a certain amount of engineering judgement; but probably the greatest difficulty lies not in the ability to predict performance, hard though that sometimes is, but in working out just which of the rehabilitation options on offer represents the most effective strategy in a given case. Whether explicitly or otherwise, the decision requires a balance between uncertainty in future performance and the consequences, should expected levels of performance not be realised, and the measure of 'value' used should ideally include disruption to users, safety and environmental issues, as well as direct costs.

However, in order to stand a chance of taking the right decision one has to be as confident as possible in predicting the performance expected from the various design options. This therefore is the starting-point.

4.5.1 Drainage improvement

It is fair to say that this is not the conventional place to start. Yet many are the experts who have been proud to state that good drainage is the most essential feature of pavement design. Whether this is strictly true or not is open to debate, but drainage is certainly extremely important and it does not lose its importance at the rehabilitation stage. The point has been made that it is normal to find that the uppermost 100–500 mm of subgrade has softened considerably in comparison to underlying material, and the cause is certainly water. It is common to observe that the presence of a particularly serious crack in a pavement is associated with significant subgrade softening. As a pavement deteriorates, the passage of water through the bound layers and into the foundation becomes ever easier, and the greater the time during which a pavement foundation is subjected to high levels of water, the greater the rate and extent of subgrade softening. Now clearly, if an overlay is applied, the water source is shut off – or at least greatly restricted. But without functioning drainage, the subgrade will not easily regain its original strength and stiffness.

So what can be done? The first question is whether anything needs to be done at all. Whether or not advanced technology is used such as closed-circuit television to inspect otherwise inaccessible pipe runs, much information can be obtained from visual inspection of drains. Direct symptoms of drainage problems are:

- the complete absence of any sign of a drain
- side ditches silted up
- no sign of a direct connection between granular foundation layers and a side drain (usually investigated by digging a trial pit)
- lack of water flow though catch-pits.

None of these is sufficient for immediate panic on its own. However, the combination of a softened upper layer of subgrade and a clear drainage fault presents a likelihood that the pavement would benefit from drainage improvement of some sort. But it is still too early to panic. One must first be convinced that the softening of the subgrade really has contributed to pavement deterioration – since it doesn't

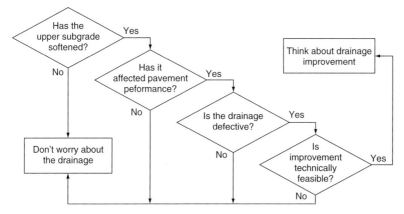

Fig. 4.20 Decision chart – drainage improvement

always. Cracking of an asphalt pavement may appear severe, but if it is top-down and does not extend beyond around 100 mm then the subgrade is unlikely to have contributed to the problem. The same is true of rutting in an asphalt; it may also apply to reflective cracking problems over a hydraulically-bound base. There is little point spending time and money correcting a very real fault if it isn't the fault which is actually causing the observed pavement distress. It sounds an obvious point – and it is – but that does not mean it is always followed. Figure 4.20 is a flowchart describing the decision-making process.

Notice that even after answering yes to all questions in Fig. 4.20, the advice is only to 'think about' drainage improvement. The final decision simply cannot be taken at this, purely technical, stage. That will depend on factors such as economics. However, one further technical evaluation which the engineer can at least attempt is to quantify the long-term benefit likely to be derived from drainage improvement. The basic question is what the stiffness modulus and/or strength of the subgrade is likely to revert to once drainage becomes effective, and the most visually understandable means of estimating this can be seen in a dynamic cone penetrometer (DCP) trace. Figure 4.21 makes the point.

It would appear likely that, in the example shown in Fig. 4.21, the subgrade originally had a CBR of 7–8% immediately beneath the granular layers, and this has reduced to 1–2% due to water ingress. However, following restoration of drainage function, the soil is unlikely to return all the way to 7–8%. A clue is often to be seen in other DCP results, from less water-affected locations; but in the absence of any actual data, it is suggested that a conservative assumption, in this case perhaps 5%, is sensible. In terms of stiffness, the influence is clearly also

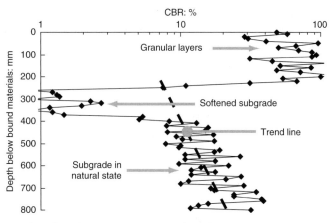

Fig. 4.21 Subgrade softening seen in DCP data

dependent on the thickness of the affected layer. It would be possible to carry out a multi-layer linear elastic calculation in order to estimate the influence that improvement of the affected layer would have on the overall effective stiffness modulus of the foundation; however, Calculation Sheet 4.2 presents a simplified assessment – which is acceptable bearing in mind the large uncertainty inherent in any such prediction.

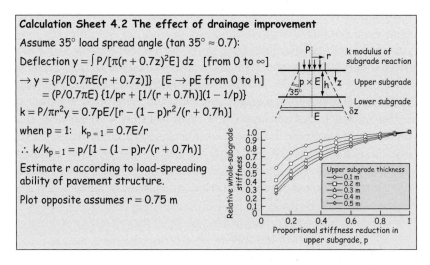

Calculation Sheet 4.2 allows the increase in overall whole-subgrade stiffness due to drainage improvement to be estimated. For example, in the case shown in Fig. 4.21, stiffness is reduced over a thickness h of about 0.3 m; the reduction ratio p is probably about 0.25, increasing to 0.7, say, after drainage improvement. The graph in Calculation Sheet

4.2 then shows that the relative whole-subgrade stiffness would increase from about 0.6 to 0.9, a 50% increase. Thus, if FWD data suggest a current whole-subgrade stiffness of 30 MPa for example, this might be expected to reach 45 MPa after drainage improvement. It's crude; but it's a great deal better than pure guesswork.

Armed with an estimate of the long-term foundation stiffness, it is now possible to use the tools described in Part 3 and to predict the influence that drainage improvement might have on pavement life.

4.5.2 Overlays/inlays to asphalt pavements

Though the benefits of drainage improvement are too frequently neglected, they may still be insufficient to ensure adequate future life; hence the likely need for additional fresh material to be added. The term *overlay* refers to the addition of a new layer or layers without the removal of any of the existing pavement (other than removing 10 mm or so to ensure a good key between old and new materials). An *inlay* refers to the situation where a certain depth of existing pavement is planed out and the same depth is replaced with new materials. It is of course possible (and common) to combine the two by planing out some of the existing pavement but then over-filling, giving an increased overall thickness. This section includes consideration of all such options.

The techniques for predicting the life of an overlaid or inlaid pavement are basically the same as those for a new pavement and the difficulties are similar to those already introduced in Section 4.4 when making a prognosis. The structure becomes one in which a certain thickness of new asphalt material overlies whatever is allowed to remain of the existing pavement layers. The choice as to how much (if any) of the existing pavement is removed prior to applying new material will depend on numerous practical factors as much as anything strictly technical. However, the key point for the engineer is that it must be possible to evaluate the likely pavement life provided by each option.

4.5.2.1 *Rutting within the asphalt layers*

Naturally, the application of a new surface means that rutting is reset to zero. If there was little rutting in the original pavement then it is not necessary to consider the matter further other than ensuring that new materials meet appropriate specifications and therefore have sufficient deformation resistance. If rutting is considered to be a potential problem, however, it is quite possible to carry out a calculation of the sort

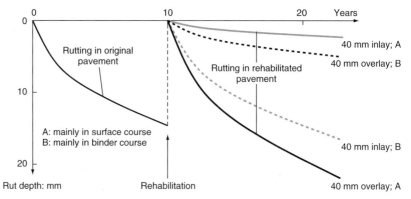

Fig. 4.22 *Conceptual illustration of rutting after rehabilitation*

introduced in Part 3 (Section 3.3.3), assigning mixture viscosities to both old and new pavement layers. Alternatively, a qualitative judgement can be made. The most damaging shear stresses occur within the upper 100 mm of the pavement, particularly between 50 mm and 100 mm below the surface. This means that, ideally, no potentially deformable layer from the existing pavement should be left within 100 mm of the surface – and this requirement may significantly affect the design. Figure 4.22 illustrates the point.

For the inexperienced engineer it is tempting to assume that all clearly defined rutting, including shoulders, is occurring in the surface course – which means that it is easy to take the wrong maintenance decision. However, at the cost of relatively few tests on specimens from cores (tests such as the repeated load axial test), the truth can be discovered and the right decision made.

4.5.2.2 Rutting within foundation layers

In general, it is fair to say that if this mode of deterioration has not been present in the past then it is unlikely to occur following rehabilitation – whatever the calculations may show. This is an important point; it is not at all easy to make confident prediction of deformation in unbound materials, and the best evidence on which to base future predictions is definitely past performance. Calculations are sometimes still worthwhile, particularly if future traffic is much higher than has been the case in the past, or if the design traffic load is to be increased, as may sometimes occur during airfield or industrial pavement development; but these predictions should always be 'calibrated' where feasible based on experience of past performance.

The methods for prediction are those presented in Part 3 (Sections 3.3.1 and 3.3.2), remembering that appropriate long-term stiffness moduli have to be used in any computation of stress or strain under load, including adjustment of foundation stiffness if drainage improvement is to be made.

4.5.2.3 Pavement cracking

This is usually a significant element, often the controlling factor, in design of overlays and inlays. The same decisions have to be made as introduced already in Section 4.4 as to whether existing pavement layers are to be considered intact or not – and the same general advice holds as to the most appropriate methods of analysis. This could mean, as shown in Fig. 4.23, that the resulting structure comprises: fully intact and undamaged material (the inlay/overlay); over intact but partially damaged material (upper asphalt from existing pavement); over substantially damaged and therefore non-intact materials (lower asphalt or hydraulically-bound base); over an unbound foundation. This is slightly more complicated than any of the cases covered in Section 4.4 in that the intact material is a combination of both damaged and undamaged components. This affects the application of Miner's law, the law which says that relative damage (i.e. proportion of life used) can never be recovered. A pragmatic approach would appear sensible, based on the ratio of thickness of new undamaged material to older damaged material. Take as an example a case where 100 mm of existing intact material is retained and it is concluded that 40% of its life has been used already. This is to be overlaid with 150 mm of new material. The effective damage might therefore be taken as 16% (40 × 100/250) for the total intact asphalt layer. If, say,

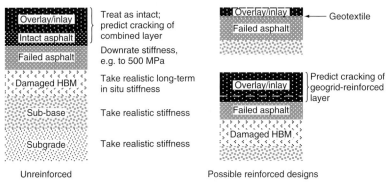

Fig. 4.23 Possible overlay/inlay designs to asphalt pavements

the calculated life with respect to fatigue cracking is 100 million vehicle passes, this therefore reduces to 84 million.

It is often sensible to check the fatigue life in more than one way. In addition to the type of calculation illustrated in the last paragraph, which would usually involve computation of the horizontal strain at the base of the lowermost intact asphalt layer, a further calculation could be carried out assuming that none of the existing pavement was still intact. This is particularly applicable to cases where it is suspected that there is a degree of full-depth cracking through the existing asphalt. The uppermost existing asphalt layers should in this case be assigned a much lower stiffness modulus, typically 500–1000 MPa as discussed in Part 3 (Section 3.4.2.10) for cracked base layers, and it is the horizontal strain within the overlay which controls predicted life. No allowance for damage would then be needed. The conservative designer might take the lower of the two pavement lives found – or would at least consider carefully which prediction is the more appropriate in a particular case.

The point here is that a responsible engineer will not wish to base a design on a single approach, but will consider various means of obtaining an estimate of pavement life, including use of design manuals where they allow such a prediction.

4.5.2.4 Use of interlayers

This situation, an asphalt overlay/inlay to a damaged pavement, is one of those which most obviously lend themselves to the use of what might be described as 'interlayer systems' – techniques for enhancing the effectiveness of an overlay. Broadly, the options are as follows, two of which were illustrated in Fig. 4.23:

- a geogrid or strong geotextile, providing actual enhanced strength
- a standard geotextile, acting as a separation layer
- a high-durability asphalt layer
- an open-graded asphalt layer
- a granular interlayer.

Clearly the effects of these different systems are not all the same. *Geogrids* and *strong geotextiles* actually slow down the rate of crack propagation; Part 2 (Section 2.4.3.2) suggested by a factor of up to around 4, depending on the product used. Part 3 (Section 3.4.2.11) has also discussed performance prediction. A secondary benefit, particularly of those geogrids which develop an efficient interlock with surrounding asphalt, is that cracks are prevented from opening even after penetrating full depth. Unfortunately, this benefit is hard to quantify, but it does at least mean that the slowing down of deterioration will continue throughout the life of the pavement.

Although the above list draws a distinction between 'strong' and 'standard' *geotextiles*, this is really just for convenience. Most geotextiles are capable of providing a degree of reinforcement, and this is particularly true for thin overlays on lightly trafficked roads. The nature of the reinforcement is not that it gives direct strength increase but rather that the asphalt is encouraged to 'recover' after each load application, being slowly pulled back into its original state as tension in the geotextile fibres dissipates. Under ideal conditions (thin overlay, fragmented underlying pavement, low traffic) the increase in pavement life can be dramatic – although rather hard to quantify. It should also be remembered that geotextiles, which are placed into a layer of sprayed bitumen (usually around 1 litre per square metre) act as a sealant, preventing rapid water ingress even after cracking commences. Their role as separators, where the systems probably come under the heading of *stress-absorbing membrane interlayers* (or SAMIs),[23] relates principally to cases where relative horizontal movement occurs across cracks, usually due to thermal effects in a hydraulically-bound base. A thick viscous layer such as is provided by a bitumen-soaked geotextile allows slip to occur (slowly) between the overlay and the existing pavement, thus inhibiting thermally-induced reflective cracking.

The description *high-durability asphalt layer* is intended to refer to specialist products which can be placed over significant underlying cracks, for example major transverse cracks initiated by thermal or shrinkage effects in a hydraulically-bound base layer. The idea is that the crack finds it difficult to propagate through the product, which will usually include modified binder and often fibre reinforcement. These systems, which are also often categorised as SAMIs, can certainly be highly effective where the main danger comes from horizontal thermally-induced movement in a hydraulically-bound base. Effectiveness is reduced where there is significant traffic-induced relative vertical movement across cracks.

The final two systems, an *open-graded asphalt* and a *granular interlayer*, are both intended to form a layer through which a crack cannot propagate. They are applicable to cases where the existing pavement contains large discrete cracks, often associated with a hydraulically-bound material. The effectiveness of the granular interlayer is obvious in that the material is 'ready-cracked' and hence cannot physically

407

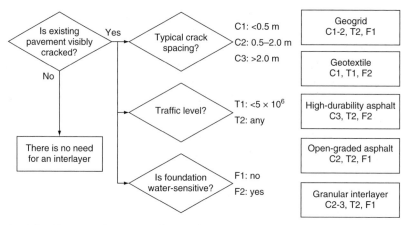

Fig. 4.24 Decision chart – interlayer selection

transmit a discrete crack. The resulting pavement comes under the heading 'sandwich construction', as described in Part 3 (Section 3.6.3).

The effect of an open-graded asphalt (logically, a cold-mix asphalt would be suitable) is similar. It is a stiffer material (perhaps 1000 MPa – depending on design temperature), but forms a less complete break to reflection of underlying cracks. It would theoretically be best suited to cases where cracks in an underlying pavement are more frequent (e.g. 2 m spacing or less) and therefore reflective cracking is a slightly less dominant issue. However, this is certainly an area where confident prediction is impossible.

Figure 4.24 is included here as an aid to decision making. Please note that the guidance contained is of a general nature and should not be seen as prescriptive. It is always important to ascertain the type of cracking present, in particular the nature of likely movement across cracks in the future. Note that the category 'F1' in Fig. 4.24 is not intended to disqualify the use of any interlayer systems, but simply to indicate which systems will actively protect the subgrade from water ingress. Note also that it is possible to combine geogrids and geotextiles into composite products, thus combining the two sets of benefits.

4.5.2.5 Repairs prior to overlay

This is an area which should not be overlooked. When a pavement is at the design stage, it is 100% uniform. As soon as it is constructed, variations in subgrade quality, material composition, compaction, layer thickness etc. immediately introduce a degree of variability. By the time major maintenance is required, this variability will be greater again, as water finds its way into some sections and not others or as debonding occurs in some places and not others. The result is that there may be some sections which are in relatively good condition while others are suffering from advanced full-depth cracking. If an overlay or inlay is applied uniformly then that variability will of course still be present. The obvious solution is to bring those sections which are showing the most advanced signs of deterioration up to a certain minimum standard, for which the overlay or inlay can then be designed. In practical terms this might mean:

- replacing localised areas of badly crazed asphalt
- trenching and replacing asphalt at severe transverse cracks[24]
- planing out severely rutted areas, at least to the depth of the rut.

The question is: just how much is worth doing? And the answer depends, of course, on the economics of each individual case. However, as a guideline, it is probably not worth replacing more than about 10% of the total pavement area due to crazing. If crazing is more widespread, then the overlay or inlay should be designed to cope with the crazed condition. In the case of severe transverse cracks, it may be economic to treat them if they are 20 m or so apart; much more frequent than this and the condition can be considered as 'general' and the overlay or inlay designed accordingly. Planing of ruts, on the other hand, is a much less expensive operation and is advised in every case where they exceed 15 mm or so.

It is also strongly advised that *local strengthening* is considered. The point is that localised crazing occurs for a reason and, even after carrying out a full-depth reinstatement with new asphalt, that reason may still remain. It is most likely to be due to foundation properties, and these will not usually be significantly improved during rehabilitation. The alternative, therefore, is to use either materials of enhanced strength and durability in these local reinstatements or else to increase asphalt thickness locally. The fact that reinstatements are rarely given the same level of compaction as the original pavement (due to difficulties at edges and corners) makes such strengthening or thickening doubly desirable.

The same principle applies to repairs to severe transverse cracks. It will never be possible to completely prevent their reoccurrence, but it is certainly possible to slow down the process. A trench repair may make use of material with enhanced 'elasticity', meaning increased ability to cope with high strains without cracking. A polymer-modified binder is an obvious choice. The use of interlayer systems (see previous section) should also be considered.

4.5.2.6 Ultra-thin white-topping

This is a more radical solution, illustrated in Fig. 4.25. It is a thin concrete overlay – which at first sight would appear to be a strange choice to make since a thin concrete slab is inherently fragile. However, when the calculations are carried out, using techniques such as finite-element analysis, it is found that the support given by an underlying asphalt pavement can certainly be adequate. However, cracked asphalt is unsuitable; it will cause stress concentrations in the concrete and will lead to fracture. The technique is therefore restricted to structurally intact asphalt pavements – which begs the question as to why one would ever want to carry it out. However, there is a very real circumstance where ultra-thin white-topping has proved highly effective, notably in some US states,[25] namely where serious rutting is taking place, which often means at heavily used highway intersections. In these cases, the continuity of support provided by the asphalt offers suitable insurance against concrete cracking, while the rigidity of the concrete prevents any further permanent deformation from occurring in the asphalt. In these particular cases, the combination provides an ideal solution. Particular points to watch are as follows:

- The concrete must be jointed and it is recommended that joints are spaced at no more than about 1 m. They can consist of simple saw-cuts, through to a depth of about half the slab thickness, which are then sealed.
- The slab should be reinforced to give adequate toughness and, in practice, this dictates the use of fibres since the thickness is usually insufficient to allow conventional reinforcement.
- It is very important that the concrete is well bonded to the asphalt. This is best achieved by thoroughly cleaning and then washing the prepared asphalt surface.

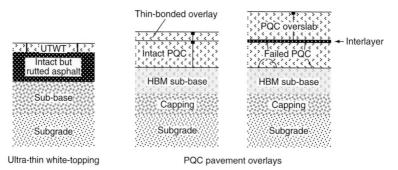

Ultra-thin white-topping   PQC pavement overlays

Fig. 4.25 *Cementitious overlay options*

- The asphalt surface does not have to be particularly even, although ruts greater than about 15 mm should be reduced by planing so as to avoid excessive variation in slab thickness.
- Design thickness will normally be in the range 50–100 mm.
- Placement is best achieved by slip-form paving, although hand-laying is acceptable in low-speed applications such as at intersections.
- The surface should be textured as for any other concrete pavement.

The greatest difficulty facing the engineer is how to judge the design thickness of ultra-thin white-topping. Current practice appears to base recommendations on proven past experience. However, the principle is that the asphalt acts as a stiffener for the concrete rather than as part of the foundation. This drastically reduces the value of tensile stress which would otherwise occur at the base of the concrete under bending. Calculation Sheet 4.3 presents an approximate, two-dimensional analysis, illustrating the way in which the system works; multi-layer

Calculation Sheet 4.3 Stress in ultra-thin white-topping

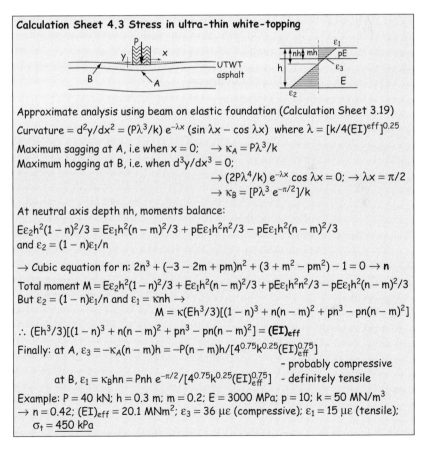

Approximate analysis using beam on elastic foundation (Calculation Sheet 3.19)

Curvature $= d^2y/dx^2 = (P\lambda^3/k) e^{-\lambda x} (\sin \lambda x - \cos \lambda x)$ where $\lambda = [k/4(EI)^{eff}]^{0.25}$

Maximum sagging at A, i.e. when $x = 0$; $\rightarrow \kappa_A = P\lambda^3/k$

Maximum hogging at B, i.e. when $d^3y/dx^3 = 0$;

$$\rightarrow (2P\lambda^4/k) e^{-\lambda x} \cos \lambda x = 0; \rightarrow \lambda x = \pi/2$$
$$\rightarrow \kappa_B = [P\lambda^3 e^{-\pi/2}]/k$$

At neutral axis depth nh, moments balance:

$E\varepsilon_2 h^2(1 - n)^2/3 = E\varepsilon_1 h^2(n - m)^2/3 + pE\varepsilon_1 h^2 n^2/3 - pE\varepsilon_1 h^2(n - m)^2/3$

and $\varepsilon_2 = (1 - n)\varepsilon_1/n$

$\rightarrow$ Cubic equation for n: $2n^3 + (-3 - 2m + pm)n^2 + (3 + m^2 - pm^2) - 1 = 0 \rightarrow n$

Total moment $M = E\varepsilon_2 h^2(1 - n)^2/3 + E\varepsilon_1 h^2(n - m)^2/3 + pE\varepsilon_1 h^2 n^2/3 - pE\varepsilon_1 h^2(n - m)^2/3$

But $\varepsilon_2 = (1 - n)\varepsilon_1/n$ and $\varepsilon_1 = \kappa n h \rightarrow$

$$M = \kappa(Eh^3/3)[(1 - n)^3 + n(n - m)^2 + pn^3 - pn(n - m)^2]$$

$\therefore (Eh^3/3)[(1 - n)^3 + n(n - m)^2 + pn^3 - pn(n - m)^2] = \mathbf{(EI)_{eff}}$

Finally: at A, $\varepsilon_3 = -\kappa_A(n - m)h = -P(n - m)h/[4^{0.75}k^{0.25}(EI)_{eff}^{0.75}]$

- probably compressive

at B, $\varepsilon_1 = \kappa_B hn = Pnh \, e^{-\pi/2}/[4^{0.75}k^{0.25}(EI)_{eff}^{0.75}]$ - definitely tensile

Example: $P = 40$ kN; $h = 0.3$ m; $m = 0.2$; $E = 3000$ MPa; $p = 10$; $k = 50$ MN/m^3

$\rightarrow n = 0.42$; $(EI)_{eff} = 20.1$ MNm^2; $\varepsilon_3 = 36$ µε (compressive); $\varepsilon_1 = 15$ µε (tensile);

$\sigma_t = \underline{450 \text{ kPa}}$

linear elastic analysis would generate a much more accurate estimate of stress.

4.5.3 Overlays/inlays to concrete pavements

In truth, an 'inlay' to a concrete-surface pavement is not a likely choice, although level constraints could in theory dictate its use. However, so long as the remaining pavement has a concrete surface prior to placement of new materials then it falls into the category of treatment covered in this section.

4.5.3.1 Thin bonded concrete overlays

This solution, illustrated in Fig. 4.25, can only be applied successfully if the existing PQC slab is intact. Basically, it is a means of increasing slab thickness; hence the need for bond. The thickness can in theory be as little as permitted by stone size and the needs of workability; 30 mm or so probably represents a sensible practical minimum. Bond, which is absolutely critical to success, is achieved by milling and thorough cleaning of the existing surface.

This treatment has been extensively employed in the US and has proved highly successful. The key is undoubtedly forward planning since it can only be carried out on intact slabs. It is a particularly logical choice where pavement usage is about to change, for example if heavier aircraft or port equipment are to be employed. Issues are as follows:

- The material used must be compatible with the existing PQC in terms of its thermal properties. In general, aggregate with low thermal expansion coefficient such as limestone is preferred.
- Thickness design is exactly the same as for a new pavement, and the assumption should be made that the strength of the composite slab is the lower of those of the overlay and the existing concrete.
- Joints in the existing pavement must be replicated (and sealed) immediately above in the overlay. If expansion joints are present, they should be formed by use of filler board or similar compressible medium.
- Paving technique and surface finish are the same as for new concrete pavements.

There is no fundamental reason why thin bonded overlays should not be used over CRC, despite the inevitable presence of relatively close-spaced transverse cracking. The overlay will, of course, also crack immediately above cracks in the existing concrete. The issue of prime concern is that the presence of so many cracks may place excessive strain on the integrity of the bond between old and new materials. It is also essential that any local deterioration in the existing slab is repaired in advance.

4.5.3.2 Overslabbing

For the designer, this is a very simple case, also illustrated in Fig. 4.25. It is appropriate when the existing concrete is severely damaged, in which case the entire existing pavement is relegated to the role of a foundation and the new slab is designed as in Part 3 (Section 3.4.1). Equivalent foundation modulus can be based on FWD data. If a modulus of subgrade reaction k is required, empirical relationships with foundation modulus can be found in several design manuals;[26] alternatively, multi-layer linear elastic calculations can be carried out to try to determine an equivalence in a particular case;[27] or one can simply divide the equivalent foundation modulus (in MPa) by 2 to obtain a very rough estimate for k (in MN/m^3).

Note that, although overslabbing is most commonly used over existing concrete pavements, it can actually be used over any pavement type. The only quantity which the designer has to worry about is the support stiffness.

Note also that concrete pavements, particularly CRC pavements, are tolerant of wide variation in support stiffness. The design should be based on a conservatively low value, but required thickness is actually relatively insensitive to this quantity. This means that it is not usually economic to carry out any local repairs to the existing pavement prior to overslabbing.

However, there is one aspect to overslabbed pavements which is of critical importance, and that is the interface between the new pavement and the old. The new slab needs to be independent of the old in terms of horizontal movement, otherwise cracks in an existing slab may be reflected in the new slab. This typically presents two options:

1. a heavy-duty polythene membrane
2. an asphalt (or mastic) interlayer.

There is much debate and disagreement between experts as to which, if either, is the more desirable. However, there is no doubt that, in engineering terms, the effects of the two solutions are different. The polythene forms a clear break in bond, allowing free vertical separation

Table 4.4 Asphalt overlay options over existing concrete pavement

Pavement type	Condition	Treatment advice
CRC	Good	No special treatment needed
	Poor	Consider an interlayer
Jointed reinforced	Any	Saw-cut, crack and seat
Jointed unreinforced	Good	either: Form joints in asphalt
		or: Crack and seat
	Poor	either: Crack and seat
		or: Rubblise

and reasonably easy shear movement. An asphalt or mastic layer (usually no more than 25 mm thick) will give good bond under load but will allow relative shear movement over a longer timescale, i.e. in response to thermally induced expansion and contraction effects. This author's view is that the asphalt or mastic solution is to be preferred if the underlying concrete has any significant remaining integrity, since it fulfils the separation need sufficiently while allowing a greater composite pavement strength. Where the underlying slab has negligible contribution to make then this argument no longer applies.

Clearly, for overslabbing of asphalt-surface pavements no interface treatment is required.

4.5.3.3 Asphalt overlays

Asphalt will usually be the favoured material for strengthening simply because it can be applied much more rapidly than concrete, and for airfield runways and major highways time is often the determining factor. However, except in the case of properly functioning CRC, design involves a choice between several quite different options. Table 4.4 lists the alternatives. Figure 4.26 illustrates the processes referred to in the table.

In general, overlay thickness design will be influenced by two considerations. The first only applies where the existing PQC is in good condition and is to remain intact, and it is that the stress induced in the concrete under load should be restricted in order to avoid further cracking. This is exactly the same design criterion as is used in new concrete pavement design (see Part 3, Section 3.4.1) except for the presence of the asphalt layer. If multi-layer linear elastic analysis is to be used, then this has to include the asphalt layer, at a conservatively

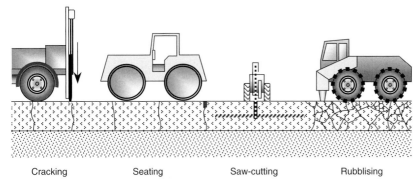

| Cracking | Seating | Saw-cutting | Rubblising |

Fig. 4.26 Concrete pre-treatment options prior to asphalt overlay

low stiffness, corresponding to relatively warm weather. Alternatively, the thickness of asphalt may be converted to an approximate equivalent PQC thickness by dividing by 4.

The second consideration is *reflective cracking*. Only in the case of an overlay to an intact CRC can reflective cracking be ignored. All joints and cracks will tend to reflect; the trick is to understand the mechanisms involved. According to Part 3, there are two basic mechanisms. The first is thermally driven and is caused by joints and cracks opening and closing as the concrete cools and heats over each 24-hour period. The second is traffic driven and is caused by differential vertical movement across joints and cracks under each passing wheel load. To combat the first, it is essential to minimise the length of concrete slab between cracks (or joints), ensuring only a small opening and closing movement at each. To combat the second, each crack (or joint) must have good load transfer properties, which means narrow cracks only. The obvious answer is to break the concrete into short lengths, providing large numbers of relatively narrow cracks. This is the *cracking* operation illustrated in Fig. 4.26; it is carried out using a large 'guillotine' device, dropping a heavy steel sheet onto the pavement surface, and is highly effective for unreinforced concrete.

The next operation shown, namely *seating*, ensures that any local gap between the underside of the slab and the foundation material is closed and that each individual element of concrete is properly supported.

An important issue is the optimum crack spacing. Here three factors compete. The first is that closer spacing means better load transfer and less thermal movement. The second is that closer spacing means a lower overall pavement stiffness and the danger that conventional fatigue cracking might take over from reflective cracking as the dominant mode of asphalt failure. The third is that the cracking operation costs both time and money. The favoured compromise seems to be a spacing of around 1 m, usually allowing an asphalt thickness of 150 mm or less.[28] See Part 3 (Sections 3.4.2.9 and 3.4.2.10) for further advice on reflective crack prediction and thickness design.

Unfortunately, jointed reinforced concrete presents a difficulty. Cracking and seating is no problem, but the continuity of the reinforcing steel means that, even after cracking, thermally induced movement will still be concentrated at joints, joints which are usually well over 10 m apart. This is certainly a recipe for reflective cracking. The difficulty can be overcome by *saw-cutting* through each slab at regular intervals (e.g. 3 m) to over half depth in order to cut the reinforcement – but it's an expensive operation. It should only be undertaken after careful consideration of the alternatives – for example, putting up with the reflective cracking.

Two further options present themselves for jointed concrete. One is 'do less'; the other is 'do more'. The 'do less' option is an acceptable solution when the existing pavement has relatively close-spaced joints (<6 m or so) and is in good condition. The overlay thickness is designed simply to reduce stress in the concrete to an acceptable level; no pre-treatment is carried out, but joints are *saw-cut* into the surface of the asphalt directly over those in the original slab, and then sealed – as in the case of a bonded concrete overlay.[29]

The 'do more' option is *rubblising*. Basically, this involves pulverising the concrete into small pieces, none more than about 150 mm in size, reducing it to a granular material. The correct design stiffness for this layer is debatable and doubtless depends on the details of the rubblisation process. Some suggest up to 1000 MPa, although this may be rather optimistic; the figure advised here is no more than about 250 MPa. Asphalt thickness design then follows that for conventional asphalt pavements.

The only other case is that of CRC in poor condition, one of the most difficult maintenance headaches of all. The poor condition undoubtedly means that many of the cracks are relatively free-moving, despite the presence of reinforcing steel, since much hidden spalling has almost certainly occurred. This means that reflective cracking through any overlay is likely. It also means that confident thickness design is practically impossible. The suggestion made in Table 4.4 that an interlayer treatment should be considered is simply advice to take out an 'insurance policy'. Geogrid reinforcement is probably the most effective option since it should at least hold the asphalt together well, even if reflective cracking occurs, whereas there is little to be gained from treatments which merely allow shear movement between the asphalt and the concrete; the problem is traffic-induced vertical movement.

4.5.4 Hot in situ recycling of asphalt

All the principles of asphalt or hydraulically-bound mixtures apply equally whether the aggregate used is virgin rock, industrial waste or recycled pavement. Similarly, the behaviour of bitumen in an asphalt is essentially similar whether it is fresh bitumen or whether it is residual binder from recycled asphalt planings. The viscosity may be different, and this has to be taken into account in mix design, arriving at a blend of old and new which gives the appropriate properties. The technology of production may also be different, requiring indirect heating of planings (by transferring heat from super-heated aggregate) but, so long as the products are still mixed off site in a batching plant, they can be controlled in a similar manner to that of a 100% virgin mixture. This is not the case for in situ recycled materials.

Hot in situ recycling represents a significant challenge for equipment manufacturers; however, the pavement engineering is much less challenging. Basically, the aim is to transform an aged and partially failed asphalt surface layer into a good-as-new product. The process requires that the surface of the pavement is heated to a temperature at which it can be reworked, healing all cracks and reshaping any deformed profile. In the so-called *Repave* process, the uppermost materials are scarified (i.e. loosened) while hot (above about 90°C), and additional new hot-mix asphalt material is added, typically increasing the level by around 20 mm. The hope is that the heated old material blends with the new to form a single contiguous surface course with fully restored properties. The bitumen grade and mixture composition of the added material is selected to balance out any defects in the composition of the existing material.

Remix is the name given to a slightly more sophisticated process in which the heated existing surface material is physically scraped up and mixed together with fresh hot-mix material before being relaid as a new surface course. This ensures a fully integrated and blended layer. Figure 4.27 illustrates the concept of the Remix process.

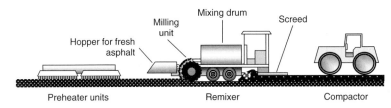

Fig. 4.27 Schematic diagram of hot in situ recycling of asphalt

417

Both these processes are excellent in that they actually do transform a failing surface into an intact new layer. However, they have their limitations:

- The existing surface material must be suitably uniform in composition (i.e. not too many patches or other material changes).
- The transformation is only effective to the depth to which the asphalt can be heated. This means that the treatment can potentially cure surface course rutting, top-down cracking or ravelling, but that it does nothing to overcome deeper problems.

A key issue here is the depth to which the treatments can extend, which depends on the efficiency of the heating. Naturally, this is an area in which technology is making regular improvements. At the time of writing (2007), heating can be achieved directly, by naked flame or infrared, or indirectly, by feeding super-heated gases over the pavement surface. Direct heating has traditionally only managed a workable depth of 20–30 mm; indirect heating is claimed to heat to at least 75 mm. Clearly, if 75 mm is 'restored' and a further 20 mm is added, this provides a new 95 mm thick layer, which could make a serious contribution to the strength of the pavement as a whole; i.e. the process is becoming more than a mere surface course treatment.

For the designer, the finished pavement can be treated as new for calculation purposes, making suitable allowance – following the advice given in Section 4.5.2.3 – for any fatigue life 'used up' in lower asphalt or hydraulically-bound layers.

4.5.5 Cold in situ recycling

This is a massive subject and one which is likely to become increasingly important in the future. The concept is that an existing pavement is milled to a certain depth – machines with capability up to 350 mm exist – and that the broken fragments are then mixed with a new binder and compacted – see Fig. 4.28. The result, if everything goes to plan, is a strong new pavement, although it will normally be necessary to apply a new surface course since it is unlikely that the requisite surface properties will be present from the recycled material itself.

The potential is obvious. No matter how cracked, deformed, worn, aged etc. the existing pavement is, so long as its broken remains fulfil the role of aggregate, then it is still useful. There is no need for expensive and disruptive transportation of materials (other than binder); there is no requirement for quarrying of virgin rock; there is a much

418

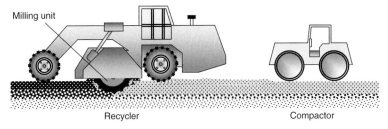

Milling unit

Recycler   Compactor

Fig. 4.28 Cold in situ recycling

reduced energy requirement since no heating of aggregates is called for. All that is needed is the addition of an effective binder. Of course there are difficulties, and the following are seen as the major issues confronting practitioners and designers.

- Binder is unlikely to be uniformly mixed into the material.
- All pavements are to a certain extent non-homogeneous, notably in layer thickness. In many cases, this means that the milled material will present varying proportions of asphalt, base (including hydraulically-bound materials), sub-base and even subgrade.
- Water content can only be controlled approximately.
- Compaction beyond about 250 mm depth will be increasingly ineffective.
- The need to work with cold, wet aggregate restricts the choice of binder.

4.5.5.1 Material variability
The first three points in the above list relate to variability. This is an issue which cannot be dismissed – nor can technical improvements to the process ever fully overcome it. Unfortunately it is an issue where data are: (1) hard to come by and (2) hard to interpret. In the one relevant data set of which the author has direct knowledge, the recycled product was only marginally more variable than an adjacent fresh hot-mix asphalt when tested with an FWD, with a coefficient of variance about 1.2 times that for hot-mix. However, when individual cores were extracted and tested, the variability was much higher – three to four times that of hot-mix. This is logical enough; it means that the variability occurs over very short distances, presumably as more or less binder reaches individual regions and due to fluctuations in the composition of recycled material. Over a metre or so – the zone of influence of an FWD test – these fluctuations even out.

The question which has to be asked (and which can barely be answered) is whether dramatic, short-wavelength fluctuations in quality matter; after all, over a thickness of 250 mm or more, deformation susceptibility might be expected to even out. Similarly, cracking would not be able to advance far unless it propagated through both good and poor regions of the material. These are reasonable arguments and they suggest that one should not necessarily panic over apparent variability from tests on cores. On the other hand, in some respects variability really does matter. Permeability is critically affected by small changes in gradation and void content, which suggests that an in situ recycled material will always be relatively permeable since there will always be high-void routes through it.

In conclusion, the following advice is offered:

- Reduce the design stiffness modulus slightly from that derived from laboratory-mixed specimens to take account of variability, perhaps by around 10%.
- Be aware that water will be able to ingress. This means that the durability of the recycled material under wet conditions should be assessed – see Part 2 (Sections 2.2.3.1 and 2.3.6.2) – and that the issue of water reaching the foundation should be recognised.

4.5.5.2 Compaction

Again, direct data are hard to come by. However, it has been found that modern compactive equipment is able to achieve high density in a granular pavement material such as a base or sub-base to a thickness of around 250 mm, and the recycled materials under consideration are effectively granular at the time of compaction. Beyond that depth, the relative density will tend to decrease. Calculation Sheet 4.4 presents an approximate assessment of the likely effect of this in

---

Calculation Sheet 4.4 Under-compaction at base of layer

0.25 m E h_n —
h pE

Use approach in Calculation Sheet 4.3 to determine neutral axis depth h_n and effective bending stiffness EI_{eff}.

Also from Calculation Sheet 4.3:
$$\varepsilon_t = \kappa(0.25 + h - h_n) \approx P(0.25 + h - h_n)/[4^{0.75}k^{0.25}(EI)_{eff}^{0.75}]$$

Then calculate h_{eq} to give the same ε_t with $p = 1$ (i.e. no under-compaction)

Example: $P = 40$ kN; $k = 50$ MN/m^3; $p = 0.8$ at $h = 0.05$ m, 0.7 at $h = 0.1$ m, 0.6 at $h = 0.15$ m $\rightarrow h_{eq} \approx 50$-60% of h

---

terms of the strain at the base of the layer under vehicle wheel loading, the stiffness reduction shown in the example being nothing more than an estimate. If this illustration were to be correct, the deduction would be that the designer should assume a reduced thickness for any material deeper than 250 mm, applying a multiplier of around 0.6.

4.5.5.3 Choice of binder

Mixing at ambient temperature dictates the use of either a hydraulic binder, bitumen emulsion or foamed bitumen, which means that full strength cannot be achieved immediately. Even in the case of Portland cement, adequate strength to prevent structural damage under traffic load would only be achieved after some days. The other binders all demand a long curing period, often months rather than weeks – which presents a dilemma. It will almost certainly not be economic to avoid use of the pavement for such a long period but, if it is used, then structural damage has to be expected, even while curing is taking place. The unknown quantity is the extent to which such damage will self-heal during subsequent curing, and also how long the curing process takes.

4.5.5.4 Hydraulic binders

The aim of using a hydraulic binder is to achieve a base of comparable quality to a plant-mixed hydraulically-bound layer, accepting the increased variability and the lower density expected at the bottom of the layer. However, the issue of damage during early life cannot be ignored, particularly in the case of a slow-curing material. Laboratory testing clearly indicates that the intensity of early-life trafficking can dramatically affect the final state of a slow-curing material.[30] Unfortunately, the current state of knowledge means that it is impossible to make confident predictions. The advice contained in Table 4.5 should therefore be seen as relatively 'high risk'. It is extrapolated from experimental data obtained at the University of Nottingham and assumes that normal traffic levels are allowed onto the pavement within a few days of the layer being recycled. Actual behaviour will naturally also be a function of the details of pavement construction.

Once a long-term stiffness modulus is determined, this can then be used in the relevant pavement design approaches in Part 3 (Sections 3.4.1.10–3.4.1.13). The clear conclusion is that this type of pavement is best suited to low-traffic cases – or at least cases where early-life traffic can realistically be either excluded or greatly restricted.

421

Table 4.5 Early-life trafficking of hydraulically-bound layers

Time to 90% of design strength: days	Suggested design stiffness: % of fully cured undamaged		
	0.1 msa/year	0.3 msa/year	1 msa/year
28	60%	30%	12%
56	40%	20%	7%
90	30%	12%	4%
180	20%	7%	2.5%

4.5.5.5 Cold bituminous binders

The actions of bitumen emulsion and foamed bitumen are similar, in that both binders tend to coat particles of aggregate (in this case recycled road fragments) unevenly and both take time to gain in effectiveness. These issues were detailed in Part 2 (Section 2.3.7.5). Pavement design approaches were presented in Part 3 (Section 3.6.1), where expected stiffness modulus values were suggested as a proportion of what would be expected from a hot-mix using the same aggregate. Curing (i.e. strength gain) is critically dependent on water loss from the material, which means that open-graded materials are preferred, allowing air to access the voids and hasten evaporation. This should in theory present no problem for in situ recycled pavements since recycled asphalt layers are typically low in fine material but, on the other hand, the variability inherent in an in situ process will mean that there will be some regions with lower voids and which therefore lose water less easily. The inclusion of around 1% cement or lime is a technique commonly used to reduce the free water content and so to encourage curing. Clearly, the timing of surfacing application is another important factor in the equation and a responsible organisation will be careful to take account of the weather, not applying the surface immediately after rain has raised the water content for example.

It is not really possible to advise on the relative advantages of emulsion and foamed bitumen for in situ recycling since continuing progress continues to be made in both technologies.

The issue of early-life damage applies to cold-mix asphalt in a similar way as to hydraulically-bound materials. The difference, however, is the inherent ability of a bituminous material to self-heal. However, in the early stages of curing of cold-mix asphalt, the material is undeniably very weak indeed. If significant load is to be taken during the first few hours, then it is essential that the aggregate has sufficient shear strength to avoid rutting. As regards long-term stiffness modulus, Table 4.5 can be taken to apply equally to cold-mix asphalt as to hydraulically-bound material (remembering that it is purely an estimate based on limited evidence). In the same way as for hydraulically-bound material, the conclusion has to be that this type of pavement is really best suited to cases where early-life trafficking is light.

Pavement design can be carried out following the principles given in Part 3 (Section 3.6.1) for cold-mix asphalt pavements.[31] The recycled layer can be treated as a conventional asphalt so long as the long-term stiffness is expected to be sufficiently high for it to be considered intact. If not, then the recycled layer has to be considered as an exceptionally high-quality unbound base and the surfacing above designed on this basis.[32]

4.5.6 Summary

Although it would be possible to include advice on other pavement types, such as block paving, grouted macadam or even granular pavements, the main principles are now in place. Block paving, if it is to be strengthened, will usually be removed, leaving a standard base and sub-base; grouted macadam is basically an asphalt and can be treated as such in any strengthening analysis; a granular pavement will readily form the foundation to any future bound pavement structure. As for all the more conventional pavement types already covered, the secret is to make appropriate assumptions on long-term properties; the actual analysis techniques are similar to those for new pavements.

So, in an ideal world, the advice contained up until this point would enable soundly based engineering decisions on future maintenance to be made, and a range of excellent rehabilitation design options to be developed. The question is: how does this fit into the real world, where resources are never sufficient and time windows are not always available? This is not solely an engineering matter, although some of the constraints will be due to engineering issues; it is a management matter, and the topic is known as 'pavement management'.

4.6

Pavement management

Pavement management is a subject which this book can only touch on, and is part of the much larger subjects of 'highway management', 'airfield management' etc. However, it is important that the pavement engineer understands the wider impact of the computations and predictions which he or she makes, together with the fact that there is never any one right answer (although there may be numerous wrong ones). The first matter which needs to be addressed is the fact that there are often good practical reasons why certain otherwise excellent maintenance solutions have to be rejected – or else given a high price tag. Once these constraints have been appreciated, it will then be possible to look at the principal underlying decisions such as whether to continue with increasingly costly minor maintenance or whether to adopt a more radical rehabilitation solution with a much higher up-front cost.

Incidentally, although this section is presented in terms of 'cost', this is not necessarily entirely financial. The sustainability issues touched on early in Part 3 represent environmental or social costs, and these can always be added into the equation using a suitable equivalence factor – a highly political decision.

4.6.1 Practical constraints
In general, nothing in pavement engineering is impossible – but some things are rather impractical. In most cases the impracticality is obvious and it is not the intention here to labour points unnecessarily. However, the issues are worth listing.

424

4.6.1.1 Multi-lane highways

The point here is that one cannot raise (or lower) the surface level of one lane without doing the same to all other lanes on a carriageway. Thus, while a simple overlay solution may appear to be the most cost-effective in isolation, the full cost (both monetary and in delays) has to be added in, i.e. similar overlays to all lanes. The only relaxation on this is where the cross-fall of the pavement surface can be made either steeper or shallower within the constraints of the specification for a particular highway class.

4.6.1.2 Highway structures

The clearance to overbridges places an obvious upper limit on raising levels. It is not difficult to carry out checks on the actual clearance, nor particularly costly, and the information is vital so that inappropriate solutions can be rejected right at the outset.

Less obviously, the carrying capacity of underbridges also has a limit, and even a thin overlay adds a significant extra load. This too must be established at an early stage to allow efficient design.

Of course, even if structures limit the thickness of overlay permitted, this constraint only applies to the pavement actually over or under the structure. It is quite possible to ramp the surface up or down either side, over a length which depends on the vertical alignment constraints for that class of highway.

4.6.1.3 Kerbs and barriers

Both kerbs and barriers can be raised – but at a cost. In both cases there is usually a degree of flexibility, allowing small increases in pavement level, and it is therefore important to know just how much flexibility is available in a particular case.

It is fair to say that this particular restriction is one of the prime drivers towards the use of geosynthetic interlayers, the philosophy being that their use at least maximises what can be achieved within the level constraints applying.

4.6.1.4 Airport runways

The situation here is similar to that for multi-lane highways in that it is generally only the central 20 m width, from a pavement that may be 60 m wide in total, which is damaged by aircraft. This often means

425

that it is desirable to apply an overlay to this central part only, which is of course not permissible. However, it is often permissible to ramp down from a relatively thick overlay over the central part of the runway to little or zero thickness at the edge. The cross-fall constraints are tight on a runway (generally 1–1.5%) and so the 'feathering out' of the overlay may only be possible at a cross-fall difference of around 0.5% (at which rate a 100 mm overlay takes 20 m to reduce to zero thickness).

4.6.1.5 *Absolute utilisation requirements*

In general, closure of an airport for more than a matter of hours is not a viable economic option. This means that processes which can be carried out at night such that the airport is fully operational the next morning may be acceptable; processes which demand a longer period without traffic are not. The range of maintenance options on runways is therefore limited. Closure of runway ends may be possible for longer periods, since operations can still continue with a reduced runway length. Closure of taxiways and aprons may also be acceptable where alternative routes or stand areas are available.

A similar restriction may apply to highways. Authorities generally specify that a certain number of lanes have to be kept open at all times, restricting access to the work area. This means that processes which take a long time to complete (or cure fully) carry too high a price on major highways. It may also mean that some processes physically cannot be carried out because of the restricted working width.

Finally, in industry, 'time is money', which means that industrial pavements may also carry a similar requirement for continuous usability. The designer has to be aware of all such restrictions before even thinking about possible designs.

4.6.1.6 *Absolute safety requirements*

These requirements come in the following guises:

- Maintain a minimum skid resistance coefficient.
- Do not exceed a maximum rut depth.
- Avoid all loose material (on an airport runway).

Any of these requirements may dictate that a new surface is required no matter what the structural strength of the pavement may be, thereby cutting back significantly the maintenance options available.

4.6.2 Project-level optimisation

This section will set out the principles to be followed. The problem is that the interface between network-level management and project-level design is not an easy one to manage (an issue that has already arisen in relation to pavement evaluation planning). It is not particularly easy for an engineer to come up with a confident maintenance design; it is quite impossible to 'second-guess' the budget constraints which apply. On the other hand, until the magnitude of maintenance requirements is known, it is impossible to manage the budget properly. It is a classic 'vicious circle'.

In practice, the most common way in which this circle is broken is for the authority to stipulate design lives to which the pavement engineer has to work, but this is not a particularly efficient system and is always likely to result in some work being carried out either earlier or to a higher design life than is really required, while other projects languish unfunded.

4.6.2.1 Working with a predetermined design life

At a straightforward level, the designer may simply be asked to come up with the best solution to strengthen the pavement to take another x years – say 20 – of traffic, assuming that the strengthening is carried out in the immediate future. In this case, it is simply a matter of costing up all the practical alternatives, taking into account any add-on costs due to practical constraints. Take, for example, the case of a two-lane carriageway with a paved shoulder, for which lane 1 requires significant strengthening (either inlay or overlay) whereas lane 2 only requires a new surface (for safety reasons). The shoulder requires no treatment. The resulting options might be as shown in Fig. 4.29.

Clearly, if the constraints are ignored and the lane 1 cost is looked at in isolation then the simple overlay solution is the cheapest. On the other hand, when the necessary lane 2 and shoulder works are added in, then the most cost-effective option is to plane 100 mm and replace with 140 mm (requiring a 40 mm overlay to both lane 2 and the shoulder).

But what happens when non-pavement costs are taken into account? Of course, circumstances vary greatly from situation to situation, but in this case it may well be that the 180 mm inlay solution might become the most favourable, because of the time saved due to the shoulder needing no treatment. It also scores well from the point of view of tonnage of material used, an environmental issue, and the negative

427

Option	Cost: £/linear metre			
	Lane 1	Lane 2	Shoulder	Total
120 mm overlay	£45	£45	£30	£120
Plane 50 mm; replace 130 mm	£50	£33	£22	£105
Plane 100 mm; replace 140 mm	£55	£24	£14	£93
Plane 150 mm; replace 170 mm	£67	£23	£10	£100
180 mm inlay	£71	£24	£0	£95

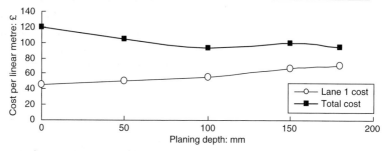

Fig. 4.29 Pavement costs – example highway project

impact of the additional planings depends on their quality. In many situations asphalt planings are a valuable resource, not a waste product.

Admittedly, the engineer is not usually asked to take any account of delay or environmental costs – but it isn't difficult to derive an estimate. If the agency in charge of the highway adopts a standard rate for lane closure time, quarried volume, land-fill volume etc., and provides this information to the engineering team, they will be more likely to produce an optimised solution.

4.6.2.2 Variable design life

In the previous section the designer was working to a set design life and, in the example given, this led to a minimum total pavement cost of £93 per metre of carriageway. However, there is no reason why one should not consider alternative design lives in order to minimise whole-life costs. Of course, the procedure now takes on a much more complex nature, and it is fair to say that a lot of estimation is needed. The following additional information is required:

- an estimate of annual maintenance costs as a function of time: (1) since the last major strengthening treatment, and (2) since the last resurfacing
- resurfacing cost and likely frequency required

428

- a set of designs and associated costs for different design lives
- a projection of how these design costs would increase (due to ongoing pavement deterioration) with every year for which they were delayed
- a discount rate for future costs.

The first of these can be standardised (on paper; not in reality) by the highway (airport etc.) authority for different types of road (or other pavement) and traffic level. The second is even easier to standardise. The third represents the main task for the designer. The fourth can again be estimated according to a set of standardised rules. The fifth is a political choice; it was mentioned at the beginning of Part 3 (Section 3.1.2) and is discussed below.

Turning to the designer's main task, what is required is to carry out the exercise described in the previous section for perhaps three different design lives (e.g. 10 years, 20 years and 40 years). Carrying on from the example in Fig. 4.29, it is assumed that these costs are found to be £80, £93 and £110 per metre respectively, at today's prices.

The annual maintenance cost has to be derived from the records of the particular authority, or from research carried out within a particular country. For purposes of illustration it is assumed that the following equation is found as a best fit to the data:

Annual maintenance cost $(£/m) = 2 + Y_1 \times 0.5 + Y_2 \times 0.25$

where Y_1 = years since last major maintenance; Y_2 = years since last resurfacing.

It is further assumed that it is currently 25 years since the last major maintenance (or original construction) and that it is 12 years since the last resurfacing; also that resurfacing is required every 12 years and that the cost is £20 per metre.

The strengthening costs (£80, £93 and £110) are for today's conditions. It will be assumed that they increase linearly with the number of years since the last strengthening. It sounds complicated, but it is not difficult to calculate on a spreadsheet.

The final and admittedly critical element is the discount rate. The idea is that a certain sum of money today is assumed to increase in purchasing power with time due to continuing economic growth. The corollary is that future costs can therefore be 'discounted' at a certain annual rate. A debate rages as to the correctness of this assumption in our 21st century world – and the result is that discount rates range from zero to about 10%. One further issue is that though

Table 4.6 A comparison of project-level maintenance strategies

Interval between major strengthenings: years	Discounted 60-year cost: £/m			
	Maintain	Strengthen	Resurface	Total
10	182	275	0	457
12	200	249	0	449
15	214	222	31	467
20	243	194	25	462
25	267	187	34	488
30	297	165	33	495

economics may sometimes indicate that it is sensible to design for 100 years, no one can be at all sure that the need for any particular pavement will extend anything like this long. The recommendation here is that, no matter what the economic arguments, the uncertainty element demands the use of a discount rate. In this example 3% will be used.

The results are shown in Table 4.6.

This is only a hypothetical example of course, but the finding in this case is that the most efficient strategy for this pavement is to strengthen every 12 years, avoiding the need for any separate resurfacing operations.

However, the problem is that this only takes account of pavement costs. And this is where the equation becomes much more speculative and political. Once user costs are factored in, the picture might well look quite different, with 30-year or even 40-year designs coming out as favourite. This is certainly the view taken by several highway authorities for maintenance of major routes.

4.6.3 Network-level optimisation

This is a subject which stretches the scope of this book. However, if pavement management is to be successful at network level then there has to be a sound basis of project-level optimisation in place. If an authority is able to generate simple simulations such as that illustrated in the previous two sections, perhaps by allowing design engineers access to an appropriately populated spreadsheet, then this immediately puts some of the tools in place for network-level decision making. 'What if?' scenarios can be explored, examining the effect of delaying maintenance for example, enabling operators to distribute the available budget in the most cost-effective manner. It also allows engineers to generate the sort of data which politicians need to see in order for them to appreciate the effect of budget restrictions.

However, network-level pavement management forces non-pavement costs to be taken seriously, including costs which are not strictly financial. These have already been introduced in Part 3 (Section 3.1.3) in relation to new pavement design, and they should play a significant role in sensible management.

4.6.3.1 The cost equation

Pavement costs are clear enough and have been dealt with in previous sections. The non-pavement costs which could be taken into account are:

- user costs (due to speed restrictions, vehicle wear and tear, fuel consumption and delays at maintenance works)
- accident costs
- environmental costs (air pollution, energy usage).

The most common method of dealing with user costs is to link them to the parameter known as the *International Roughness Index* (IRI), defined in Section 4.2.2.1. The following are examples of the forms of equation typically used for this.[33]

$$\text{Vehicle operating cost (VOC)} = \text{VOC}_{\text{low IRI}}$$
$$\times (1 + 0.06[\text{IRI} - 3]) \quad [\text{IRI} > 3]$$
$$\text{Time cost (TC)} = \text{TC}_{\text{low IRI}} \times (1 + 0.03 \times \text{IRI})$$

There is nothing fundamental about these two equations or any of the many others which have been developed around the world; they are based on experience and estimation, and should definitely not be applied outside the limits of the data upon which they are based. The problem is that the economic equation is so different in different countries, even in different parts of one country, that it is quite impossible to give guidance other than that calibration is *always* required.

Accident costs can be linked to *skid resistance coefficient* (μ) and to *pavement condition*, but only very approximately. Once again, example equations are given.[34]

$$\text{Skidding accident cost} \propto \text{Traffic flow} \times 10^{(1 - 1.8\mu)}$$

$$\text{Accident cost due to pavement} \propto \text{Traffic flow}$$
$$\times (\text{rut depth} - 10\,\text{mm})$$

The issue of environmental costs is bound to grow in importance. At present there seems little will to address the environmentally damaging effects of congestion (social costs as well as pollutants), but in the end the pavement will have little effect on congestion until it reaches such a degraded state that it is well outside the range of pavement conditions dealt with in this book. And where pavements reach such a level, pollution and social issues are probably not top of the political agenda.

Energy usage, however, has a closer link to pavement type and condition. It is an area which is still subject to research, with claim and counter-claim. It is very clear that energy cost is related to overall pavement unevenness, as measured by IRI and as included in equations such as that given above for vehicle operating costs; it is less clear whether there is any significant difference between the energy required to travel on different pavement types, when in good condition (see Part 3, Section 3.1.3.3).

Returning to the main issue, the key point is that network-level management should include a means of assessing the day-to-day cost of using each element of the network, and a convenient way of achieving this, in some countries at least, is to base equations on IRI – or an alternative pavement condition indicator.

4.6.3.2 Practical management

In the end, network-level management is often simply a matter of avoiding damaging mistakes, particularly due to delaying maintenance too long. Every section of highway, airfield, cycle track, footway, industrial pavement etc. requires continuing investment in order to maintain it at a certain operational standard. In theory it is possible to work out an approximate minimum expenditure with an optimum maintenance strategy for each individual section, but if the sum total of all these expenditures is not available each year then the task simply cannot be achieved. However optimised the network-level budget allocation, if the total spend is insufficient then the unavoidable consequence is a reduction in operational standard. Routine maintenance would have to be scaled back, which means that ride quality and safety standards would suffer, but with considerable savings to be made – at the expense of extra costs to the vehicle operators of course. These are all issues which are not difficult to explore once a sound foundation of project-level projections is made and a suitable relationship between pavement properties and 'running costs' is formulated. Unfortunately, integration of project-level predictions into network-level management requires a very clearly thought-out system and so is generally only carried out in a relatively superficial manner.

4.6.4 Summary

Politicians would be lost without a supply of soundly based information from the real world, and those politicians, both local and national, who deal with spend on transportation infrastructure are no exception. It is therefore very important that serious engineering input goes into the development of systems for managing pavements, alongside the required input from other disciplines (economics, sociology etc.). The trouble is that there are numerous different ways in which a pavement system can be mismanaged and funds wasted, and mismanagement is almost certain unless the practical skills of engineers are brought in.

4.7

Conclusion to Part 4

The ratio of spend on new pavement construction to spend on maintenance and rehabilitation will continue to swing the way of maintenance throughout the developed world. Yet maintenance is a subject which is rarely treated scientifically. It is hoped that this book has gone some way towards rectifying this situation. Of course, no amount of guidance can possibly replace the wisdom that comes from experience, but maybe the guidance given in these pages can at least kick-start the process of developing that wisdom.

If one subject were to be picked out from this part of the book, it would be that of uncertainty and risk. Pavement engineering is a subject full of uncertainty even if it is not always admitted, and the uncertainty when dealing with maintenance and rehabilitation is greater than anywhere else. There is never a complete set of data to work with; future pavement usage is never known with complete confidence; design methods when dealing with materials which are already damaged are, at best, questionable. The engineer must therefore become an expert at assessing the level of uncertainty and tailoring design recommendations accordingly. The right answer isn't always the one that drops straight out of an analytical package. It is even less likely to be the one assumed by a pavement management system.

Notes

1. The influence of temperature on the set of rapid-hardening concretes can be considerable, a mere 5°C drop in temperature potentially causing a dramatic slowing of the curing process. Users should heed suppliers' warnings carefully.
2. Crack stitching is usually restricted to longitudinal cracks. The problem with transverse cracks is that there can be day–night thermally induced opening and closing taking place, and crack stitching is not designed to combat this.
3. See County Surveyors Society (1994) for a thickness design guide.
4. Road Note 39 (Nicholls, 2002) from the UK Transport Research Laboratory gives a full set of design and construction guidelines.
5. The so-called 'Pavement Condition Index' (PCI), developed by the US Army Corps of Engineers, is one of the most commonly used measures of visual condition. It is based on a summation of the contributions from different distress types (ravelling, cracking, rutting etc.).
6. The International Roughness Index (IRI) was developed from trials carried out in Brazil in the early 1980s under World Bank sponsorship. See Paterson (1988).
7. There are so many different pieces of equipment on the market these days (2007) that it would be unfair to make recommendations. Names include 'Road Surface Profiler', 'Automatic Road Analyzer', 'Multifunction Road Monitor' and 'Road Assessment Vehicle'.
8. See for example CEN (1999).
9. Here too there are far too many alternatives for any to be recommended. Well-known names include 'Tire Traction Tester', 'Mu Meter', 'Griptester' and 'Skiddometer'.

435

10. An unbound material sampler is a device which drives a steel tube into the ground, containing within it a plastic inner tube in two halves. The inner tube (containing the sample) is later extruded from the steel outer tube, and separated into its two halves, releasing the sample for inspection and testing.

11. This equation was developed by the UK Transport Research Laboratory and is now incorporated into UK standards (Highways Agency, 2006c).

12. These images were provided by Scott Wilson Ltd.

13. The Leutner test is described in Forschungsgesellschaft für Strassen- und Verkehrswesen (1999) and the torque test in British Board of Agrément (2004).

14. See Stöckert (2001).

15. The sensitivity of GPR is a function of the wavelength used. Short wavelength (i.e. high frequency – that is, ≥ 1 GHz) will give good resolution but poor penetration into the pavement; it is suited to identifying bound layer interfaces. Longer wavelength (lower frequency) is better suited to identifying pavement foundation issues.

16. The device was developed by A.C. Benkelman in the 1950s. See Highway Research Board (1954; 1955).

17. See Kennedy and Lister (1978).

18. There is a vast literature on the FWD, mainly in connection with interpretation. Space precludes going into detail here.

19. This statement sounds very much like wishful thinking. However, studies have shown (Mamlouk and Davies, 1984) that the error involved in ignoring dynamic effects is rarely more than a few per cent for any of the back-calculated stiffness values. Other error sources (non-homogeneity, edge effects, lack of bond) will certainly be the same under traffic as under the FWD.

20. For example, the UK Highways Agency maintains around 15 weigh-in-motion stations around the country, purely to monitor national trends. From time to time, as changes occur, this has led to changes in the relevant design standard, (Highways Agency, 2006a).

21. See AASHTO (1993).

22. Miner's law (or Miner's rule – see Miner, 1945) is a general law applied to fatigue damage, not only to damage of pavement materials. It is an approximate rule rather than an exact law.

23. The term SAMI is applied to a variety of interlayer systems, with or without a geotextile, the common theme being that they are tough, flexible, bitumen-rich layers that allow slow viscous slip to occur but provide a high level of crack resistance.

436

24. 'Trenching' refers to the removal of a strip of asphalt either side of a crack, of total width less than 1 m. This can be replaced by fresh asphalt, with or without an interlayer system (geogrid, SAMI).

25. Several US states have used ultra-thin white-topping and some have brought out guidance or specification. However, 'design' in the sense of scientifically selecting a strength and thickness does not appear to be advanced.

26. For example, British Airports Authority (1993) – see note 28 of Part 1.

27. The idea is to compute the deflection under a suitably large circular load area, reflecting the likely spread of load under the new PQC slab. The modulus of subgrade reaction is then given by the applied stress divided by the computed deflection.

28. See Highways Agency (1994) for UK guidance.

29. The problem with this otherwise excellent solution is that future resurfacing will also have to include the same pattern of saw-cutting – and saw-cutting is not cheap.

30. See for example Thom and Wood (2004).

31. Empirical design guidance on cold recycled pavements can be found in Merril *et al.* (2004).

32. The stiffness assumed for the recycled layer would normally be lower than that for an equivalent plant-mixed material because of the greater variability of in situ treated mixtures.

33. These equations are adapted from proposals made in a recent study led by the University of Birmingham, for heavy goods vehicles.

34. As note 33.

References

Standards and specifications

AASHTO (1999) *Standard method of test for soundness of aggregate by use of sodium sulfate or magnesium sulfate*, T104. American Association of State Highway and Transportation Officials, Washington, DC, USA.

AASHTO (2002a) *Standard method of test for resistance to degradation of small-size coarse aggregate by abrasion and impact in the Los Angeles machine*, T96. American Association of State Highway and Transportation Officials, Washington, DC, USA.

AASHTO (2002b) *Standard method of test for resilient modulus of subgrade soils and untreated base/sub-base materials*, T307. American Association of State Highway and Transportation Officials, Washington, DC, USA.

AASHTO (2006a) *Standard method of test for viscosity determination of asphalt using rotational viscometer*, T240. American Association of State Highway and Transportation Officials, Washington, DC, USA.

AASHTO (2006b) *Standard method of test for effect of heat and air on a moving film of asphalt (rolling thin-film oven test)*, T316. American Association of State Highway and Transportation Officials, Washington, DC, USA.

AASHTO (2006c) *Standard method of test for resistance of coarse aggregate to degradation by abrasion in the Micro-Deval apparatus*, T327. American Association of State Highway and Transportation Officials, Washington, DC, USA.

AASHTO (2007a) *Standard method of test for soundness of aggregates by freezing and thawing*, T103. American Association of State Highway and Transportation Officials, Washington, DC, USA.

Asphalt Institute (2003) *Binder specifications and testing*, Superpave Series No. 1 (SP-1), 3rd edn. Asphalt Institute, Kentucky, USA.

ASTM (2001) *Standard practice for classification of soils for engineering purposes (Unified Soil Classification System)*, D2487. American Society of Testing and Materials, West Conshohocken, Pennsylvania, USA.

ASTM (2002) *Standard test method for pull-off strength of coatings using portable adhesion testers*, D4541. American Society of Testing and Materials, West Conshohocken, Pennsylvania, USA.

ASTM (2003) *Standard test method for resistance to degradation of large-size coarse aggregate by abrasion and impact in the Los Angeles machine*, C535. American Society of Testing and Materials, West Conshohocken, Pennsylvania, USA.

ASTM (2004) *Standard test method for effect of heat and air on a moving film of asphalt (rotating thin-film oven test)*, D2872. American Society of Testing and Materials, West Conshohocken, Pennsylvania, USA.

ASTM (2006a) *Standard test method for resistance to degradation of small-size coarse aggregate by abrasion and impact in the Los Angeles machine*, C131. American Society of Testing and Materials, West Conshohocken, Pennsylvania, USA.

ASTM (2006b) *Standard test method for penetration of bituminous materials*, D5. American Society of Testing and Materials, West Conshohocken, Pennsylvania, USA.

ASTM (2006c) *Standard test method for softening point of bitumen (ring-and-ball apparatus)*, D36. American Society of Testing and Materials, West Conshohocken, Pennsylvania, USA.

ASTM (2006d) *Standard test method for viscosity determination of asphalt at elevated temperatures using a rotational viscometer*, D4402. American Society of Testing and Materials, West Conshohocken, Pennsylvania, USA.

ASTM (2006e) *Standard test methods for resistance of coarse aggregate to degradation by abrasion in the Micro-Deval apparatus*, D6928. American Society of Testing and Materials, West Conshohocken, Pennsylvania, USA.

ASTM (2007) *Standard test methods for frost heave and thaw weakening susceptibility of soils*, D5918. American Society of Testing and Materials, West Conshohocken, Pennsylvania, USA.

British Board of Agrément (2004) Torque bond test, *Guidelines document for the assessment and certification of thin surfacing systems for highways*, Report SG3/05/234. British Board of Agrément, Watford.

BSI (1989) Method for determination of the polished stone value, BS 812, *Testing aggregates: Part 114*. British Standards Institution, London.

CEN (1996) Determination of the resistance to wear (micro-Deval), EN 1097, *Tests for mechanical and physical properties of aggregates: Part 1*. Comité Européen de Normalisation, Brussels.

CEN (1998a) Methods for the determination of resistance to fragmentation, EN 1097, *Tests for mechanical and physical properties of aggregates: Part 2*. Comité Européen de Normalisation, Brussels.

CEN (1998b) Magnesium sulphate test, EN 1367, *Tests for thermal and weathering properties of aggregates: Part 2*. Comité Européen de Normalisation, Brussels.

CEN (1999) Sideway force coefficient routine investigation machine, EN 7941, *Methods for measuring the skid resistance of pavement surface: Part 1*. Comité Européen de Normalisation, Brussels.

CEN (2002) Compliance test for leaching of granular waste materials and sludges: two stage batch test at a liquid to solid ratio of 2l/kg and 8l/kg for materials with a high solid content and with a particle size below 4 mm (without or with size reduction), EN 12457, *Characterisation of waste – leaching: Part 3*. Comité Européen de Normalisation, Brussels.

442

CEN (2003a) Test methods for hot mix asphalt – determination of the water sensitivity of bituminous specimens, EN 12697, *Bituminous mixtures: Part 12*. Comité Européen de Normalisation, Brussels.

CEN (2003b) Test methods for hot mix asphalt – wheel tracking, EN 12697, *Bituminous mixtures: Part 22*. Comité Européen de Normalisation, Brussels.

CEN (2003c) Method for measurement of slip/skid resistance of a surface – the pendulum test, EN 13036, *Road and airfield surface characteristics – test methods: Part 4*. Comité Européen de Normalisation, Brussels.

CEN (2003d) Test methods for laboratory dry density and water content – vibrating hammer, EN 13286, *Unbound and hydraulically bound mixtures: Part 4*. Comité Européen de Normalisation, Brussels.

CEN (2003e) Test method for the determination of the direct tensile strength of hydraulically bound mixtures, EN 13286, *Unbound and hydraulically bound mixtures: Part 40*. Comité Européen de Normalisation, Brussels.

CEN (2003f) Test method for the determination of the modulus of elasticity of hydraulically bound mixtures, EN 13286, *Unbound and hydraulically bound mixtures: Part 43*. Comité Européen de Normalisation, Brussels.

CEN (2004a) Test methods for laboratory dry density and water content – Proctor compaction, EN 13286, *Unbound and hydraulically bound mixtures: Part 2*. Comité Européen de Normalisation, Brussels.

CEN (2004b) Cyclic load triaxial test for unbound mixtures, EN 13286, *Unbound and hydraulically bound mixtures: Part 7*. Comité Européen de Normalisation, Brussels.

CEN (2004c) Test method for the determination of CBR, immediate bearing index and linear swelling, EN 13286, *Unbound and hydraulically bound mixtures: Part 47*. Comité Européen de Normalisation, Brussels.

CEN (2004d) Accelerated swelling test for soil treated by lime and/or hydraulic binder, EN 13286, *Unbound and hydraulically bound mixtures: Part 49*. Comité Européen de Normalisation, Brussels.

CEN (2007a) Determination of needle penetration, EN 1426, *Bitumen and bituminous binders*. Comité Européen de Normalisation, Brussels.

CEN (2007b) Determination of the softening point – ring and ball method, EN 1427, *Bitumen and bituminous binders*. Comité Européen de Normalisation, Brussels.

CEN (2007c) Determination of the resistance to hardening under influence of heat and air – RTFOT method, EN 12607, *Bitumen and bituminous binders*. Comité Européen de Normalisation, Brussels.

Forschungsgesellschaft für Strassen- und Verkehrswesen (1999) Prüfung des schichtenverbundes nach Leutner, *Arbeitsanleitungen zur prüfung von asphalt ALP A-StB*, Part 4. Forschungsgesellschaft für Strassen- und Verkehrswesen, Köln, Germany.

Highways Agency (2007) Specification for highway works, *Manual of Contract Documents for Highway Works*, Vol. 1. Stationery Office, London.

United Facilities Guide Specifications (2006), 'Aggregate Surface Course', USGF-32 15 00, US Corps of Engineers, Hyattsville, Maryland.

Design guides

AASHTO (1993) *Guide for design of pavement structures*. American Association of State Highway and Transportation Officials, Washington, DC, USA.

AASHTO (2007b) *Guide for mechanistic empirical design of new and rehabilitated pavement structures*. American Association of State Highway and Transportation Officials, Washington, DC, USA.

Asphalt Institute (1984) *Mix design methods for asphaltic concrete and other hot mix types*, Manual Series No. 2 (MS-2). Asphalt Institute, Kentucky, USA.

Asphalt Institute (1996) *Superpave mix design*, Superpave Series No. 2 (SP-2). Asphalt Institute, Kentucky, USA.

Asphalt Institute (1999) *Thickness design: asphalt pavements for highways and streets*, Manual Series No. 1 (MS-1), 9th edn. Asphalt Institute, Kentucky, USA.

British Airports Authority (1993) *Pavement design guide for heavy aircraft loading*. BAA plc, Group Technical Services Aircraft Pavements, London.

Committee of Land Transportation Officials (1996) *Structural design of interurban and rural road pavements*, TRH4. Department of Transport, Pretoria, South Africa.

Concrete Society (2003) *Concrete industrial ground floors: a guide to design and construction*, Report TR34, 3rd edn. The Concrete Society, Camberley.

County Surveyors Society (1994) *Road haunches – a guide to maintenance practice*, Report PA/SCR243. Transport and Road Research Laboratory, Crowthorne.

Defence Estates (2006) *A guide to airfield pavement design and evaluation*, 2nd edn, Design and Maintenance Guide 27. Defence Estates, London.

FAA (1995) *Airport pavement design and evaluation*, AC150/5370–6D. Federal Aviation Administration, Washington, DC, USA.

FEHRL (2006) *Guidance manual for the implementation of low noise road surfaces*, Report 2006/02. Forum of European National Highway Research Laboratories, Brussels.

Highways Agency (1994) Maintenance of concrete roads, HD32, *Design manual for roads and bridges Vol. 7: Pavement design and maintenance – pavement maintenance methods*. Stationery Office, London.

Highways Agency (2001) Structural assessment methods, HD29, *Design manual for roads and bridges Vol. 7: Pavement design and maintenance – pavement maintenance assessment*. Stationery Office, London.

Highways Agency (2006a) Traffic assessment, HD24, *Design manual for roads and bridges Vol. 7: Pavement design and maintenance – pavement design and construction*. Stationery Office, London.

Highways Agency (2006b) Pavement design, HD26, *Design manual for roads and bridges Vol. 7: Pavement design and maintenance – pavement design and construction*. Stationery Office, London.

Highways Agency (2006c) *Design guidance for road pavement foundations (Draft HD25)*, Interim Advice Note IAN73. Stationery Office, London.

Knapton, J. and Meletiou, M. (1996) *The structural design of heavy duty pavements for ports and other industries*, 3rd edn. Interpave and British Ports Association, Leicester, UK.

NAASRA (1987) *Pavement design: a guide to the structural design of road pavements*. National Association of Australian State Highway Authorities, Milsons Port, New South Wales.

Nicholls, J.C. (2002) *Design guide for road surface dressing*, Road Note 39, 5th edn. Transport Research Laboratory, Crowthorne.

Shell (1978) *Shell pavement design manual – asphalt pavements and overlays for road traffic*. Shell International Petroleum Company Ltd, London.

Transport Research Laboratory (1993) *A guide to the structural design of bitumen-surfaced roads in tropical and sub-tropical countries*, Overseas Road Note 31. Transport Research Laboratory, Crowthorne, UK.

Other references

Airey, G.D., Collop, A.C., Thom, N.H. and Zoorob, S.E. (2004) Use of steel slag and recycled glass in bituminous mixtures. *Proceedings of the 3rd Eurasphalt and Eurobitume Congress*, Vienna, pp. 1218–1232.

Bell, C.A. (1989) *Aging of asphalt aggregate systems*, Strategic Highway Research Program, National Research Council, Washington, DC, Report SR-OSU-A-003A-89-2.

Benson, P.E. (1976) *Low temperature transverse cracking of asphalt concrete pavements in central and west Texas*. Texas Transportation Institute and State Department of Highways and Transportation, Cooperative Research Project, Report 175-2F.

Bonnot, J. (1988) Fissuration de retrait des chaussées à assises traitées aux liants hydrauliques. *Bulletin de Liaison du Laboratoire Centrale des Ponts et Chaussées*, No. 156 and 157, Paris.

Boussinesq, J. (1883) *Application des potentials a l'étude d'équilibre et du movement des solides élastiques*. Gautier-Villars, Paris.

Boyce, J.R. (1980) A non-linear model for the elastic behaviour of granular materials under repeated loading. *Proceedings of an International Symposium on Soils under Cyclic and Transient Loading*, Balkema, Rotterdam, pp. 149–167.

Bradbury, R.D. (1938) *Reinforced concrete pavements*. Wire Reinforcement Institute, Washington, DC, USA.

Brown, S.F. (1978) Stiffness and fatigue requirements for structural performance of asphaltic mixes. *Proceedings of Eurobitume Seminar*, London, pp. 141–145.

Brown, S.F., Brunton, J.M. and Stock, A.F. (1985) The analytical design of bituminous pavements. *Proceedings of the Institution of Civil Engineers*, Part 2, Vol. 79, pp. 1–31.

Brown, S.F., Loach, S.C. and O'Reilly, M.P. (1987) *Repeated loading of fine grained soils*, Report CR72. Transport and Road Research Laboratory, Crowthorne.

Brown, S.F., Cooper, K.E., Gibb, J.M., Read, J.M. and Scholz, T.V. (1994) Practical tests for mechanical properties of hot-mix asphalt. *Proceedings of the 6th Conference on Asphalt Pavements for Southern Africa*, Cape Town, Vol. 2, pp. 29–45.

CERTU (1999) *Chaussées poreuses urbaines*. CERTU, Lyon, France.

Chan, W.K.C. (1990) *Permanent deformation resistance of granular layers in pavements*. PhD thesis, University of Nottingham, UK.

Choi, Y.-K., Thom, N.H. and Collop, A.C. (2005) Fatigue damage accumulation measured using different laboratory techniques. *Proceedings of the 4th International MAIRPAV Symposium*, Belfast.

Collop, A.C., Choi, Y.-K., Airey, G.D. and Elliott, R.C. (2004) Development of the saturation ageing tensile stiffness (SATS) test. *Proceedings of the ICE, Transport*, Vol. 157, No. TR3, pp. 143–186.

Comité Euro-International du Béton (1993) *CEB FIP Model Code 90*. Thomas Telford, London.

Corbett, L.W. and Schweyer, H.E. (1981) Composition and rheology considerations in age hardening of bitumen. *Proceedings of the Association of Asphalt Paving Technologists*, Vol. 50, pp. 571–582.

Croney, D. and Jacobs, J.C. (1967) *The frost susceptibility of soils and road materials*, Report LR90. Road Research Laboratory, Crowthorne.

Cundall, P.A. and Strack, O.D.L. (1979) A discrete element model for granular assemblies. *Géotechnique*, Vol. 29, No. 1, pp. 47–65.

Darcy, H. (1856) *Les fontaines publiques de la ville de Dijon*. Dalmont, Paris.

Day, J.B.A. (1981) Proof testing of unbound layers. *Proceedings of the 1st Symposium on Unbound Aggregates in Roads*, Nottingham, pp. 15–20.

De Beer, M. (2006) Reconsideration of tyre–pavement input parameters for the structural design of flexible pavements. *Proceedings of the 10th International Conference on Asphalt Pavements*, Quebec City, International Society of Asphalt Pavements.

De Beer, M., Fisher, C. and Jooste, F.J. (1997) Determination of pneumatic tyre/pavement interface contact stresses under moving wheel loads and some effects on pavements with thin asphalt surfacings. *Proceedings of the 8th International Conference on Structural Design of Asphalt Pavements*, Seattle, Vol. 2, pp. 1643–1658.

Edwards, J.P., Thom, N.H., Fleming, P.R. and Williams, J. (2005) Accelerated laboratory based mechanistic testing of unbound materials within the newly developed NAT Springbox. *Transportation Research Record 1913*, Transportation Research Board, Washington, pp. 32–40.

Fraass, A. (1937) Test methods for bitumen and bituminous mixture with specific reference to low temperature. *Bitumen*, pp. 152–155.

Fuller, W.B. and Thompson, S.E. (1907) The laws of proportioning concrete. *Journal of the Transportation Division*, American Society of Civil Engineers, Vol. 59, pp. 67–143.

Griffiths, G. and Thom, N.H. (2007) *Concrete pavement design guidance notes*. Taylor & Francis, London.

Gubler, R., Baida, L.G. and Partl, M.N. (2004) A new method to determine the influence of water on mechanical properties of asphalt concrete. *Road materials and pavement design*, Vol. 5, special issue, pp. 259–279.

Hansen, J.B. (1961) A general formula for bearing capacity. *Bulletin No. 11*, Danish Geotechnical Institute.

Hazen, A. (1892) *Some physical properties of sands and gravels with special reference to their use in filtration*, 24th Annual Report. Massachusetts State Board of Health.

Hertz, H. (1895) Über die berührung elastischer Körper. *Gesammelte Werke*, (eds P. Leonard and J.A. Barth), Leipzig, Vol. 1, pp. 155–173.

Hicks, R.G. and Monismith, C.L. (1971) Factors influencing the resilient response of granular materials. *Highway Research Record 345*, Transportation Research Board, Washington, pp. 15–31.

Highway Research Board (1954) *WASHO road test*, Special Report No. 18. Highway Research Board, Washington, DC, USA.

Highway Research Board (1955) *WASHO road test*, Special Report No. 22. Highway Research Board, Washington, DC, USA.

Highway Research Board (1961) *The AASHO road test: history and description of the project*, Special Report No. 61A. Highway Research Board, Washington, DC, USA.

Hornych, P., Karzai, A. and Quibel, A. (2000) Modelling of a full scale experiment of two flexible pavement structures with unbound granular bases. *Proceedings of the 4th International Conference on Bearing Capacity of Roads and Airfields*. Balkema, Rotterdam, Vol. 3, pp. 1277–1287.

Ibrahim, H.E.M. (1998) *Assessment and design of emulsion–aggregate mixtures for use in pavements*. PhD thesis, University of Nottingham, UK.

ICAO (2004) Aerodrome design and operations. *Aerodrome standards: Annex 14*, Vol. 1, 4th edn. International Civil Aviation Organisation, Quebec, Canada.

Jones, R.H. and Jones, H.A. (1989a) Granular drainage layers in pavement foundations. *Unbound Aggregates in Roads* (eds R.H. Jones and A.R. Dawson). Butterworths, Sevenoaks, pp. 55–69.

Jones, R.H. and Jones, H.A. (1989b) Horizontal permeability of compacted aggregates. *Unbound Aggregates in Roads* (eds R.H. Jones and A.R. Dawson). Butterworths, Sevenoaks, pp. 70–77.

Kennedy, C.K. and Lister, N.W. (1978) *Prediction of pavement performance and design of overlays*, Report LR833. Transport and Road Research Laboratory, Crowthorne.

Lay, M.G. (1990) *Handbook of road technology*. Taylor & Francis, London.

Maillard, S., de la Roche, C., Hammoum, F., Such, C. and Piau, J.M. (2004) Bitumen healing investigation using a specific fracture test. *Road Materials and Pavement Design*, Vol. 5, special issue, pp. 45–63.

Mamlouk, M.S. and Davies, T.G. (1984) Elastodynamic analysis of pavement deflections. *Transportation Engineering Journal*, American Society of Civil Engineers, Vol. 110, No. 6, pp. 536–550.

Mayhew, H.C. and Harding, H.M. (1987) *Thickness design of concrete roads*, Report RR87. Transport and Road Research Laboratory, Crowthorne.

Melan, E. (1936) Theorie statisch unbestimmter Systeme aus ideal-plastischen Baustoff. *Sitzungsberichte der Akademie der Wissenschaften in Wien*, Vol. 2a, No. 145, pp. 195–218.

Merril, D., Nunn, M.E. and Carswell, I. (2004) *A guide to the use and specification of cold recycled materials for the maintenance of road pavements*, Report TRL611. Transport Research Laboratory, Crowthorne.

Meyerhof, G.G. (1962) Load carrying capacity of concrete pavements. *Journal of the Soil Mechanics and Foundations Division, ASCE*, Vol. 88, No. 3, pp. 89–116.

Meyerhof, G.G. (1963) Some recent research on bearing capacity of foundations. *Canadian Geotechnical Journal*, Vol. 1, No. 1, pp. 16–26.

Miner, M.A. (1945) Cumulative damage in fatigue. *Journal of Applied Mechanics, ASME*, Vol. 12, No. 67, pp. A159–A164.

Nunn, M.E. (2004) *Development of a more versiatile approach to flexible and flexible composite pavement design*, Report TRL615. Transport Research Laboratory, Crowthorne.

Odemark, N. (1949) *Undersökning av elasticitetegenskaperna hos olika jordarter samt teori för beräkning av belägningar eligt elasticitesteorin*. Statens Väginstitute, Stockholm.

Oliveira, J.R.M. (2006) *Grouted macadam: material characterisation for pavement design*. PhD thesis, University of Nottingham.

Packard, R.G. and Tayabji, S.D. (1985) New PCA thickness design procedure for concrete highway and street pavements. *Proceedings of the 3rd International Conference on Concrete Pavement Design and Rehabilitation*, Purdue University, USA, Vol. 9, pp. 225–236.

Paris, P.C. and Erdogan, F.A. (1963) A critical analysis of crack propagation laws. *Journal of Basic Engineering, ASME*, Vol. 85, pp. 528–534.

Paterson, W.D.O. (1988) *Road deterioration and maintenance effects*. The World Bank, Washington, DC.

Pendrys, J.P. (1989) Biodegradation of asphalt cement-20 by aerobic bacteria. *Journal of Applied and Environmental Microbiology*, Vol. 55(b), pp. 1357–1362.

Peploe, R.J. and Dawson, A.R. (2006) *Environmental impact of industrial by-products in road construction – a literature review*, Research Report 308. Land Transport New Zealand, Wellington, NZ.

Phillips, U.A. and Traxler, R.W. (1963) Microbial degradation of asphalt. *Applied and Environmental Microbiology*, Vol. 11, No. 3, pp. 235–238.

Powell, W.D., Potter, J.F., Mayhew, H.C. and Nunn, M.E. (1984) *The structural design of bituminous roads*, Report LR1132. Transport and Road Research Laboratory, Crowthorne.

Pratt, C., Wilson, S. and Cooper, P. (2002) *Source control using constructed pervious surfaces*, Report C582. CIRIA, London.

Raad, L., Weichert, D. and Haidar, A. (1989) Analysis of full depth asphalt concrete pavements using shakedown theory. *Transportation Research Record 1227*, Transportation Research Board, Washington, DC, pp. 53–65.

Rahimzadeh, B. (2002) *Linear and non-linear viscoelastic behaviour of binders and asphalts*. PhD thesis, University of Nottingham, UK.

Read, J.M. and Whiteoak, D. (2003) *The Shell bitumen handbook*, 5th edn. Shell Bitumen UK, Chertsey.

Sandberg, U. and Ejsmont, J.A. (2002) *Tyre/road noise reference book*. Informex, Kisa, Sweden.

Semmelink, C.J. and de Beer, M. (1995) Rapid determination of elastic and shear properties of road-building materials with the K-Mould. *Unbound Aggregates in Roads* (eds A.R. Dawson and R.H. Jones). University of Nottingham, pp. 151–161.

Stöckert, U. (2001) Schichtenverbund – Prüfung und Bewertungshintergrund. *Straße und Autobahn*, Vol. 11, pp. 624–631.

Stripple, H. (2001) *Life cycle assessment of road: a pilot study for inventory analysis*, Report B1210E, 2nd edn. IVL Swedish Environmental Research Institute, Göteborg, Sweden.

Sunarjono, S. (2008) *Influence of foamed bitumen characteristics on cold mix asphalt properties*. PhD thesis, University of Nottingham, UK.

Terzaghi, K. and Peck, R.B. (1967) *Soil mechanics in engineering practice*, 2nd edn. Wiley, New York.

Thom, N.H. (1988) *Design of road foundations*. PhD thesis, University of Nottingham, UK.

Thom, N.H. (2000) A simplified computer model for grid reinforced asphalt overlays. *Proceedings of the 4th International RILEM Conference on Reflective Cracking in Pavements*, Ottawa, pp. 37–46.

Thom, N.H. (2003) Grid reinforced overlays: predicting the unpredictable. *Maintenance and rehabilitation of pavements and technological control* (eds P. Pereira and F. Branco). University of Minho, Guimarães, Portugal.

Thom, N.H. and Brown, S.F. (1988) The effect of grading and density on the mechanical properties of crushed dolomitic limestone. *Proceedings of the 14th Conference Australian Road Research Board*, Canberra.

Thom, N.H. and Brown, S.F. (1989) The mechanical properties of unbound aggregates from various sources. *Unbound Aggregates in Roads* (eds R.H. Jones and A.R. Dawson). Butterworths, Sevenoaks, pp. 130–147.

Thom, N.H. and Cheung, L-W. (1999) Relating in situ properties of cement bound bases to their performance. *Transportation Research Record 1673*, pp. 3–8.

Thom, N.H. and Wood, O. (2004) A laboratory study of the early life performance of a slag bound base. *Pavements Unbound* (ed. A.R. Dawson). Taylor & Francis, London, pp. 259–265.

Thom, N.H., Elliott, R.C. and Cheung, L-W. (1997) Comparisons between laboratory and in situ determined asphalt concrete moduli. *Proceedings of the 8th International Conference on Structural Design of Asphalt Pavements*, Seattle, Vol. 2, pp. 1433–1442.

Thom, N.H., Osman, S.A., Collop, A.C. and Airey, G.D. (2006) Fracture and fatigue of binder and binder/filler mortar. *Proceedings of the 10th International*

Conference on Asphalt Pavements, Quebec City. International Society of Asphalt Pavements, White Bear Lake, Minnesota, Vol. 1, pp. 798–807.

Thompson, I. (2001) *Use of steel fibres to reinforce cement bound roadbase.* PhD thesis, University of Nottingham, UK.

Thompson, I., Peaston, C.H. and Thom, N.H. (1999) Fibre reinforced cement bound roadbase. *Proceedings of the 2nd Asia Pacific Specialty Conference on Fibre Reinforced Concrete*, Singapore, pp. 213–220.

Ullidtz, P. (1979) A fundamental method for the prediction of roughness, rutting and cracking in asphalt pavements. *Proceedings of the Association of Asphalt Paving Technologists*, Vol. 48, pp. 557–586.

Van der Poel, C. (1954) A general system describing the visco-elastic properties of bitumens and its relation to routine test data. *Journal of Applied Chemistry*, Vol. 4, pp. 221–236.

Webber, N.B. (1971) *Fluid mechanics for civil engineers.* Chapman & Hall, London.

Westergaard, H.M. (1926) Stresses in concrete pavements computed by theoretical analysis. *Public Roads*, Vol. 7, No. 2, pp. 25–33.

Woods Ballard, B., Kellagher, R., Martin, P., Jeffries, C., Bray, R. and Shaffer, P. (2007a) *The SUDS Manual.* CIRIA, London, Report C697.

Woods Ballard, B., Kellagher, R., Martin, P., Jeffries, C., Bray, R. and Shaffer, P. (2007b) *Site Handbook for the Construction of SUDS.* CIRIA, London, Report C698.

Yap, P. (1987) *Factors affecting truck fuel economy.* Goodyear Tyre and Rubber Company, Akron, Ohio, Report No. 862-932-513, pp. 63–79.

Yu, H-S. (2006) *Plasticity and geotechnics.* Springer, New York.

Zaniewski, J. (1982) *Vehicle operating costs, fuel consumption and pavement type and condition factors*, Report No. FHWA/PL/82/001. Federal Highway Administration, Washington, DC.

451

Index

Note: Page number in *italics* refer to figures